INTRODUCTION TO POLYMER CHEMISTRY

INTRODUCTION

TO POLYMER

CHEMISTRY

JOHN K. STILLE

UNIVERSITY OF IOWA

547.94
Sti

JOHN WILEY AND SONS, INC.

NEW YORK   LONDON

Library of Congress Catalog Card Number: 62–15192
Printed in the United States of America

PREFACE

Only recently has polymer chemistry become recognized as a separate branch of chemistry, and it receives little attention in the undergraduate courses in the chemistry curriculum of our universities and colleges. Consequently, few graduating seniors are aware of even the most basic aspects of polymer chemistry. In addition, there are few schools that offer a graduate course in this field. Entering graduate students, because of their unfamiliarity with the subject, tend to reject a research problem which involves any study even remotely related to polymer chemistry. The graduate organic chemist visions polymer research as a physical chemical treatment of the tars and gums which he has probably encountered in a course in organic preparations instead of the broad, fascinating, relatively new field in chemistry which lies ahead.

The result is that we are not properly educating and preparing organic chemists in their field. A recent survey[1] shows that one third of the American chemists and chemical engineers are employed in industries connected with polymeric materials. From this it is assumed that a much larger portion of recent graduates are in positions in industry dealing mainly with polymers.[2] One half of the graduate degrees (M.S. and Ph.D.) awarded are given by institutions who do not have anyone who could be considered a polymer chemist on their staff, whether a formal course is offered or not.[3]

This book is written for a one semester first course in polymer chemistry

[1] F. W. Billmeyer, Jr., *Textbook of Polymer Chemistry*, Interscience Publishers, Inc., New York, 1957, p. 1.

[2] G. B. Butler, *J. Chem. Ed.*, **36,** 171 (1959).

[3] *Chem. and Eng. News*, March 25, 1957, 54–56.

for both seniors in chemistry and first year graduate students in organic chemistry. No attempt is made to rigorously treat the physical chemistry of polymers. Only the fundamental physical chemical principles, which are necessary to the organic chemist working in this field, are briefly treated. The course is designed to help prepare organic chemists for the polymer chemistry that most of them face at one time or another during their careers.

There is no attempt here to discuss every polymer which has been made or studied. Most of the various types of polymers or polymerization reactions are covered at least in part, but only the most industrially or scientifically important examples of any type are treated in any detail. In addition, new developments in the field are given perhaps a larger degree of consideration in relation to what might be warranted in a comprehensive picture of polymer chemistry.

JOHN K. STILLE

Iowa City, Iowa
April, 1962

CONTENTS

1
INTRODUCTION

The fundamental concept that high polymers are actually high molecular weight compounds containing *covalent bonds* as the force holding together atoms or smaller molecular fragments was not generally accepted until 1930. These high molecular weight compounds, for example, rubber, cellulose, protein, resins, and gums, had been known to chemists for years, but they were believed to be made up of colloidal aggregates of small molecules which were held together by some undefined binding force. This belief held back developments in the field of polymer chemistry for nearly half a century.

The first statement that these naturally occurring substances were polymeric in nature, as we define polymeric today, was made in 1871 by Hlasiwetz and Habermann.[1] Proteins and carbohydrates were described as isomeric and polymeric species which differed in their degree of molecular condensation. The prime requisite, however, for acceptable research in organic chemistry at this time was to isolate pure molecular compounds which could be defined by a simple molecular formula. This discipline, with which the organic chemist was so successful, depended on elementary analyses and molecular weight determinations. Herein lay much of the trouble which led to confusion in the polymer field.

No good methods were available for the determination of molecular weights of high molecular weight compounds. Cryoscopic methods and vapor density methods were not good in the high molecular weight ranges. Although Raoult's diffusion laws were applicable to high molecular weight materials, the necessity of extrapolation of measurements to zero concentration was not generally observed. Through these inaccurate molecular weight observations, the colloidal theory became more firmly entrenched.

Another barrier to the elucidation of polymer structures was the inability of investigators to account for end groups. Since ozonolysis of natural rubber produced levulinic acid,[2] the chain structure was rejected in favor of a cyclic dimer (I). Later, the dimer structure was changed in favor of larger rings.[3]

$$CH_2-CH=C-CH_2$$
$$CH_2-C=CH-CH_2$$

with CH_3 groups on the central carbons

I

The same ideas were carried over to synthetic polymers. Generally, colloidal aggregates of simple molecules were formulated, and, in order to account for end groups, cyclic monomers and dimers were depicted. Only Lourenço correctly described polyethylene glycol[4] and polyethylene succinate[5] as $HO-(C_2H_4O)_n-H$ and $-[OCH_2-CH_2OCOCH_2CH_2CO]_x$. These materials were accurately described as having different degrees of condensation (molecular weight range). However, these ideas were lost with time, and later polyethylene succinate was assigned a cyclic formula.

In 1920, Staudinger[6] proposed chain formulas for polystyrene(II) and polyoxymethylene(III).

$$-CH_2-CH-CH_2-CH-   \qquad -CH_2-O-CH_2-O-$$
$$C_6H_5 \qquad C_6H_5$$

II   III

Perhaps most important here was his vigorous attack on his colleagues for ignoring the evidence supporting such structures and clinging to older ideas. Even after extensive investigation and further proof by Staudinger of the nature of polymers, his views were not widely accepted until ten years later. During this ten-year period, Meyer and Mark added support to the high molecular weight theory with several x-ray investigations of polymer structure.

In 1929, W. H. Carothers started a series of investigations in which polymeric molecules were prepared through known organic reactions and the properties of the products were then correlated with polymer structure.[7] This work was particularly effective in breaking the last resistance to the new theories, opening up the field of polymer chemistry to synthetic polymers, and establishing polymer chemistry on a firm chemical footing. Since that time, this new field in chemistry has advanced rapidly.

In the period during the Second World War, the American chemical industry was forced to develop and perfect synthetic polymers. The already-known synthetic polymers, which were available mainly through Carothers' work, were made better and were more thoroughly investigated.

The United States was forced to produce synthetic elastomers as Germany had done twenty-five years before and was now doing. The stimulus of war now advanced polymer chemistry as it had advanced other scientific fields in previous times.

Thus began the upswing which has climbed so rapidly and at an ever-increasing pace. In the postwar years, the demand for consumer goods and, for the first time on a large scale, a methodical scientific investigation of polymers and polymerization reactions provided the driving force behind some remarkable discoveries.

Some basically new polymerization reactions are being discovered today; however, most of the reactions which are employed in the formation of polymers are well known. The biggest postwar advances have come either through a higher degree of perfection of certain reactions or through a tailoring of polymer molecules guided by what has been learned about the physical chemistry of polymers.

These polymerization reactions have been perfected through the use of catalysts. Certainly the "stereospecific" catalysts of the 1950's have had a tremendous effect on the polymer field. New techniques in polymerization are providing useful forms of polymers which had been prepared previously but were only low molecular weight forms with undesirable physical properties and were therefore cast aside. Polyformaldehyde is an outstanding example of a "rediscovered" polymer.

Now that polymer chemists can better correlate polymer structure with properties and have a better understanding of, and appreciation for, polymerization reactions, more and more polymers are being tailor-made to suit special needs. In a few short years, polymer chemistry has risen from nothing to a large part of our chemical industry, and it is still in its infancy.

REFERENCES

1. H. Hlasiwetz and J. Habermann, *Ann. Chem. Pharm.*, **159,** 304 (1871).
2. C. Harries, *Ber.*, **37,** 2708 (1904); **38,** 1195, 3985 (1905).
3. C. Harries, *Ann.*, **406,** 173 (1914).
4. A. V. Lourenço, *Compt. rend.*, **51,** 365 (1860).
5. A. V. Lourenço, *Ann. chim. et phys.*, [3], **67,** 257 (1863).
6. H. Staudinger, *Ber.*, **53,** 1073 (1920).
7. H. Mark and G. S. Whitby, eds., *Collected Papers of Wallace Hume Carothers,* Interscience Publishers, New York and London, 1940.

2

DEFINITIONS

Before proceeding with a description of the physical chemistry, characterization, mechanisms of formation, and preparation of polymers, certain terms in the vocabulary of the polymer chemist must be understood.

2.1 FUNDAMENTAL DEFINITIONS

The word *polymer* was first used to describe compounds with the same composition but different molecular weights. Polymer means many of a unit.[1] Carothers[2] defined polymerization as a reaction which is functionally capable of proceeding indefinitely. The structure of a polymer is generally described in terms of its *structural unit*. Structural units are groups having two or more available bonding sites and are linked to one another through covalent bonds in a polymer molecule. Most polymers can be described in terms of their structural unit or units.

The units can be arranged and connected in a variety of ways. In the most straightforward type of polymer, the *linear polymer*, the units are connected to one another in a chain arrangement such as X—M—M—M—M $\cdots$ Y or X—(M)$_n$—Y, where M is a structural unit or a *monomer* and n is the *degree of polymerization*. The degree of polymerization (d.p.) describes the molecular size. High molecular weight polymers, especially synthetic polymers, have varying degrees of polymerization or a *molecular weight distribution* among the chains within an individual polymer batch. The chain of structural units M is terminated on either end by X and Y. Whereas M must be at least bivalent (two bonding sites), X and Y, the *end groups*, are monovalent (one bonding site). X and Y may be identical or different.

On the other hand, the structural recurring unit may be trivalent (trifunctional) or polyvalent (polyfunctional). Polymers made up of these units can have *nonlinear* or *branched* structures. At least some of the units

4

must be trivalent for a branched molecule. Polymer molecules such as that depicted can be interconnected to have a *network* structure, which may be a *planar network* or a three-dimensional *space network*.

$$
\begin{array}{c}
\text{Y} \\
| \\
\text{M} \\
| \\
\text{X—M—M—M—M—T—M—M—T--M—M—Y} \\
| \\
\text{M} \\
| \\
\text{M—M—X}
\end{array}
$$

Poly(ethylene adipate) and polyethylene may be taken as examples of *linear polymers*. In polyethylene, the *structural recurring unit* is two atoms long and in poly(ethylene adipate) the unit is ten atoms long, since the polymer is described in terms of both the acid and alcohol fragments which are the structural recurring units.

$$n + 2\, CH_2{=}CH_2 \longrightarrow CH_3{-}CH_2{-}(CH_2{-}CH_2)_n{-}CH_2{-}CH_3$$

$$nHOCH_2CH_2OH + nHOOC(CH_2)_4COOH \longrightarrow$$

$$H{-}\left[O{-}\overset{\displaystyle O}{\overset{\|}{C}}(CH_2)_4{-}\overset{\displaystyle O}{\overset{\|}{C}}{-}O{-}CH_2{-}CH_2\right]_n OH + 2nH_2O$$

In the example of polyethylene, the structural unit and the monomer from which the polymer is made have the same formula. Only the electronic structure has been changed. In the second example, water has been lost, and the recurring unit consists of two different structural units. The ethyl end groups for polyethylene and the H and OH end groups for poly(ethylene adipate) are shown. Often the end groups for a polymer are not even known and the polymer structure is written only in terms of the structural unit, the end groups being left off. In many cases the elementary analyses will not distinguish end groups in a high molecular weight compound. Even end groups on different polymer chains produced from the same polymerization reaction can be different. Since a structural unit can have a valence of two or more, the monomer must be capable of joining with two or more other monomers. If the monomer joins with only two other monomers, it is a *bifunctional* monomer. In this sense, ethylene glycol, adipic acid, and even ethylene are bifunctional and the unit is a *bifunctional unit*. Thus branching units are made from *polyfunctional monomers*. Glycerin, a polyfunctional monomer, and maleic anhydride, a bifunctional monomer, form a nonlinear (branched) polymer:

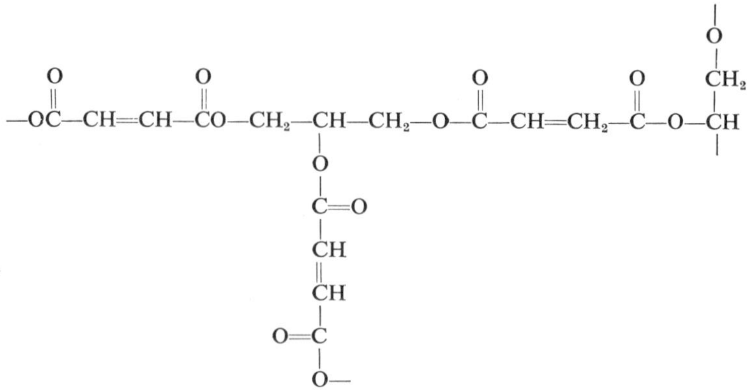

$$
\begin{array}{c}
\overset{\displaystyle |}{O} \\[2pt]
\overset{\displaystyle |}{CH_2}
\end{array}
$$

$$-OC\!\!\overset{\displaystyle O}{\overset{\|}{}}\!\!-CH\!=\!CH-CO\!\!\overset{\displaystyle O}{\overset{\|}{}}\!\!-CH_2-CH-CH_2-O-\overset{\displaystyle O}{\overset{\|}{C}}-CH\!=\!CH_2-\overset{\displaystyle O}{\overset{\|}{C}}-O-CH$$

$$
\begin{array}{c}
O \\
| \\
C=O \\
| \\
CH \\
\| \\
CH \\
| \\
O=C \\
| \\
O-
\end{array}
$$

Likewise, the polymerization of divinylbenzene and styrene can yield a network polymer:

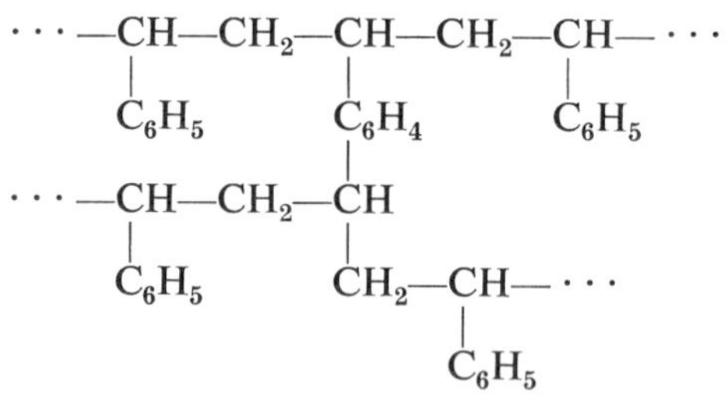

$$\cdots -CH-CH_2-CH-CH_2-CH- \cdots$$
$$C_6H_5 \qquad C_6H_4 \qquad C_6H_5$$
$$\cdots -CH-CH_2-CH$$
$$C_6H_5 \qquad CH_2-CH- \cdots$$
$$C_6H_5$$

In practice, this theoretical description of a linear polymer is sometimes not realized, since the smallest trace of a polyfunctional unit in an otherwise linear polymer would lead to a branched structure. Ordinarily, a polymer which is intentionally made from bifunctional monomers is considered linear even though it may contain a few branches.

Oftentimes it becomes impossible to write an accurate description of a branched polymer. In the case of the phenol-formaldehyde resin, formaldehyde is a difunctional monomer. Phenol may act part of the time as a difunctional monomer, in which formaldehyde can condense at the two ortho positions or one ortho and one para position, or part of the time it may act as a trifunctional molecule, in which formaldehyde condenses at three positions. Therefore, the polymer cannot be conveniently expressed in terms of a recurring unit and is usually represented as shown at top of facing page.

Polymers containing a single repeating unit, such as polyethylene, are referred to as *homopolymers*. This type of polymer is made from one monomer and is homogeneous in this respect. On the other hand, polymers containing two or more structural units, for example poly(ethylene adipate) or phenol-formaldehyde, are *copolymers*. The copolymer may be composed of two bifunctional units and may alternate to give a well-defined recurring unit or may be joined in a random fashion in which no recurring unit can be written:

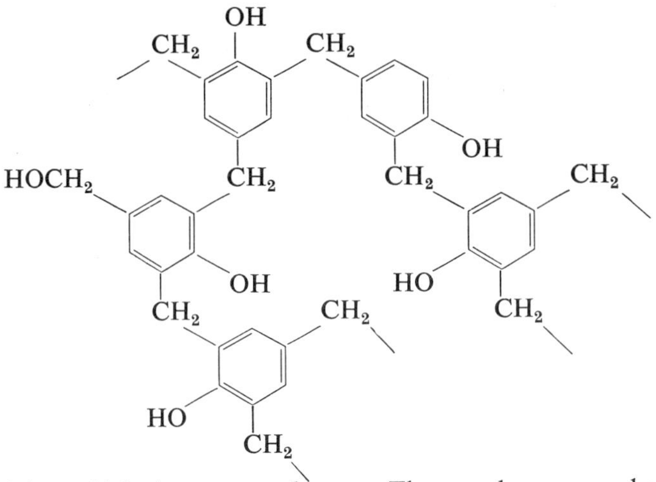

$$\cdots -M_1-M_2-M_1-M_2-M_1-M_2- \cdots \quad -(M_1-M_2)_n- \quad \text{(Alternating)}$$
$$\cdots -M_1-M_2-M_1-M_1-M_2-M_2-M_2-M_1-M_2- \cdots \quad \text{(Random)}$$

Both random and alternating types are referred to as *linear copolymers*.

2.2 POLYMER CLASSIFICATION

Carothers recognized the need for classification of polymers and divided all polymers into two types: *condensation polymers* and *addition polymers*.[3]

A condensation polymer is one which does not have the same composition as the monomer or monomers from which it was formed or to which it may be degraded by chemical means. These polymers are formed from bi- or polyfunctional monomers with the elimination of some smaller molecule as a by-product, usually water, methanol, or hydrogen chloride. Poly(ethylene terephthalate) is an example of a condensation polymer which is formed through an ester interchange with the loss of methanol:

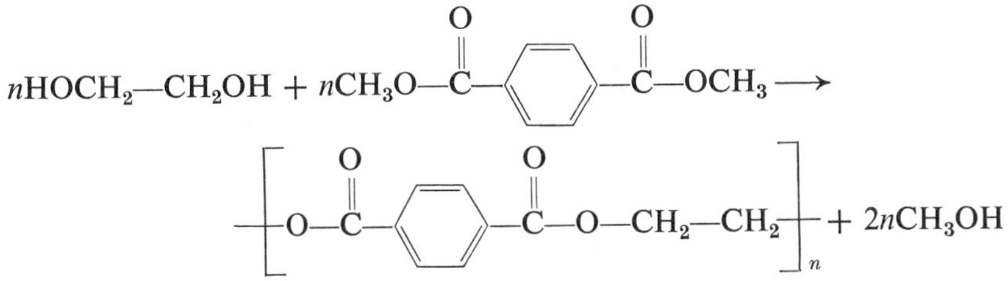

An addition polymer is one in which the recurring units have the same composition as the monomer or monomers from which they were formed. The polymer is formed from a bi- or polyfunctional monomer by the addition of one monomer to another without the loss of any portion of the monomer. Polymers formed from the polymerization of vinyl monomers are the most common of this class:

$$n\text{CH}_2\!\!=\!\!\text{CH} \longrightarrow \left[\text{CH}_2\!\!-\!\!\text{CH}\right]_n$$
$$\phantom{n\text{CH}_2=}\overset{|}{\text{X}} \phantom{\longrightarrow \left[\text{CH}_2-\right.}\overset{|}{\text{X}}$$

Flory[4] has argued that the significant difference between addition and condensation polymerization is not a matter of similarity or difference in the composition of the monomer and structural unit, but is a matter of the reactions which form the polymers. Condensation polymerizations proceed by a stepwise intermolecular condensation, while addition polymerizations are associated with a chain mechanism involving active centers on the growing chain. This difference will be clearly pointed out in a later discussion of the kinetics of polymerization (Chapter 5). The structural units of a condensation polymer are joined by internal functional groups, while addition polymers usually have a carbon chain backbone.

$$\begin{array}{cc} & \overset{\displaystyle \text{F}\quad \text{F}\quad \text{F}}{\overset{\displaystyle |\quad |\quad |}{}} \\ -\text{R}-\text{F}-\text{R}-\text{F}- & -\text{R}-\text{R}-\text{R}- \\ \text{\small Condensation} & \text{\small Addition} \end{array}$$

It can be seen that there are several difficulties with Carothers' definition. The formation of some condensation polymers takes place without a change in the composition in going from monomer to structural unit and does not split off a small molecule during the course of polymerization. The reaction of a diol with a diisocyanate to form a polyurethane demonstrates this:

$$n\text{HOROH} + n\text{OCN—R}'\text{—NCO} \longrightarrow$$

$$\text{HO}\left[\text{R—O—}\overset{\displaystyle \text{O}}{\overset{\displaystyle \|}{\text{C}}}\text{—NH—R}'\text{—NH—}\overset{\displaystyle \text{O}}{\overset{\displaystyle \|}{\text{C}}}\text{—O}\right]_{n-1}\text{R—O—}\overset{\displaystyle \text{O}}{\overset{\displaystyle \|}{\text{C}}}\text{—NHR}'\text{NCO}$$

According to Flory's definition, this reaction would fall into the condensation class from the standpoint of both mechanism and internal functional groups.

The conversion of caprolactam to nylon 6 can be classed either as an addition polymerization or as a condensation polymerization by the same definitions. The same polymer can be obtained, however, from ε-amino caproic acid by the loss of water:

$$CH_2—(CH_2)_4—CO \longrightarrow \left[NH—(—CH_2)_5—\overset{\overset{\textstyle O}{\|}}{C} \right] \xleftarrow{-H_2O} H_3\overset{\oplus}{N}(CH_2)_5CO_2^{\ominus}$$
$$\underset{NH}{|}$$

Condensation polymers. Condensation polymers must be made by utilizing a reaction which is functionally capable of proceeding indefinitely. The monomer or monomers must have two or more groups which will enter into the condensation reaction. The chemistry involved in the formation of a condensation polymer is the chemistry of simple organic reactions. Esterification by the reaction of an acid and an alcohol, an acid chloride and an alcohol, an acid anhydride and an alcohol, or trans-esterification are all widely used, and the kinetics or mechanism type in these polymerization reactions are similar. Steric factors encountered in the reactions of monofunctional molecules can also be applied in the poly-merization reactions of polyfunctional molecules; thus steric considera-tions are important. Some examples of polyesters as well as other condensation polymers are given in Table 2.1.

The polymerization reaction must be an extremely efficient process. For this to be so, the monomers must be free from impurities which would terminate the reaction. In the formation of a polyester from a diol and a dibasic acid, mere traces of monobasic acid would reduce the molecular weight considerably. It has been pointed out[5] that more time has been wasted in industrial research by the use of impure monomers in studying polymer-forming reactions than any other way. The process must be free from side reactions which would act as growth terminators, especially those which would use up functional groups without producing a link in the polymer chain. Stoichiometric balance in a condensation reaction of two monomers must be as exact as possible for the formation of high molecular weight polymers.

Such caution is not necessary in the formation of nonlinear condensation polymers. In the formation of a resin from a dibasic acid and a triol, the functionality of the polymer increases as its molecular weight increases, and therefore, even if some functional sites are destroyed, others will continue the chain.

There is one other important consideration with difunctional molecules. Intramolecular reactions to give cyclic compounds sometimes occur. Termination by reaction of one end of the molecule with a functional group on the other end is favored when five- and six-membered rings can be

TABLE 2.1
Condensation polymers

Polymer	Example
1. Polyester	$nHORCO_2H \longrightarrow $ ╉$O-R-CO$╊$_n + nH_2O$

$$HOROH + HO_2CR'CO_2H \longrightarrow \text{╉}O-R-O-\underset{\underset{O}{\parallel}}{C}-R'-\underset{\underset{O}{\parallel}}{C}\text{╊} + 2nH_2O$$

$$HOROH + R' \overset{CO}{\underset{CO}{<}} O \longrightarrow \text{╉}O-R-O-\underset{\underset{O}{\parallel}}{C}-R'-\underset{\underset{O}{\parallel}}{C}\text{╊} + nH_2O$$

$$HOROH + Cl-COR'COCl \longrightarrow \text{╉}O-R-O-\underset{\underset{O}{\parallel}}{C}-R'-\underset{\underset{O}{\parallel}}{C}\text{╊} + 2nHCl$$

$$HOROH + R''-O-COR'CO_2R'' \longrightarrow \text{╉}O-R-O-\underset{\underset{O}{\parallel}}{C}-R'-\underset{\underset{O}{\parallel}}{C}\text{╊} + 2nR''OH$$

$$RHC\overset{O}{\underset{CH_2}{\triangle}}CHR + HO_2CR'CO_2H \longrightarrow HO_2R'CO_2CHR-CHROH \longrightarrow \text{╉}O-CHR-CHR-O-\underset{\underset{O}{\parallel}}{C}-R'-\underset{\underset{O}{\parallel}}{C}\text{╊} + nH_2O$$

$$CH_2\overset{O}{\underset{}{\triangle}}CH-R-CH\overset{}{\underset{}{\triangle}}CH_2 + HO_2R'CO_2H \longrightarrow \text{╉}O-CH-R-CH-R-O-\underset{\underset{O}{\parallel}}{C}-R'-\underset{\underset{O}{\parallel}}{C}\text{╊}$$
$$\qquad\qquad\qquad CH_2OH \quad CH_2OH$$

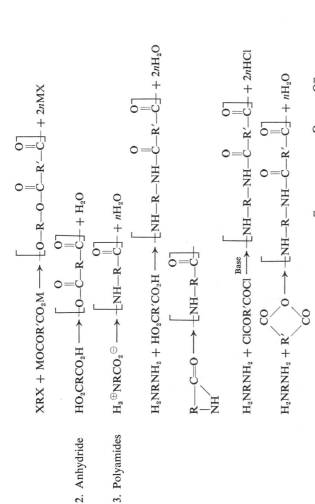

$$\mathrm{XRX + MOCOR'CO_2M \longrightarrow \left[O{-}R{-}O{-}\overset{O}{\overset{\|}{C}}{-}R'{-}\overset{O}{\overset{\|}{C}}\right] + 2\mathit{n}MX}$$

2. Anhydride

$$\mathrm{HO_2CRCO_2H \longrightarrow \left[O{-}\overset{O}{\overset{\|}{C}}{-}R{-}\overset{O}{\overset{\|}{C}}\right] + H_2O}$$

3. Polyamides

$$\mathrm{H_3{}^{\oplus}NRCO_2{}^{\ominus} \longrightarrow \left[NH{-}R{-}\overset{O}{\overset{\|}{C}}\right] + \mathit{n}H_2O}$$

$$\mathrm{H_2NRNH_2 + HO_2CR'CO_2H \longrightarrow \left[NH{-}R{-}NH{-}\overset{O}{\overset{\|}{C}}{-}R'{-}\overset{O}{\overset{\|}{C}}\right] + 2\mathit{n}H_2O}$$

$$\mathrm{\underset{\displaystyle \backslash NH /}{R{-}C{=}O}} \longrightarrow \mathrm{\left[NH{-}R{-}\overset{O}{\overset{\|}{C}}\right]}$$

$$\mathrm{H_2NRNH_2 + ClCOR'COCl \xrightarrow{Base} \left[NH{-}R{-}NH{-}\overset{O}{\overset{\|}{C}}{-}R'{-}\overset{O}{\overset{\|}{C}}\right] + 2\mathit{n}HCl}$$

$$\mathrm{H_2NRNH_2 + R'\!\begin{matrix} CO \\ CO \end{matrix}\!\!>\!O \longrightarrow \left[NH{-}R{-}NH{-}\overset{O}{\overset{\|}{C}}{-}R'{-}\overset{O}{\overset{\|}{C}}\right] + \mathit{n}H_2O}$$

$$\mathrm{H_2NHRNH_2 + R''OCOR'CO_2R'' \longrightarrow \left[NH{-}R{-}NH{-}\overset{O}{\overset{\|}{C}}{-}R'{-}\overset{O}{\overset{\|}{C}}\right] + 2\mathit{n}R''OH}$$

TABLE 2.1 (Continued)

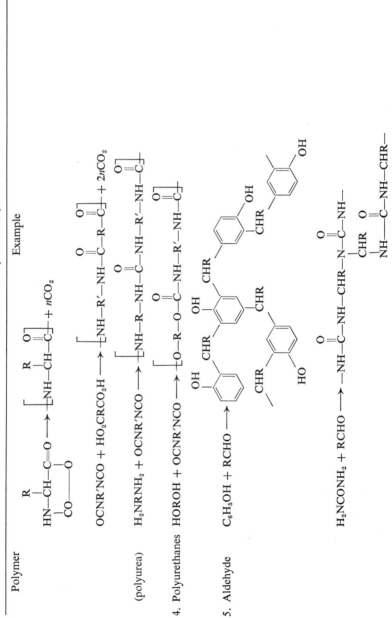

6. Polyacetals

$$HOROH + CHR'(OR'')_2 \longrightarrow +[O-R-O-CHR']+ + 2nR''OH$$

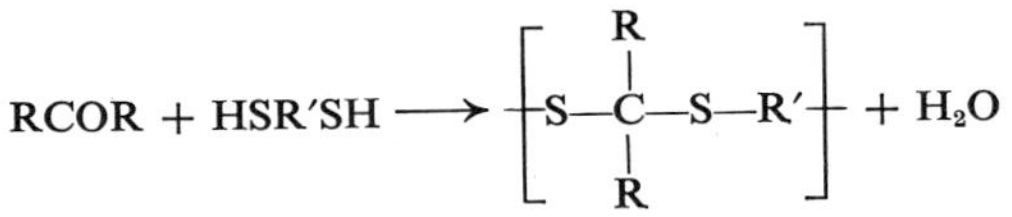

$$RCOR + HSR'SH \longrightarrow \left[S-\underset{R}{\overset{R}{C}}-S-R' \right] + H_2O$$

7. Polysulfides

$$XRX + Na_2S \longrightarrow [S-R] + 2NaX$$

$$XRX + Na-S-R'-S-Na \longrightarrow +[R-S-R'-S]+ + 2NaX$$

$$HSRSH \xrightarrow{[O]} [R-S-S]$$

$$HSRSH + CH_2=CHR'CH=CH_2 \longrightarrow +[S-R-S-CH_2-CH_2-R'-CH_2-CH_2]+$$

8. Polyethers

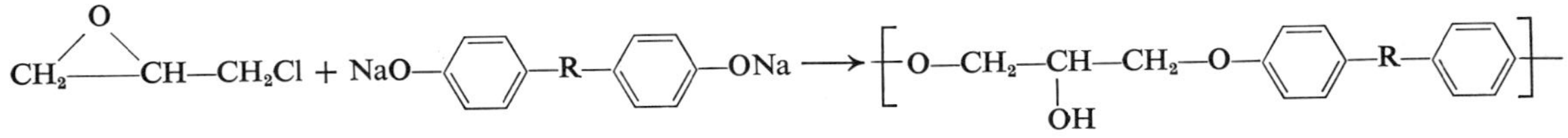

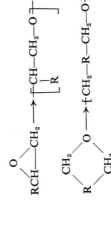

$$RCH\overset{O}{\diagdown}CH_2 \longrightarrow +[CH-CH_2-O]+ \quad [R]$$

$$\underset{H_2O}{\overset{CH_2}{R}\diagup O \diagdown \overset{CH_2}{}} \longrightarrow +[CH_2-R-CH_2-O]+$$

9. Silicones

$$R_2SiCl_2 \longrightarrow +[SiR_2-O]+ + 2nHCl$$

formed. For example, high molecular weight polymers of the α-, β-, γ-, and δ-hydroxy acids are not formed since the α-hydroxys give lactids, the β-hydroxys form α,β-unsaturated acids, and the γ- and δ-hydroxy acids form lactones. The same is true with the amino acids. When the ring that can form is less than five- or greater than six-membered, polymerization takes place instead of ring formation.

Some examples of large-ring formation can be cited, even in fairly concentrated media. As much as 10 to 15% of cyclic dimer (eighteen-membered ring) is formed as a by-product in the polymerization of ethylene glycol and isophthalic acid:[6]

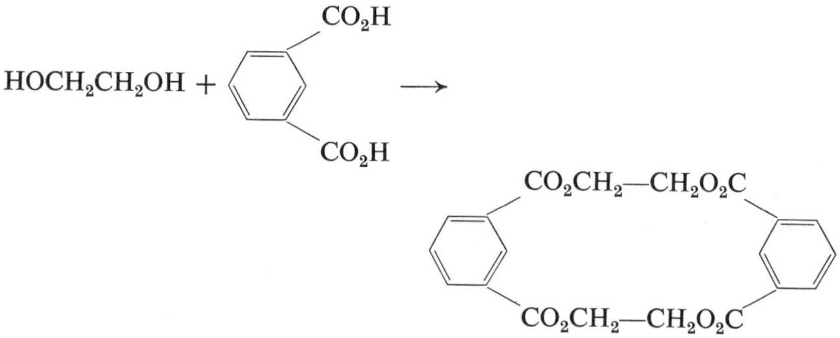

Cyclic mercaptals are formed in the reaction of acetone and decamethylene-dithiol:[7]

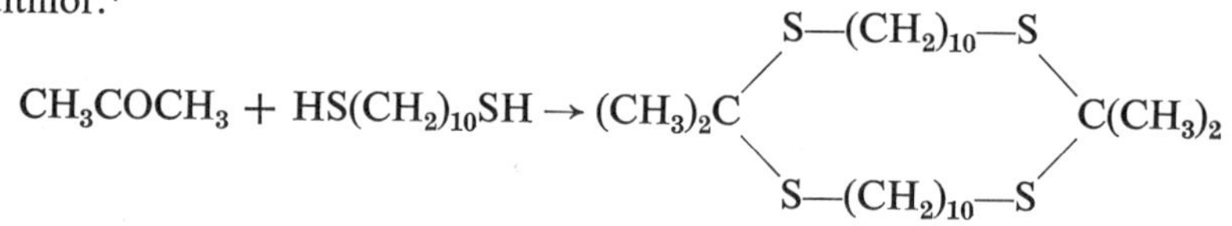

$$CH_3COCH_3 + HS(CH_2)_{10}SH \rightarrow$$

Macrocyclic lactones,[8] urethanes,[9] and esters[10] are also reported:

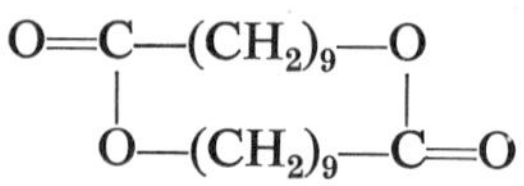

Lactone

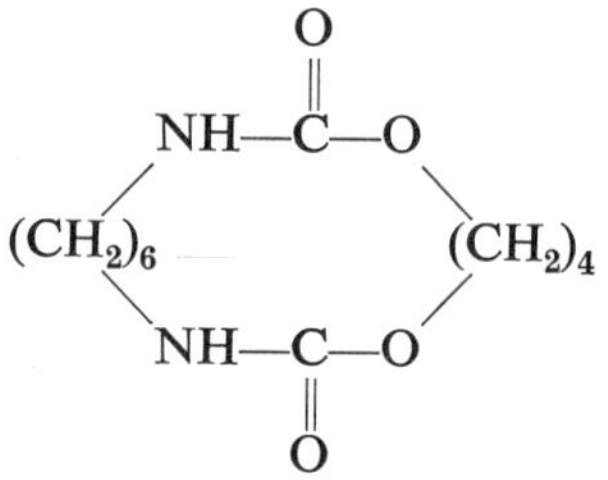

Urethane

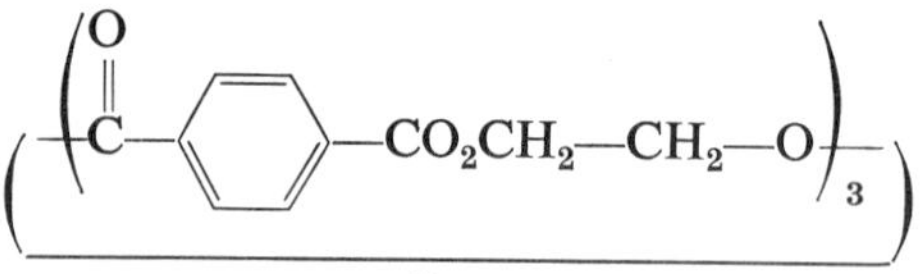

Ester

Large-ring compounds have also been isolated for a variety of polyamide polymers. The formation of cyclic mers of nylon 66 has been reported,[11,12] and it has been shown that in the polymerization of caprolactam, large rings are formed to the extent of 3 %.[13]

$$\left(\underline{-NH(CH_2)_6NHCO(CH_2)_4CO} \right)_n) \qquad \left(\underline{-NH(CH_2)_5CO} \right)_n)$$

$$(n = 1\text{--}4) \qquad\qquad (n = 5\text{--}9)$$

The structures of the various compounds were confirmed by an independent synthesis and the largest ring found contained sixty-three atoms in the ring.

Some of the polymers listed under condensation polymers could also be included under addition polymers. In almost every case, a polymer prepared by the conversion of a cyclic monomer to a polymer can also be prepared by the condensation of linear monomers according to the definition of Carothers. For example, the carboanhydrides form polyamides by splitting of a small molecule, and the product possesses the typical condensation structure. Yet the polymerization proceeds by a mechanism characteristic of addition polymerization. The polymerization of an epoxide to a polyether proceeds by a mechanism characteristic of addition polymerization, and the polymer cannot be degraded by hydrogen iodide into a glycol. However, the polymer could conceivably be formed by an alternative method. In order to avoid confusion on the basis of the two definitions, Flory[4] has suggested that the polymer be classed according to the reverse polymerization reaction, or the monomers into which a polymer can be degraded. The polymerization of a lactone, lactam, cyclic anhydride, or carboanhydride falls into the condensation class (Table 2.1). The opening of these ring compounds usually proceeds by an interchange reaction either catalytically or by traces of end-group-producing substances.

Addition polymers. Addition polymerization of vinyl monomers to give high molecular weight polymers proceeds by a chain mechanism. Whether the mechanism is of a free radical, cationic, or anionic type, this polymerization features an active site at the end of the growing polymer chain. Addition polymerization proceeds by the following mechanism, and the polymerization is finally terminated by some other reaction to give a polymer of finite length:

$$M + I^* \longrightarrow IM^* \xrightarrow{M} IM\text{---}M^* \xrightarrow{M} IM_2M^* \longrightarrow I\text{---}(M)_n\text{---}M^*$$

I^* can be some free radical initiator, cationic initiator, or anionic initiator. Therefore, a free radical, cation, or anion is present on the end of the growing chain. In this type of propagation, the synthesis of a complete polymer molecule is very fast and the overall conversion of all the monomers to polymer chains is slow, so that there are few low or intermediate molecular weight polymer molecules.

In general, 1,2-disubstituted ethylenes do not polymerize well under free radical conditions, and ethylene itself is the only aliphatic hydrocarbon which will form high molecular weight polymers.

$$n\text{RCH}=\text{CH}_2 \longrightarrow \left[\begin{array}{c} \text{CH}-\text{CH}_2 \\ | \\ \text{R} \end{array} \right]_n$$

Substituted ethylenes of the type $CH_2=CHX$ (where X is a halogen), $-CO_2H$ (or derivative), $-OCOR$, $-OSO_2R$, $-\overset{\displaystyle O}{\overset{\|}{C}}-R$, or aryl are susceptible to free radical polymerization. Monomers of the type $CH_2=CX_2$, $XCH=CX_2$, or $X_2C=CX_2$, where X is halogen, are the only polysubstituted ethylenes which are readily polymerized.

Conjugated diene monomers of the butadiene type undergo free radical addition polymerization with either 1,2- or 1,4-addition. Generally both are observed in free radical polymerizations and the chain contains a random mixture of both 1,2- and 1,4-units.

$$(m+n)\text{CH}_2=\text{CH}-\text{CH}=\text{CH}_2 \longrightarrow$$

$$\left[\text{CH}_2-\text{CH}=\text{CH}-\text{CH}_2 \right]_m \left[\begin{array}{c} \text{CH}_2-\text{CH} \\ | \\ \text{CH} \\ \| \\ \text{CH}_2 \end{array} \right]_n$$

The monomer types suitable for cationic and anionic addition polymerization are quite different from one another as well as being different from the free radical type. Ethylenes substituted by groups which favor or stabilize the formation of carbonium ions or carbanions will form high molecular weight polymers by these mechanisms. Isobutylene and α-methylstyrene polymerize best by cationic initiation where the existence of a stable tertiary carbonium ion in the growing chain is favored:

$$\cdots\text{CH}_2-\overset{\displaystyle CH_3}{\underset{\displaystyle CH_3}{\overset{|}{C}}}{}^{\oplus} \qquad \cdots\text{CH}_2{\overset{\delta+}{=\!=\!=}}\overset{\displaystyle CH_3{}^{\delta+}}{\underset{\displaystyle CH_3{}^{\delta+}}{\overset{\|}{C}}} \qquad \cdots\text{CH}_2-\overset{\displaystyle CH_3}{\underset{\displaystyle C_6H_5}{\overset{|}{C}}}{}^{\oplus} \qquad -\text{CH}_2-\overset{\displaystyle CH_3}{\underset{\displaystyle \boxed{+}}{\overset{|}{C}}}$$

Acrylonitrile may be polymerized by anionic initiators since the carbanion in the growing chain is stabilized:

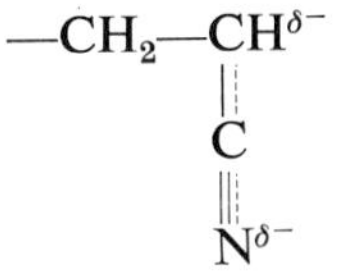

$$-CH_2-CH^{\delta-}$$
$$|$$
$$C$$
$$|||$$
$$N^{\delta-}$$

Copolymers of vinyl monomers can be readily formed, and in fact, many vinyl monomers which fail to undergo homopolymerization reactions will form copolymers. Nonlinear addition polymers are obtained by copolymerizing a nonconjugated divinyl monomer with a vinyl monomer.

Unusual condensation and addition polymers. Certain polymers are formed by reactions which are similar to addition polymerization reactions, but have the characteristics of condensation polymers. These are not the cyclic monomers which polymerize by ring opening, and the polymers that are formed cannot usually be made by other condensation reactions. The free radical initiated reaction of a nonconjugated diolefin and a dithiol is an example:

$$HSRSH + CH_2=CH-R'CH=CH_2 \longrightarrow$$
$$+S-R-S-CH_2-CH_2-R'-CH_2-CH_2+$$

The copolymers formed from sulfur dioxide and olefins are also unusual in that the polymerization reaction is believed to proceed first through an SO_2-olefin complex, followed by polymerization:

$$CH_2=CH_2 + SO_2 \rightarrow +SO_2-CH_2-CH_2+$$

This reaction has all the earmarks of an addition reaction but the polymer has the condensation structure.

The formation of Diels-Alder polymers (Chapter 8), on the other hand, should proceed by a stepwise addition, but the polymers do not have the characteristic condensation structure and cannot be formed by a different method.

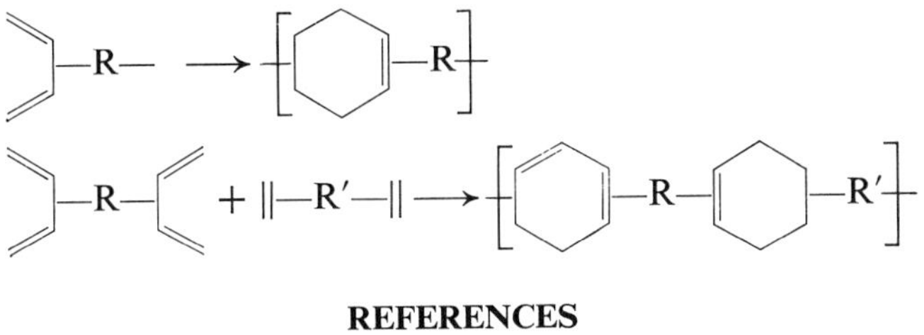

REFERENCES

1. J. J. Berzelius, *Jahresbericht*, **12**, 63 (1833).
2. W. H. Carothers, *Chem. Revs.*, **8**, 353 (1931).

3. W. H. Carothers, *J. Am. Chem. Soc.*, **51**, 2548 (1929).

4. P. J. Flory, *Principles of Polymer Chemistry*, Cornell University Press, Ithaca, N.Y., 1953.

5. C. S. Marvel, *An Introduction to the Organic Chemistry of High Polymers*, John Wiley and Sons, New York, 1959, p. 13.

6. C. E. Berr, *J. Polymer Sci.*, **15**, 591 (1955).

7. C. S. Marvel and R. C. Farrar, Jr., *J. Am. Chem. Soc.*, **79**, 986 (1957).

8. W. H. Carothers and F. J. van Natta, *J. Am. Chem. Soc.*, **55**, 4714 (1933).

9. O. Bayer, *Ann.*, **549**, 286 (1941).

10. S. D. Ross, E. R. Coburn, W. A. Leach, and W. B. Robinson, *J. Polymer Sci.*, **13**, 406 (1954).

11. H. Zahn, P. Miro. and F. Schmidt, *Chem. Ber.*, **90**, 1411 (1957).

12. C. J. Brown, A. Hill, and P. V. Youle, *Nature*, **177**, 128 (1956).

13. H. Rothe, *J. Polymer Sci.*, **30**, 227 (1958).

3

PHYSICAL CHEMISTRY
OF POLYMERS

There are many factors which determine the physical properties of simple molecules as well as polymer molecules. Some of the most important of these factors are molecular weight, the nature of the primary and secondary valence bonds, and the symmetry, arrangement, and configuration of the molecule. These factors influence the crystallinity of the molecule, which in turn, and in combination with these factors, determines such simple physical properties as melting point, tensile strength, solubility, viscosity, etc. An attempt is made here to discuss, correlate, and show the interdependence of these factors and the physical properties.

3.1 CHEMICAL BONDS

In addition to the covalent bonds which hold together the structural units of a polymer chain, there are other bonding forces, as in simple organic compounds, which must be considered in order to account for many of the physical properties of the polymer. These bonds are the secondary valence or intermolecular forces, which can be broken down into several types.

Dipole forces arise from a difference in electronegativity of two atoms in a molecule which produces a polar bond. When two different areas of the molecule have equal and opposite charges or when the resultant of all the centers of charge does not add up to zero, the molecule has a permanent dipole moment. At small distances between molecules, there is an attraction between molecules at the unlike poles of the molecules. Such dipole interaction, for example, can be found in polyesters (see top of next page).

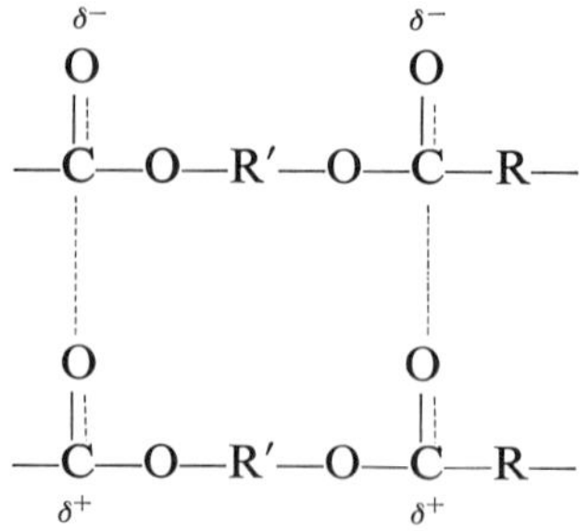

$$\begin{array}{ccccccccc}
 & \overset{\delta^-}{O} & & & & \overset{\delta^-}{O} & & & \\
 & \parallel & & & & \parallel & & & \\
-C & - & O & - & R' & - & O & - & C & - & R & - \\
\end{array}$$

$$-\underset{\delta^+}{\overset{O}{\underset{\parallel}{C}}}-O-R'-O-\underset{\delta^+}{\overset{O}{\underset{\parallel}{C}}}-R-$$

There are undoubtedly some examples of dipole-induced dipoles which have an effect on the physical properties. A strong permanent dipole may induce a dipole in a nearly covalent bond as it approaches the covalent bond. Similarly, in even the relatively dipole-free hydrocarbon polymers, induced dipole interactions (dispersion forces) arise where neither molecule has a permanent dipole. The strongest and most influential of the secondary valence forces (when it exists) is the hydrogen bond. This type of bonding accounts for the most marked changes in the physical chemical properties of large molecules. The classical example of this is the hydrogen bonding which occurs in polyamides:

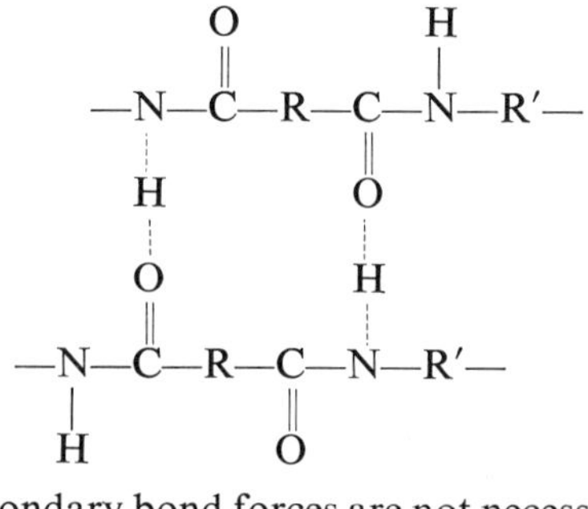

$$\begin{array}{cccccc}
 & O & & & H & \\
 & \parallel & & & | & \\
-N-C-R- & C & -N-R'- \\
| & & \parallel & \\
H & & O & \\
\end{array}$$

$$-N-\overset{O}{\overset{\parallel}{C}}-R-\underset{\parallel}{\overset{}{C}}-N-R'-$$

Whereas these secondary bond forces are not necessary for the formation of a stable polymer chemically, through the aggregation of polymer chains, they greatly influence the physical properties of the polymer.

3.2 CONFIGURATION AND STRUCTURE OF POLYMER CHAINS

The structural recurring unit of a linear condensation polymer formed from either a difunctional monomer or two different difunctional monomers must, by the nature of the chemical reaction, be quite simple. The recurring unit will be ordered in its structure, and along the backbone of the polymer chain there will be an internal functional group at predictable carbon intervals.

The structural recurring unit of a vinyl polymer is not quite so simple or obvious. The addition of a free radical, cation, or anion to a simple vinyl monomer can occur in either of two ways:

$$R* + CH_2{=}CHX \begin{cases} (a)\ RCH_2{-}CHX* \\ (b)\ R{-}CHX{-}CH_2* \end{cases}$$

(* = a radical, —, or +)

Which mode of addition takes place will depend on the stability of the resulting free radical, cation, or anion throughout the growing process. This stability depends upon the substituent X and the fact that there is a choice between a primary, secondary, or tertiary free radical, carbonium ion, or carbanion. In free radical addition, path a would be followed since a secondary free radical is formed. One further factor to consider is the steric hindrance encountered in the approach of the free radical source to the vinyl monomer. If this type of addition persists throughout the growing of the polymer chain, the polymer molecule will be arranged in an orderly *head-to-tail* fashion rather than a *head-to-head–tail-to-tail* fashion or even in a random fashion.

$$-CH_2{-}CH{-}CH_2{-}CH{-}CH_2{-}CH{-}$$
$$\qquad\ \ |\qquad\qquad |\qquad\qquad |$$
$$\qquad\ \ X\qquad\quad\ \ X\qquad\quad\ \ X$$

Head-to-tail

$$-CH_2{-}CH{-}CH{-}CH_2{-}CH_2{-}CH{-}CH{-}CH_2{-}$$
$$\qquad\ \ |\quad\ |\qquad\qquad\qquad\ |\quad\ |$$
$$\qquad\ \ X\quad X\qquad\qquad\qquad X\quad X$$

Head-to-head–tail-to-tail

The proof of the structural arrangement of the vinyl polymer chains will be considered later.

There is occasion during vinyl polymerization, especially free radical vinyl polymerization, for a branch to occur along the polymer chain. The atom at the site of the branch is made trifunctional when this occurs. There are generally two types of branching, long- and short-chain, which may give to the polymer molecule a feather-like arrangement or a structure more like a three-dimensional polymer:

Short-chain branching   Long-chain branching

The mechanism by which this branching occurs will be discussed in Chapter 5, but it is important to the physical properties of the polymer in that it brings disorder to the chain.

There is yet a more subtle consideration in the structure of a vinyl polymer made from a monomer of the type $CH_2{=}CHR$. When $CH_2{=}CHR$

polymerizes, asymmetric centers are generated along the chain backbone. The carbon atom bearing the R substituent can take up either a *d*- or an *l*-configuration and in most polymerization processes a completely random arrangement is obtained. If the R substituent is not optically active in its own right, then because of the random character (*d* and *l*) of the backbone carbon atoms, the polymer will not exhibit any optical activity. In the polymer chain —CH_2—CHR— there is a possibility that the tertiary carbon atoms will have the same configuration with respect to the other tertiary carbon atoms.

The various arrangements can be visualized by placing the zigzag chain backbone in the same plane and arranging the R groups on the alternate tertiary carbon atoms. When all the R groups are on the same side of the plane, either above or below, the regular sequence of head-to-tail monomer units has every other carbon atom of the same conformation, and the polymer has an isotactic structure:[1]

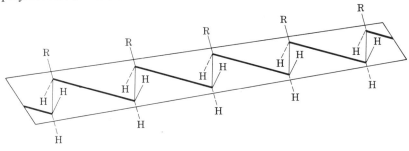

Isotactic

In polymer molecules with different end groups on an isotactic polymer, the polymer is optically active, but in practice optical activity is not observed since its mirror image is produced in an equal amount.

If the R groups are alternately above and below the plane of the zigzag backbone, the polymer has a syndiotactic structure. A polymer containing the random structure with no regular sequence is referred to as an atactic polymer.

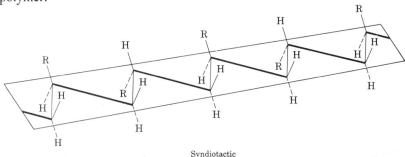

Syndiotactic

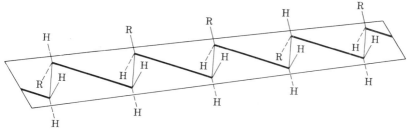

Atactic

   The actual spatial arrangement of a solid isotactic polymer is rarely in the planar zigzag conformation as depicted.   More often there is a large steric interaction between R groups so that the chain is forced out of the planar arrangement.   Suitable rotations around the carbon-carbon single bonds relieve the interaction, and the R substituents serve as a free rotation barrier.   Many such chains in the solid state will fit into a spiral spatial arrangement, where a full $360°$ spiral may require three or more structural recurring units in a vinyl polymer.

   A much more complex situation can result from the polymerization of a conjugated diene monomer.   To illustrate the structures and conformations of a diene, consider a 2-substituted-1,3-butadiene.   In the free radical polymerization, especially, there are three paths for polymerization: by 1,2-, 3,4-, or 1,4-addition.

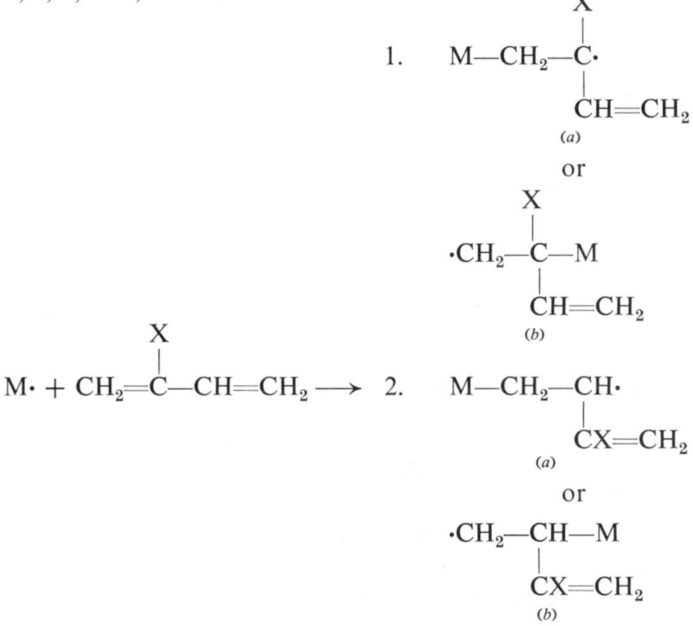

$$
\text{1.} \quad M-CH_2-\overset{\displaystyle X}{\underset{\displaystyle CH=CH_2}{C\cdot}}
$$
(a)

or

$$
\cdot CH_2-\overset{\displaystyle X}{\underset{\displaystyle CH=CH_2}{C}}-M
$$
(b)

$$
M\cdot + CH_2=\overset{\displaystyle X}{C}-CH=CH_2 \longrightarrow \quad \text{2.} \quad M-CH_2-\underset{\displaystyle CX=CH_2}{CH\cdot}
$$
(a)

or

$$
\cdot CH_2-\underset{\displaystyle CX=CH_2}{CH}-M
$$
(b)

$$3. \quad M—CH_2—\overset{\overset{\displaystyle X}{|}}{C}=CH—CH_2\cdot$$
(a)

or

$$\cdot CH_2—\overset{\overset{\displaystyle X}{|}}{C}=CH—CH_2—M$$
(b)

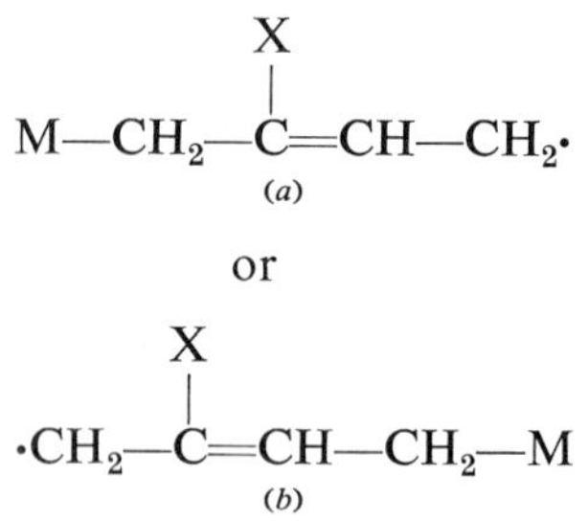

Whether the addition takes place at end *a* or *b* of any given path is of no consequence to the overall structure of the polymer chain as long as the addition always proceeds either at end *a* or end *b*. All three modes are known, and all one structure may exist throughout in a given polymer chain or the three may be mixed at random in any one chain. Which type is formed depends again on the type of polymerization (free radical, anionic, cationic) and the relative stability of the radical or ion in question.

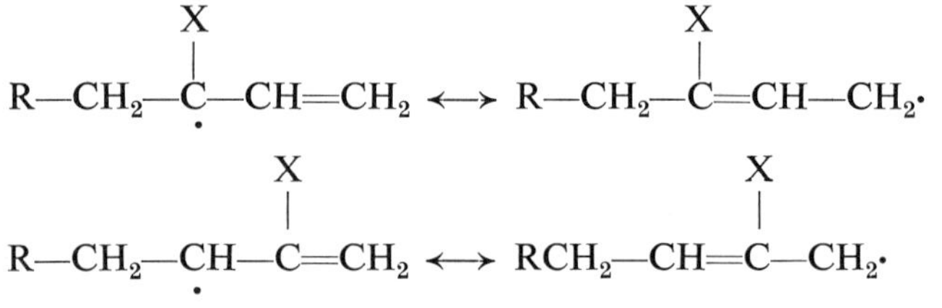

$$R—CH_2—\overset{\overset{\displaystyle X}{|}}{\underset{\cdot}{C}}—CH=CH_2 \longleftrightarrow R—CH_2—\overset{\overset{\displaystyle X}{|}}{C}=CH—CH_2\cdot$$

$$R—CH_2—CH—\overset{\overset{\displaystyle X}{|}}{\underset{\cdot}{C}}=CH_2 \longleftrightarrow RCH_2—CH=\overset{\overset{\displaystyle X}{|}}{C}—CH_2\cdot$$

The 1,4-unit may occur either as the *cis*- or the *trans*-isomer, and the 1,2- or 3,4-units may be arranged in an isotactic, syndiotactic, or atactic chain. In the case of the syndiotactic polymers, there is no need to depart from the zigzag chain in solid polymers.

The copolymers formed from condensation reactions, for example from a diacid and a dialcohol, must by the nature of the reaction have a regular chain with alternating alcohol and acid units along the backbone. Vinyl copolymers made from monomers A and B may have a range of incorporation of A and B units in the chain, and the polymer is rarely a perfect 1:1 copolymer. In addition, the A and B units may or may not alternate along the chain in the 1:1 copolymer and will not have the arrangement shown, for example, in a 3:1 copolymer.

$$—A—A—A—B—A—A—A—B—$$

The arrangement in this case has at least some degree of randomness, and more often than not copolymers of this type will have a range of concentration of any one unit among different chains.

3.3 RELATION OF POLYMER STRUCTURE TO PHYSICAL PROPERTIES[2]

Molecular weight. The molecular weight and molecular weight distribution of polymers plays an important role in the physical properties of the polymer. In general, a narrow molecular weight distribution gives more useful polymers.[3] Most natural polymers and all of the synthetic polymers contain a wide range of molecular weights for the polymer molecules.

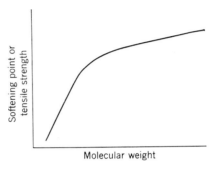

Fig. 3.1.

The softening point and tensile strength of a polymer can be related to its molecular weight and its other structural features. Low molecular weight polymers have low melting points and tensile strengths. Within a given polymer, the melting point and tensile strength increase as the molecular weight increases, as shown in Fig. 3.1. At lower molecular weights the melting point and tensile strength are very much affected by the molecular weight. At some molecular weight which is characteristic of the individual polymer, a break in the curve occurs and higher molecular weights have a lesser effect on the properties of the polymer. The relationship between the chain length n and the crystalline melting point Tm is expressed by $1/Tm = a + b/n$,[4,5] where a and b are constants.

Crystallinity. Many of the synthetic and natural polymers have some degree of crystallinity, but none of them are ever 100% crystalline. The amount of crystallinity in a polymer depends on the secondary valence bonds which can be formed, the structure of the polymer chain (degree of order), to some extent the physical treatment of the polymer, and the molecular weight of the polymer.

Crystalline polymers are most easily formed from structurally ordered chains. For a high degree of crystallinity, segments of the polymer chain must be able to fit into some sort of crystal lattice; i.e., one segment of a chain must be able to approach another segment of a different chain or the same chain where the structural features are identical.[6] This would be possible in all head-to-tail polymers, where there is regular stereochemistry in the chains. An isotactic chain, in which an ordered helix is present, or a syndiotactic chain is conducive to crystallite formation.[7] In a poly(1,3-diene), where there is a variety of structural units making up the polymer

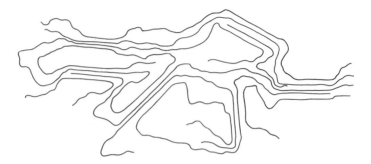

Fig. 3.2. An unoriented crystalline polymer.

chain (1,4-*cis* and -*trans*, 1,2-, and 3,4-units), there is a randomness which does not favor crystallites. If the 1,3-diene can be polymerized, for example to give a poly(*trans*-1,4-)structure throughout, the polymer can be made crystalline. Irregularities in the polymer such as chain branching or those brought about by random vinyl copolymers limit the regions of crystallinity to areas between branches or random segments. Vinyl copolymers approaching a 1:1 composition where there is no regular order to the placement of structural units along the chain are completely amorphous. Also, a crosslinked network of polymer chains, especially from vinyl polymers, where there is a high degree of disorder, will tend to be amorphous.

A crystalline polymer can be represented as shown in Fig. 3.2. X-ray studies have shown that crystalline regions in the polymer are no more than several hundred angstrom units in any direction. There will always be some amorphous regions in a polymer since segments of the polymer chains come together in a random fashion, and complete crystallization can be compared to the arranging and straightening of a tangled ball of yarn, although, as will be seen later, mechanical action, such as stretching and thermal changes, will help the formation of crystalline regions.

Whether or not a polymer tends to be crystalline depends not only on the structural order as discussed, but also on the symmetrical structure of the monomer itself and the association of chains by secondary valences, especially hydrogen bonding. In the molten state, whether or not the polymer chains can arrange themselves through secondary bonding and hold some order during cooling, plays an important role in crystallization. Polymer chains which have weak secondary bonding can be rapidly cooled past the crystalline melting point to give amorphous polymers even at low temperatures. This is analogous to the formation of a supercooled liquid. The rate of crystallization depends on the temperature at any point below

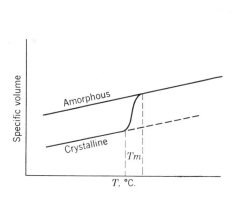

Fig. 3.3.[8]

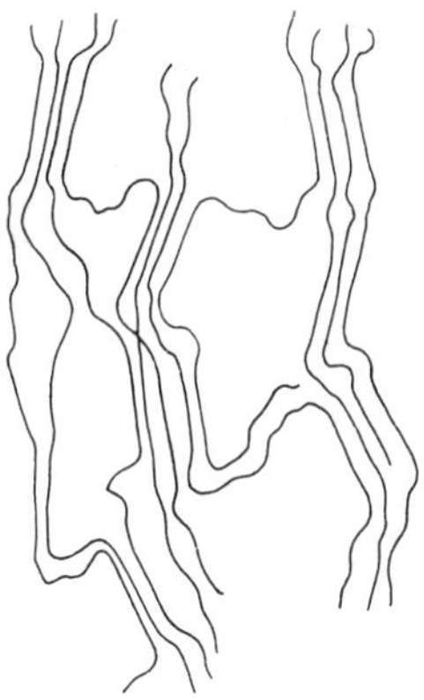

Fig. 3.4. An oriented
crystalline polymer.

the crystalline melting point. As the temperature of a polymer is raised, the crystalline regions melt over a temperature range, as shown in Fig. 3.3.[8]

When a polymer crystallizes in the absence of external forces, the crystallites tend to be oriented in a random fashion. If an external stress is applied to the polymer, it will undergo a transformation in which the crystallites are rearranged in the direction of the external stress. When this stress is applied below the crystalline melting point where crystallites are already well formed, the polymer stretches in the direction of the stress and the crystallites are oriented in this direction (Fig. 3.4). This process is referred to as *cold drawing*. The degree of crystallinity does not change if crystallinity is already well developed, but crystallinity of a largely amorphous polymer can be increased by this process. When the crystalline melting point is reached, the polymer becomes rubbery, leathery, or a viscous liquid. Discontinuous changes in density, refractive index, heat capacity, etc. are observed. Measurement of any of these properties over a range of temperatures will detect the *crystalline melting point Tm*. The transition associated with the disappearance of the crystallites is a first-order transition.

Structure and crystalline melting point. Secondary valence bonds have a great influence on the crystalline transition temperature. Where hydrogen bonding can take place, as in polyureas, polyamides, and polyurethanes, high melting points are observed.[9] Freedom of molecular motion along the chain backbone contributes to low crystal transition temperatures. For example, a chain with bulky groups, such as is found in polytetrafluoroethylene, has a higher melting point than polyethylene. Here too, dipole forces may play an important part. The substitution of inflexible units in the chain backbone raises the melting point. Insertion of a phenylene group for methylene units shows an increase in crystalline melting point. For example, poly(hexamethylene adipamide) melts at 235° while poly-(hexamethylene terephthalate) melts at 350° with decomposition.

As the number of methylene units separating polar groups or hydrogen bonding groups in a polymer increases, the polymer becomes more like polyethylene and the melting points tend to approach that of polyethylene (Fig. 3.5).[10]

It is surprising that the melting points of polyesters which contain polar groups lie below that of polyethylene, but the contributions of secondary valence bonds are apparently outweighed by the flexibility imparted to the chain in the oxygen linkages.

Within a given series of polyamides, polyureas, or polyurethanes, the melting points are also dependent on whether an odd or even number of methylene groups are contained in the polymer chain between polar groups. The example of the polyamides is shown in Figs. 3.6 and 3.7. The poly(ω-amino acids) follow a descending zigzag-odd, even line as the number of methylene groups increases.[11]

Within a series of polyhydrocarbons the melting points are affected markedly by pendant substituent groups along the chain backbone. Poly-ethylene containing chain branches cannot have a high degree of crystallinity and has a crystalline melting point of 110°C. Linear polyethylene, fractionated portions of which can be made to grow in single crystals, has a melting point of above 130°C.[13] When methyl groups are substituted along

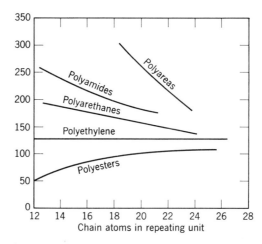

Fig. 3.5. Crystalline transition temperatures of polymers.[10]

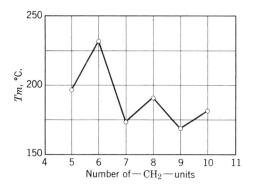

Fig. 3.6. ω-Amino acid polymers.[11]

the linear chain, as in polypropylene, and the groups are arranged in an atactic fashion, the polymer has little crystallinity and a second-order transition is observed at $-35°C$. On the other hand, isotactic polypropylene has a crystalline melting point of $165°C$.[14] The lengthening of the side chain in the higher isotactic poly(1-olefin) homologs decreases the melting point to polyhexene, at which point the melting point minimum takes an upward turn.[15] Apparently this decrease is due to the repulsion

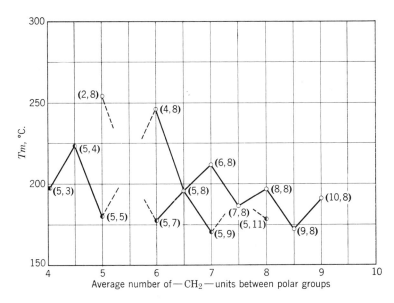

Fig. 3.7. Numbers in parentheses refer to the number of CH_2 groups in the diamine and dibasic acid respectively (e.g., 5,4 means pentamethylene diamine and adipic acid).[12]

of the bulky side groups in the crystalline regions. The upward turn is probably a result of side chain crystallites.

The relationship between the structural properties of crystalline high-melting polyhydrocarbons has been correlated.[16] In the olefin $CH_2=CH—CH—CH—CH—CH_2$, branching on the α-carbon gives the

highest melting polymers of any studied (250–360° range) of which polystyrene and poly(3-methyl-1-butene) are examples. Branching on the β-carbon, where the branching is symmetrical, gives polymers melting in the 225–240° range. Unsymmetrical branching lowers the melting point, and double branching in this position gives the highest melting polymers in the β-branching series. Poly(neopentylethylene) has a first-order transition temperature of 358°. Branching further out on the chain lowers the melting point and the terminal branches give rubbery polymers.

Copolymers have lower crystalline melting points than either of the homopolymers formed from the monomers making up the copolymer. Addition of larger and larger amounts of comonomer to a polymer chain decreases the melting point until a minimum is reached. This effect can be directly compared to eutectic formation in the melting point composition diagram of two simple crystalline organic molecules. The melting point behavior of the homologous series of poly(1-olefins) has also been likened to eutectic formation.[15]

Crystallinity—structure and other physical properties. Crystallinity and density of polymers go hand in hand. In all cases, the higher the degree of crystallinity, the higher the density. Highly crystalline polymers, such as the nylons, are characterized by high tensile strength, stiffness, hardness, and low solubility in solvents.[9]

These properties are even further enhanced by orientation or cold drawing. The solubility of any polymer depends on its molecular weight, degree of crystallinity, and structure.

The solubility in any solvent will decrease with increased molecular weight. Crystalline polymers are less easily soluble than amorphous polymers since a greater crystal binding force must be overcome. Once in solution, however, a crystalline polymer exhibits solution properties like those of a solution of the same polymer in the amorphous state. Which solvent is most suitable for any given polymer depends on the structure of the polymer and what groups are contained in the structural recurring units of the polymer. The same solubility rules which apply to simple organic molecules can be applied to polymers.

Phase transition temperature. The properties of polymers may change markedly with small changes in temperature as a result of the crystalline

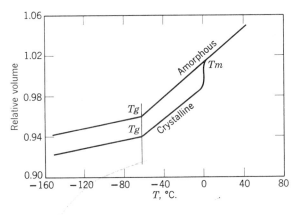

Fig. 3.8.[8]

regions in the polymer (first-order transition) or as a result of particular molecular motions within the molecule (second-order transition). The second-order transition in polymers is referred to as the glass transition, T_g, the temperature at which the polymer loses its hardness or brittleness and becomes more flexible and takes on rubbery or leathery properties. At this transition temperature, noticeable changes in the specific volume, thermal conductivity, refractive index, stiffness, heat content, and dielectric loss are apparent.

Below the transition temperature, the motion in the polymer chain is restricted to small motions of individual atoms. Above T_g, larger molecular motions are occurring in which whole segments of the polymer chain are in motion and the polymer loses its rigidity.

When the temperature of natural rubber in the supercooled amorphous state is raised, a glass transition temperature is observed. The polymer in the crystalline phase still shows a crystalline melting point above T_g (Fig. 3.8). In linear polyethylene, for example, where T_m is above 130°, T_g has not been found, since it is quite low. In general, polymers which have very high crystalline melting points have high glass transition temperatures. The same properties or adhesion forces, such as secondary valence bonding, and especially hydrogen bonding, which are to a great extent responsible for crystallinity and high crystalline melting points are also responsible for high glass transition temperatures. The relationship between molecular weight and the physical state of the polymer as related to T_g and T_m are shown in Fig. 3.9.

It is possible that a polymer will not be crystalline but will have a high glass transition temperature. This usually results when a polymer has a fair degree of secondary valence bonding but no order to the chain. For

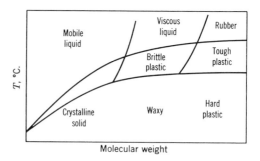

Fig. 3.9. Polymer phase changes with temperature.[8]

example, atactic poly(methyl methacrylate) is not crystalline but has a high glass transition temperature as a result of secondary valence bonding. The reverse, of course, can also be true. Witness the case of linear polyethylene, where the secondary valence bonds are weak yet the perfectly ordered chain gives it a relatively high crystalline melting point.

A polymer may have a further transition temperature from the rubbery or leathery state into a viscous melt.[17,18] In the rubbery state, polymers exhibit some sort of elastomeric properties. Their behavior can be likened to that of a gas, a liquid, or a solid. The elastomer is like a gas in that it resists compression and heats up. When it is stretched, the random motion is restricted but the elastomer cools. In both cases, entropy is lost. However, like a liquid it shows a high volume rigidity with low shape rigidity and like a solid, an elastomer undergoes elastic deformations.

A good elastomer must be able to undergo flexing with little heat build-up, and at the extent of its elongation it must have a high tensile strength. Good snap or rebound as well as creep resistance are also characteristics of good elastomers.

Polymers which exhibit these properties must be above their glass transition temperatures at the operating temperature, but the overall mobility of the chains has to be restricted to resist creep and have good snap.[19] This latter requirement is often obtained through crosslinking or vulcanization or by bond angle restrictions.[20]

Further heating of a polymer yields a viscous liquid since the motion of the polymer chains is such that they flow past one another. Since the entire polymer chain must coordinate its movements for flow, the viscosity of the polymer depends to a large extent on the chain length,[17] but is influenced to a large degree by hydrogen bonding.[21]

Three-dimensional networks. Space network polymers exhibit complete insolubility in all solvents and high fluid flow melting points. Vinyl monomers may be suitably crosslinked with a few hundredths of a per cent of divinyl monomer to give three-dimensional networks. During a polymerization, the point (molecular weight) at which a polymer becomes insoluble is usually sharp for any given polymer and is called the gel point. This is the point at which the solvent no longer supports the polymer chains. Actually a gelled polymer may consist of somewhat short segments of low molecular weight chains, but since the chains are linked together, the overall molecular weight is high.

If the polymer is below its glass transition temperature, it is a tough thermosetting plastic. If it is above its glass transition temperature, it is a tough elastomer, as is vulcanized latex. These three-dimensional networks are amorphous and show no crystalline regions.

REFERENCES

1. G. Natta and F. Danusso, *J. Polymer Sci.*, **34**, 3 (1959).
2. A. V. Tobolsky, *Properties and Structure of Polymers*, John Wiley and Sons, New York, 1960.
3. C. S. Marvel, *An Introduction to the Organic Chemistry of High Polymers*, John Wiley and Sons, New York, 1959, p. 9.
4. C. P. McClelland and R. L. Bateman, *Chem. and Eng. News*, **23**, 247 (1945).
5. C. A. Sperati, W. A. Franta, and H. W. Starkweather, Jr., *J. Am. Chem. Soc.*, **75**, 6127 (1953).
6. W. P. Slichter, *J. Polymer Sci.*, **36**, 259 (1959).
7. G. Natta, *J. Polymer Sci.*, **34**, 531 (1959).
8. F. W. Billmeyer, Jr., *Textbook of Polymer Chemistry*, Interscience Publishers, New York, 1957.
9. H. W. Starkweather, Jr., C. E. Moore, J. E. Hansen, T. M. Roder, and R. E. Brooks, *J. Polymer Sci.*, **21**, 189 (1956).
10. R. Hill and E. E. Walker, *J. Polymer Sci.*, **3**, 609 (1948).
11. D. D. Coffman, N. L. Cox, E. L. Martin, W. S. Mochel, and F. J. van Natta, *J. Polymer Sci.*, **3**, 85 (1948).
12. D. D. Coffman, G. J. Berchet, W. R. Petersen, and E. W. Spanagel, *J. Polymer Sci.*, **2**, 306 (1947).
13. L. Marker, R. Early, and S. L. Aggarwal, *J. Polymer Sci.*, **38**, 369 (1959).
14. G. Natta, F. Danusso, and G. Moraglio, *J. Polymer Sci.*, **25**, 119 (1957).
15. P. F. Reding, *J. Polymer Sci.*, **21**, 547 (1956).
16. T. W. Campbell and A. C. Haven, Jr., *J. Appl. Polymer Sci.*, **1**, 73 (1959).
17. A. V. Tobolsky, *Sci. American*, Sept. 1957, p. 120.
18. W. P. Slichter, *J. Chem. Education*, **36**, 185 (1959).
19. G. Salomon and C. Koningsberger, *J. Polymer Sci.*, **2**, 522 (1947).
20. P. J. Flory, C. A. J. Hoeve, and A. Ciferri, *J. Polymer Sci.*, **34**, 337 (1959).
21. R. Longworth and H. Morawetz, *J. Polymer Sci.*, **29**, 307 (1958).

4

CHARACTERIZATION
OF POLYMERS

4.1 MOLECULAR WEIGHT DETERMINATION[1]

The molecular weight determination of a polymer is by no means a simple task. The polymer sample usually contains mixtures of different-size molecules, which differ from one another by a weight that is some multiple of a recurring unit. Many of the usual methods which can be applied to simple organic molecules for the determination of molecular weights cannot be employed with polymers.

The determination of molecular weight through chemical end group analysis has only a very limited application. Let us suppose we wish to determine the molecular weight of a polyester by titration of carboxyl end groups. First we must know whether or not the polymer chain contains two acid end groups, or one acid end group and one alcohol end group or two alcohol end groups, and we must also know what the relative proportions of these end groups are. If the types of end groups are statistically distributed, the polymer can be treated as one which has one alcohol and one acid end group. If there is just one branch in the molecule, a third end group is introduced and the observed molecular weight will be only two-thirds of the actual molecular weight. Furthermore, at high molecular weights, the method becomes insensitive since, for example in the case of a polyester of 20,000 molecular weight, the problem becomes one of detecting 0.2% carboxyl.

Using the standard physical methods which are applied to simple organic molecules has serious limitations. The boiling point elevation method or freezing point depression method depends on the measurement of ΔT_b (Eq. 4.1) and ΔT_f (Eq. 4.2) respectively.

$$\left(\frac{\Delta T_b}{C}\right)_{c=0} = \frac{RT^2}{\rho \, \Delta H_v M} \qquad (4.1)$$

$$\left(\frac{\Delta T_f}{C}\right)_{c=0} = \frac{RT^2}{\rho \, \Delta H_f M} \qquad (4.2)$$

It can be seen from these equations that large molecular weights result in extremely small values for ΔT_b or ΔT_f, and thus a polymer of molecular weight 20,000 in a 1% solution might show a ΔT in the range of 0.002°, a value which would be difficult to measure accurately. Measurements of this type can be made through the use of a thermistor with a sensitivity of $1 \times 10^{-4}\,°C.$[2] It is possible to measure molecular weights with the thermistor by freezing point depression in the range up to 50,000 with 10% reproducibility.

Osmotic pressure measurements.[3] Van't Hoff's law, $(\pi/C)_{c=0} = RT/M$, can very conveniently be applied to a molecular weight measurement. This colligative property is more sensitive than the cryoscopic methods since a 1% solution of polymer of molecular weight 20,000 might show an osmotic pressure of 20 cm. of solvent. This method becomes ineffective at low molecular weights and is generally useless at molecular weights below 5000, depending on the particular membrane used. A lower limit must be set owing to imperfections (holes) in the membrane, but molecular weights as high as 10^6 can be accurately measured.

It must be remembered that polymers contain mixtures of different-size molecules and that measurement of colligative properties such as osmotic pressure measures the *number* of molecules in a given solution $\left(\sum_{i=1}^{\infty} N_i\right)$. Since a weighed amount of polymer is employed for the determination in order to obtain a given concentration regardless of the size of the molecules $\left(w = \sum_{i=1}^{\infty} w_i = \sum_{i=1}^{\infty} N_i M_i\right)$, a *number average* molecular weight is obtained:

$$\bar{M}_n = \frac{w}{\sum\limits_{i=1}^{\infty} N_i} = \frac{\sum\limits_{i=1}^{\infty} M_i N_i}{\sum\limits_{i=1}^{\infty} N_i}$$

Van't Hoff's equation then becomes a measure of *number average* molecular weight,

$$\left(\frac{\pi}{C}\right)_{c=0} = \frac{RT}{M_n}, \qquad \bar{M}_n = \frac{RT}{\left(\dfrac{\pi}{C}\right)_{c=0}}$$

and number average molecular weights are sensitive to small weight fractions of low molecular weight molecules and insensitive to small weight fractions of high molecular weight molecules.

Several types of osmometers and methods are available for gathering the necessary data. In the static method, the osmotic pressure of the solution is balanced by the head that develops. The height of the head is measured, and the density of the solution is assumed to be approximately that of the solvent. The dynamic method consists of applying an external pressure of measurable magnitude so that there will be no developing head. In both methods, various solutions of low solute concentrations are measured and the results extrapolated to zero concentration. Usually, in the static method, the osmometer is filled to the expected head height so that the concentration of the solution will not change by a rising or falling head. One crude determination may be necessary to get a first estimate.

Light scattering.[4] Light passing through a gas or liquid medium loses energy both by absorption of the light and conversion into energy, mainly heat, and by scattering. The intensity of the scattering in the liquid can be related to thermal fluctuations of the density of the liquid which make the liquid nonhomogeneous. In a pure solvent a beam of light will scatter in all directions and some of its energy will be lost by absorption. Scattered light is observed at wavelengths where there is no absorption. If a solute is dissolved in the solvent, solute molecules of a different refractive index are available for scattering. The scattering of a solute depends on the number and the square of the amplitude of the electronic vibrations of the solute molecules. Thus in order to count the number of molecules, the amplitude of the molecule must be known.

The change in index of refraction of the solution compared to the solvent also depends on the number of molecules of solvent and the amplitude. Thus through measurement of the increase in scattering and refraction change from solvent to solution, the two simultaneous equations can be solved.

The method should become more exact the larger the molecule, but in practice, dissymmetry corrections reduce the accuracy. For example, if n molecules of molecular weight x are dissolved in a given solvent and $n/2$ molecules of molecular weight $2x$ are dissolved in another solvent so that the weight of solute is the same for each solvent, the molecules of weight $2x$ will be half as many and in this respect have half the scattering power. However, the doubled size of the molecule of molecular weight $2x$ gives twice the amplitude, and since the scattering increases as the square of the amplitude, the contribution in this respect is fourfold. The net result of both factors is twice the scattering for the polymer of weight $2x$.

The amplitude of the scattered light is proportional to the mass of the molecule and the intensity is therefore proportional to the square of the particle mass.

$$\tau = \sum_{i=1}^{\infty} \tau_i = H \sum_{i=1}^{\infty} C_i M_i = H_c \bar{M}_w$$

where τ = scattered light
C = concentration
M = molecular weight

$$\bar{M}_w = \frac{\sum\limits_{i=1}^{\infty} N_i M_i^2}{\sum\limits_{i=1}^{\infty} N_i M_i}$$

The total scattering $\bar{M}_w$ describes a *weight average molecular weight*. $\bar{M}_w$ is always greater than $\bar{M}_n$ except in the case where all polymer molecules are the same size, in which case $\bar{M}_w = \bar{M}_n$. For example, a polymer in which half of the molecules have a molecular weight 30,000 and half 60,000, will show $\bar{M}_n = 45,000$. Since by light scattering, the molecules of 60,000 molecular weight scatter light twice as much as those of 30,000 molecular weight, one-third of the contribution comes from the small and two-thirds of the contribution from the large molecules, and $\bar{M}_w = 50,000$. Measurements by these two different methods give a measure of the molecular weight distribution of any given polymer sample.

The method described above is valid for small particles, but when the size of the polymer particle is in the same order of magnitude as the wavelength of the light, separate portions of any one particle begin to scatter. The scattered rays undergo destructive interference and the intensity of scattering is reduced. In the direction of the beam it is near zero, and it increases through a rotation of 180° to the opposite direction of the beam. The scattering is therefore a function of the angle. By taking appropriate measurements at different angles, the molecular size can be obtained.

The problem becomes one of how molecular size can be related to molecular weight. If the polymer, polyethylene for example, were stretched out in solution in a planar zigzag fashion, it would not be difficult to calculate what molecular weight belonged to a particular molecular length. This is not the case however. The molecule can take any scrambled shape. The most probable molecular size can be calculated by considering a random walk by the polymer chain in which it can take a step in any direction and then, forgetting the first direction, can take a step in any other given direction, and so on to the end of the molecule. This calculation leads to a direct distance from one end of the walk (chain) to the other which is proportional to the square root of the actual distance traveled. A polyethylene molecule of molecular weight 300,000 has about 20,000 carbon-carbon bonds, each 1.5 A. long. The calculated average diameter (end-to-end distance) of the molecule is then about 300 A. The random walk has neglected the fact that the molecule must not forget where it has stepped previously, since two carbon atoms cannot occupy the same position (the molecule cannot step where it has stepped before), the direction of each step must be approximately 109° from the previous one, and certain rotational restrictions must be observed. Corrections for the calculation lead to a molecular diameter of 1100 A.

Ultracentrifuge.[4,5] If a polymer solution is placed in the cylindrical cell of a high speed centrifuge so that the cell is perpendicular to the axis of rotation during rotation, the polymer will begin to distribute itself throughout the cell according to the mass of the individual polymer molecules. At a constant force, the larger molecules will move more rapidly toward the periphery and at equilibrium the larger polymer molecules will be found nearer the periphery. If the refraction of a light beam which passes parallel to the axis of rotation and perpendicular to the axis of the cell on each rotation can be measured, then the concentration of the polymer in any given section in the cell can be found. This enables the determination of either the velocity at which a polymer is moving toward the periphery or the gradient at equilibrium.

The force acting on any polymer particle is defined by

$$F = m(1 - \bar{v}\rho)x\omega^2$$

where x = distance of the particle from the axis of rotation
m = particle mass
$\bar{v}$ = particle specific volume
ρ = density of the medium
ω = angular velocity
This is equal to the frictional force, $F = f(dx/dt)$, where f = frictional coefficient. When the two forces are equated the expression

$$\frac{1}{\omega^2 x}\frac{dx}{dt} = \frac{m(1 - \bar{v}\rho)}{f}$$

is obtained. The term on the left of the equation is the *sedimentation constant* and is determined by measuring the rate of movement. The frictional coefficient reduces to f_0 at infinite dilution, but must be obtained independently from the diffusion constant D, since the frictional interactions even at low dilution are extreme. At infinite dilution, since

$$S = \frac{m(1 - \bar{v}\rho)}{f} \quad \text{and} \quad D = kT \frac{\left(1 + \frac{d \ln \gamma}{d \ln c}\right)}{f}$$

where γ is the activity coefficient of the solute, the equation reduces to $D = kT/f_0$ so that $S_0/D_0 = m(1 - \bar{v}\rho)/kT$ or $S_0/D_0 = M(1 - \bar{v}\rho)/RT$. Both the sedimentation constant and D are obtained by extrapolation to zero concentration.

If the conditions of sedimentation are at equilibrium and the polymer is homogeneous, an ideal (dilute) solution is considered and the molecular weight of the polymer can be related to its concentrations at any two points in the cell. When the polymer is heterogeneous, the value obtained is a weight average molecular weight, $\bar{M}_w$.

$$\bar{M}_w = \frac{2RT \ln (C_2/C_1)}{(1 - \bar{v}\rho)\omega^2(x_2^2 - x_1^2)}$$

Fig. 4.1.

Solution viscosity.[6] The solution viscosity of a polymer is a measure of the size of a polymer molecule and is empirically related to the molecular weight of a linear polymer. Two types of solution viscosities are of practical value, the *intrinsic viscosity* and the *inherent viscosity*. The *intrinsic viscosity* $[\eta_i]$ is independent of concentration since measurements are extrapolated to zero concentration. The *inherent viscosity* is taken at a given concentration, usually 0.25 g./100 ml. The viscosity of a solution is a relative measurement of the time it takes a given amount of polymer solution to flow through a capillary compared to the time it takes the solvent, and is defined by $\eta = \ln (t/t_0)/C$, where t and t_0 are the flow times of solution and solvent respectively and C is the concentration in grams/100 ml. The measurement is taken at a constant temperature in a viscometer such as is shown in Fig. 4.1.

Practically, this viscosity measurement alone gives only a relative difference in the molecular weight of different samples of the same polymer, but the intrinsic viscosity can be related to the molecular weight by $[\eta] = K'M^a$. The constants K and a can only be determined for a given polymer if the molecular weights of the samples of the polymer are known, by a plot of $[\eta]$ against the molecular weight. The value of the constant a depends both on the polymer and the solvent. Once these constants have been determined for a polymer in a particular solvent, it is not necessary to again determine the molecular weight of any sample of that polymer by the long and difficult methods previously described; the viscosity measurement will suffice. This viscosity measurement will provide either a weight average or a number average molecular weight depending on the molecular weight determination used to obtain K and a.

4.2 CHEMICAL METHODS OF STRUCTURE DETERMINATION

Some of the possible structural features of the polymer chain which were discussed in Chapter 3 can be elucidated by means of simple reactions which are known to organic chemists. The features of a condensation polymer do not usually present a problem because of the nature of the reaction by which they are formed. Vinyl polymers, however, can be made up of monomeric units in a variety of ways. In addition to the problem of determining whether a polymer is atactic, isotactic, or syndiotactic is the problem of whether the polymer has a head-to-tail, a head-to-head–tail-to-tail, or a random arrangement.[7]

The structure of poly(methylvinyl ketone) has been investigated by considering the difference in the reactions of 1,5- and 1,4-diketones.[8] The head-to-head poly(methylvinyl ketone) (I) should yield furan rings (III) on dehydration, while the head-to-tail polymer (II) should undergo an internal aldol condensation to give a series of condensed cyclohexene rings (IV).

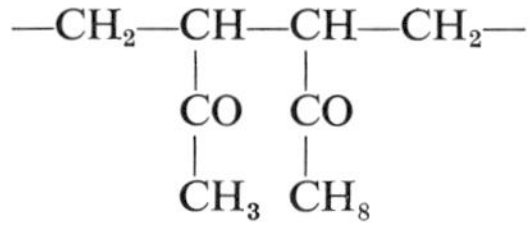

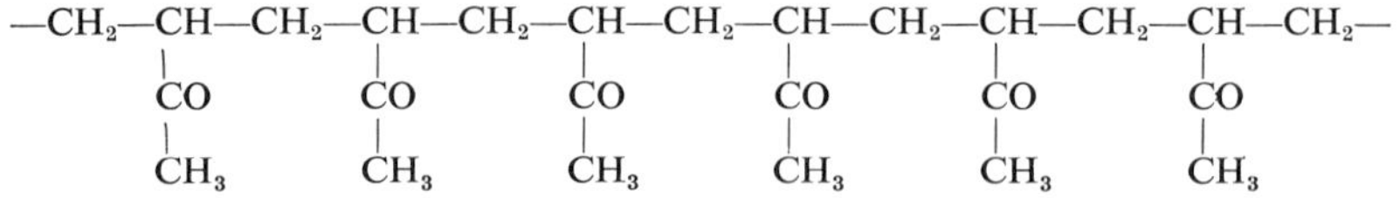

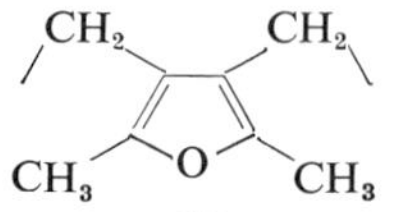

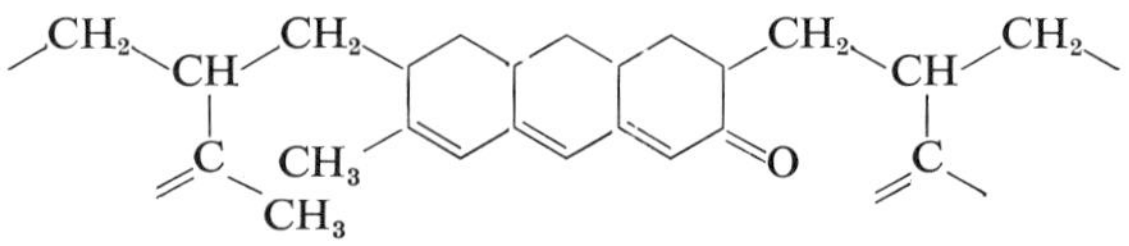

Theoretical statistical calculations[9,10] show that 81.6% of the oxygen should be lost in the reaction of the 1,5-diketone structure while only 50%

would be lost in the 1,4-structure. Experimental results are in excellent agreement with the head-to-tail structure (II).

Further proof of the head-to-tail structure is obtained by converting the polyketone (II) to the corresponding oxime and then to a polypyridine.[11] The problem of ring closure with the oxime groups again comes up here, where some groups will be isolated by the direction of the individual reactions. It has been calculated statistically[12-14] that 86% of the groups will react in a head-to-tail arrangement to form pyridine rings, and this in fact is in good agreement with the experimental results. Similar experiments have shown the head-to-tail arrangement of poly(methylisopropenyl ketone).[15]

Hydrolysis of poly(vinyl acetate) produces poly(vinyl alcohol), which will have either 1,2-diol or 1,3-diol units along the chain, depending on whether or not the poly(vinyl acetate) is a head-to-head or a head-to-tail polymer. Neither periodic acid nor lead tetraacetate, reagents which cleave glycols, were found to be consumed (within experimental error) by the polymer.[16] This would indicate a head-to-tail structure. A more sensitive indication of a reaction can be obtained by measuring the solution viscosity of the polymer both before and after treatment, since any reaction would decrease the molecular weight considerably. A considerable decrease in viscosity is noted,[17] thus indicating that at least some, but a very small fraction of the units are linked head-to-head.

$$\cdots -CH_2-\underset{\underset{OH}{|}}{CH}-CH_2-\underset{\underset{OH}{|}}{CH}-CH_2-\underset{\underset{OH}{|}}{CH}-\underset{\underset{OH}{|}}{CH}-CH_2-\underset{\underset{OH}{|}}{CH}-CH_2-\cdots$$

$$\downarrow$$

$$\cdots -CH_2-\underset{\underset{OH}{|}}{CH}-CH_2-\underset{\underset{OH}{|}}{CH}-CH_2-CHO + OHC-CH_2-\underset{\underset{OH}{|}}{CH}-CH_2-\cdots$$

The question of orientation of vinyl chloride units in poly(vinyl chloride) has been resolved by treating the polymer with zinc.[18] The head-to-head structure would leave an unsaturated polymer while the head-to-tail structure would yield cyclopropane rings.

$$\cdots -CH_2-\underset{\underset{Cl}{|}}{CH}-\underset{\underset{Cl}{|}}{CH}-CH_2-CH_2-\underset{\underset{Cl}{|}}{CH}-\underset{\underset{Cl}{|}}{CH}-CH_2-\cdots \longrightarrow$$

$$\cdots CH_2-CH=CH-CH_2-CH_2-CH=CH-CH_2 \cdots$$

$$-CH_2-\underset{\underset{Cl}{|}}{CH}-CH_2-\underset{\underset{Cl}{|}}{CH}-CH_2-\underset{\underset{Cl}{|}}{CH}-CH_2-\underset{\underset{Cl}{|}}{CH}-CH_2-\underset{\underset{Cl}{|}}{CH}-\cdots \longrightarrow$$

$$CH_2-\overset{\overset{\displaystyle CH_2}{\diagup \diagdown}}{CH}-CH-CH_2-\underset{\underset{Cl}{|}}{CH}-CH_2-\overset{\overset{\displaystyle CH_2}{\diagup \diagdown}}{CH}-CH-\cdots$$

Since only 85% of the chlorine could be removed, this fits the theoretical calculations for a head-to-tail polymer.[19,20]

Another structural question which arises when butadienes are polymerized is whether the polymer structure is obtained by 1,4-, 1,2-, or 3,4- addition. This problem was attacked quite early by Harries[21] in the determination of the structures of natural rubber, gutta-percha, and synthetic butadiene polymers. The ozonolysis of natural rubber produced levulinic aldehyde or acid, depending on the method of decomposition of the ozonide. These results show that the 1,4-arrangement is the one present in both natural rubber (*cis*-1,4-) and gutta-percha (*trans*-1,4-).

$$\cdots -CH_2-CH=\overset{\overset{\displaystyle CH_3}{|}}{C}-CH_2-CH_2-CH=\overset{\overset{\displaystyle CH_3}{|}}{C}-CH_2-\cdots$$

$$\downarrow$$

$$\cdots CH_2-CO_2H + CH_3-\overset{\overset{\displaystyle O}{\|}}{C}-CH_2-CH_2-CO_2H + O=\overset{\overset{\displaystyle CH_3}{|}}{C}-CH_2\cdots$$

These results were later confirmed, and it was shown that at least 95% of natural rubber contains the 1,4-structure.[22]

The ozonolysis of polyisoprene formed by a free radical polymerization shows a predominance of the 1,4-structure (levulinic acid) but only a few segments of head-to-head (acetonylacetone) and tail-to-tail (succinic acid) units.[21] Similarly, the structure of polybutadiene polymerized by free radical initiation has been determined.[23–26] Ozonolysis has also been useful in the determination of the structure of butadiene copolymers.[27–29] Poly(2,3-dimethylbutadiene) obtained by a free radical polymerization shows at least a 90% 1,4-structure by ozonolysis to acetonylacetone.[30] Similarly, neoprene has been shown to have at least 97% of its chloroprene units arranged in a 1,4-head-to-tail fashion.[31]

Marvel et al.[32] have elucidated the structure of polyalloöcimene prepared by polymerization with a Ziegler catalyst by use of ozonolysis techniques. The identification of acetone (58%), glyoxal (22%), and a polymeric aldehyde suggests that 40 to 50% of the units have the structure V and the remaining have the structure VI.

The amount of unsaturation in a polymer can easily be determined by the standard quantitative organic methods. Iodine monochloride seems to be a very successful reagent and has been employed in the determination of total unsaturation in polybutadiene.[33] This method does not give the type of unsaturation and thus does not allow identification of 1,2- or 1,4-units by distinguishing internal double bonds (1,4-) from pendant vinyl double bonds (1,2-). A chemical method which solves this problem takes

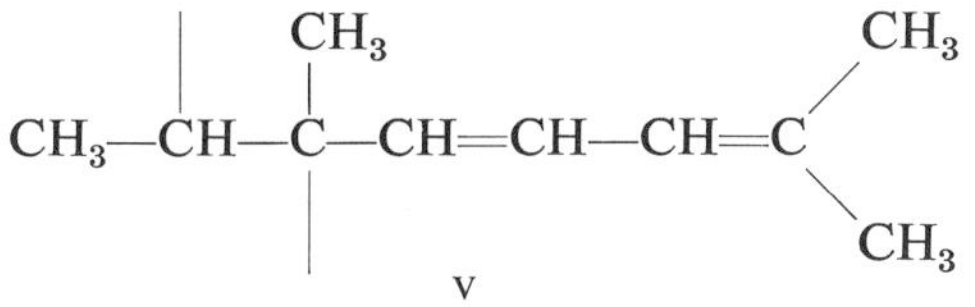

$$CH_3-CH-\underset{\underset{V}{|}}{\overset{\overset{CH_3}{|}}{C}}-CH=CH-CH=C\overset{CH_3}{\underset{CH_3}{}}$$

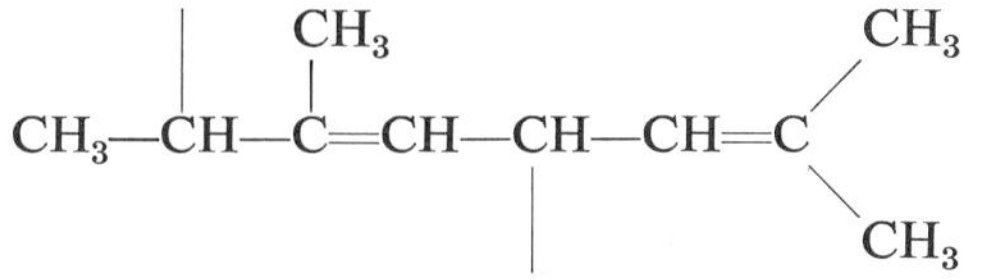

$$CH_3-CH-\underset{\underset{VI}{|}}{\overset{\overset{CH_3}{|}}{C}}=CH-CH-CH=C\overset{CH_3}{\underset{CH_3}{}}$$

advantage of the relative rates at which perbenzoic acid will react with the two types of bonds.[34,35] The internal double bond from 1,4-addition reacts twenty-five times as fast as the vinyl double bond from 1,2-addition. These techniques have been employed to determine the structure of poly(2-phenylbutadiene).[36] These methods are important in this case, where infrared techniques fail to give a good determination.

4.3 INFRARED METHODS

Through detailed study of the infrared absorption characteristics of model compounds, various absorption bands can be assigned to certain moieties. Table 4.1 gives some of the spectral assignments which are valuable in vinyl polymer structure determination.[37,38]

TABLE 4.1
Infrared assignments

Group	Vibration	Wavelength, cm.$^{-1}$
$\diagdown \!\!\!\! \diagup CH_2$	C—H str.	2924 and 2850
$=CH_2$	,,	3086 and 3000
$=CH-$	,,	3030
$-CH_3$	,,	2958 and 2874
$R_1CH=CH_2$	C—H wag	990 and 909
trans $R_1CH=CHR_2$	,,	962
$R_1R_2C=CH_2$	,,	885
$R_1R_2C=CHR_3$	,,	833
cis-$R_1CH=CHR_2$	,,	704

The infrared spectra of polybutadienes polymerized by various methods and catalysts have been shown to give a good measure of the structure (*cis-* or *trans-* 1,4- and 1,2-addition) obtained. Absorption from *cis-*1,4-addition appears at 990 and 725 cm.$^{-1}$ while that from *trans*-1,4-addition is observed at 970 cm.$^{-1}$. The amount of 1,2-addition can be determined from the band at 909 cm.$^{-1}$.[39-41]

The structures of *Hevea* (natural rubber), balata, and gutta-percha, and synthetic polyisoprene have been compared through infrared techniques.[42-47] Both *Hevea* (*cis-*1,4-) and balata (*trans*-1,4-) show bands at 840 cm.$^{-1}$ characteristic of the internal double bond and must be distinguished on the basis of the relative intensities of this band. Synthetic polyisoprenes contain all of the four possible structural arrangements. The band at 911 identifies the 1,2-structure and the one at 889 the 3,4-structure. Increased free radical polymerization temperature raises the amount of the *cis-*1,4-structure from about 10% at 0° to 30% at 100°. The amounts of *cis-* and *trans*-1,4-units in poly(2-phenylbutadiene) and poly(1-phenylbutadiene) are more difficultly determined (Table 4.2).[48]

TABLE 4.2

	1,2-	3,4-	*cis*-1,4-	*trans*-1,4-
Poly(2-phenylbutadiene)	1000–900 cm.$^{-1}$	893 cm.$^{-1}$	840 cm.$^{-1}$	—
Poly(1-phenylbutadiene)	1000–900 cm.$^{-1}$	707–697 cm.$^{-1}$	707–697 cm.$^{-1}$	965 cm.$^{-1}$

Small amounts of *cis-* 1,4-, 1,2- and 3,4-units can be detected in neoprene.[49] Increasing the polymerization temperature increases the amounts of these units from 5% at −40° to 30% at 100°C. The *cis-* and *trans*-1,4-units are observed at 1650 and 1660 cm.$^{-1}$ respectively, the 1,2- at 923 cm.$^{-1}$, and the 3,4- at 885 cm.$^{-1}$.

The infrared spectra of certain samples of polyethylene show more methyl groups than can be accounted for by the end groups alone.[50-54] (The reason for this branching will be taken up in Chapter 5). In polyethylene which has been made by methods yielding a perfectly linear sample, no absorption bands are found in the 847 cm.$^{-1}$ region characteristic of methyl groups. By removal of any unsaturation in polyethylene by hydrogenation (887 cm.$^{-1}$ interference) certain samples of polyethylene show 0.2 to 4.6 branches per 100 carbon atoms.

Infrared measurements are also useful in determining the crystallinity and the presence of other infrared active groups in polymers.

4.4 X-RAY METHODS

The x-ray diffraction technique is perhaps the ultimate tool in the determination of the structure of a molecule. Structures of size comparable to the x-ray wavelength give interference effects which will reinforce each other if the structure has an orderly arrangement. Unoriented non-crystalline polymer samples act like amorphous powder samples. Since there is little orderly arrangement in noncrystalline polymers, the x-ray patterns show a nonreinforced random pattern, and little information can be gained. In a nonoriented crystalline polymer, the pattern is typical of a crystalline powder diagram. Polymers with oriented crystallites produce the spot pattern typical of a single crystal pattern.

The crystal structure of many different polymers has been determined by the x-ray methods and this method has become increasingly important with the advent of high speed computers. The structure of polyethylene, various poly(α-olefins), polybutadienes, poly(vinyl alcohol), poly(ethylene terephthalate), various polyamides, and polypeptides has been determined. Not only does this method give the arrangement in the unit cell, but more important, it gives the ultimate structure of these molecules.[55] Crystalline polypropylene, for example, shows an identity period of 6.50 A. Since the carbon-carbon single-bond distance is 1.54 A. the calculated identity period for the backbone polymer chain lying in a zigzag fashion along one plane would be 7.67 A. for three recurring units. In this case, the chain must take a helical configuration in which each methyl group on the tertiary carbon atom is displaced 120° from the previous one to conform to the experimentally observed identity period. Thus the polymer must be isotactic. The helical arrangement in which the first and fourth methyl groups are positioned over one another when viewed down the axis of the chain might be expected since a planar polypropylene chain in an isotactic arrangement is sterically impossible.[56]

REFERENCES

1. P. W. Allen, *Techniques of Polymer Characterization*, Butterworth's Scientific Publications, London, 1959.
2. C. E. Ashby, J. S. Reitenouv, and C. F. Hammer, *J. Am. Chem. Soc.*, **79**, 5086 (1957).
3. R. U. Bonnar, M. Dimbat, and F. H. Stross, *Number Average Molecular Weights*, Interscience Publishers, New York, 1958, pp. 191–261.

4. P. J. Flory, *Principles of Polymer Chemistry*, Cornell University Press, Ithaca, N.Y., 1953.
5. T. Svedberg and K. O. Peterson, *The Ultracentrifuge*, Clarendon Press, Oxford, 1940.
6. F. W. Billmeyer, Jr., *Textbook of Polymer Chemistry*, Interscience Publishers, New York, 1957.
7. C. S. Marvel, "Organic Chemistry of Vinyl Polymers" (in *The Chemistry of Large Molecules*, R. E. Burk and O. Grummit, eds.), Interscience Publishers, 1943, p. 219.
8. C. S. Marvel and C. L. Levesque, *J. Am. Chem. Soc.*, **60**, 280 (1938).
9. P. J. Flory, *J. Am. Chem. Soc.*, **64**, 177 (1942).
10. F. T. Wall, *J. Am. Chem. Soc.*, **64**, 269 (1942).
11. C. S. Marvel and C. L. Levesque, *J. Am. Chem. Soc.*, **61**, 3234 (1939).
12. P. J. Flory, *J. Am. Chem. Soc.*, **61**, 1518 (1939).
13. F. T. Wall, *J. Am. Chem. Soc.*, **62**, 803 (1940); **63**, 821 (1941).
14. R. Simha, *J. Am. Chem. Soc.*, **63**, 1479 (1941).
15. C. S. Marvel, E. H. Riddle, and J. O. Corner, *J. Am. Chem. Soc.*, **64**, 92 (1942).
16. C. S. Marvel and C. E. Denoon, Jr., *J. Am. Chem. Soc.*, **60**, 1045 (1938).
17. P. J. Flory and F. S. Leutner, *J. Polymer Sci.*, **3**, 880 (1948); **5**, 267 (1950).
18. C. S. Marvel, J. H. Sample, and M. F. Roy, *J. Am. Chem. Soc.*, **61**, 3241 (1939).
19. P. J. Flory, *J. Am. Chem. Soc.*, **61**, 1518 (1939).
20. F. T. Wall, *J. Am. Chem. Soc.*, **62**, 803 (1940); **63**, 821 (1941).
21. C. Harries, *Ber.*, **38**, 1195, 3985 (1905); **45**, 936 (1912); **48**, 863 (1915); *Ann.*, **395**, 211 (1913); **383**, 157 (1911).
22. R. Pummerer, G. Ebermayer, and K. Gerlach, *Ber.*, **64**, 809 (1931).
23. C. S. Marvel, W. M. Schilling, D. J. Shields, C. Bluestein, O. R. Irwin, P. G. Sheth, and J. Honig, *J. Org. Chem.*, **16**, 838 (1951).
24. K. Ziegler, E. Eimers, W. Hechelhammer, and H. Wilms, *Ann.*, **567**, 43 (1950).
25. N. Rabjohn, C. E. Bryan, G. E. Inskeep, H. W. Johnson, and J. K. Lawson, *J. Am. Chem. Soc.*, **69**, 314 (1947).
26. R. Hill, J. R. Lewis, and J. L. Simonsen, *Trans. Faraday Soc.*, **35**, 1067 (1939).
27. C. S. Marvel and R. E. Light, Jr., *J. Am. Chem. Soc.*, **72**, 3887 (1950).
28. J. Rehner, Jr., *Ind. Eng. Chem.*, **36**, 46 (1944).
29. R. Hill, J. R. Lewis, and J. L. Simonsen, *Trans. Faraday Soc.*, **35**, 1073 (1939).
30. C. Harries, *Ann.*, **395**, 264 (1913).
31. A. Klebanskii and K. Chevychalova, *Zhur. Obschei Khim.*, **17**, 941 (1947).
32. C. S. Marvel, P. E. Kiener, and E. D. Vessel, *J. Am. Chem. Soc.*, **81**, 4694 (1959).
33. A. R. Kemp and H. Peters, *Ind. Eng. Chem.*, **15**, 1108 (1943).
34. I. M. Kolthoff and T. S. Lee, *J. Polymer Sci.*, **2**, 206 (1947).
35. I. M. Kolthoff, T. S. Lee, and M. A. Mairs, *J. Polymer Sci.*, **2**, 199 (1947).
36. P. de Radzitzki and G. Smets, *Bull. soc. chim. Belges*, **62**, 320 (1953).
37. J. J. Fox and A. E. Martin, *Proc. Roy. Soc. (London)*, **A175**, 208 (1940).
38. L. H. Cross, R. B. Richards, and H. A. Willis, *Discussions Faraday Soc.*, **9**, 235 (1950).
39. R. R. Hampton, *Anal. Chem.*, **21**, 923 (1949).
40. E. J. Hart and A. W. Meyer, *J. Am. Chem. Soc.*, **71**, 1980 (1949).
41. R. S. Silas, J. Yates, and V. Thornton, *Anal. Chem.*, **31**, 529 (1959).
42. J. E. Field, D. E. Woodward, and S. D. Gehman, *J. Appl. Phys.*, **17**, 386 (1946).
43. G. B. B. M. Sutherland and A. V. Jones, *Discussions Faraday Soc.*, **9**, 281 (1950).
44. G. Salomon, A. C. van der Schee, J. A. A. Ketelaar, and B. J. van Eyk, *Discussions Faraday Soc.*, **9**, 291 (1950).
45. W. S. Richardson and A. Sacher, *J. Polymer Sci.*, **10**, 353 (1953).

46. W. S. Richardson, *J. Polymer Sci.*, **13**, 229 (1954).
47. J. Binder and H. C. Ransaw, *Anal. Chem.*, **29**, 503 (1957).
48. P. de Radzitzski, M. C. de Wilde, and G. Smets, *J. Polymer Sci.*, **13**, 477 (1954).
49. J. T. Maynard and W. E. Mochel, *J. Polymer Sci.*, **13**, 251 (1954).
50. L. H. Cross, R. B. Richards, and H. A. Willis, *Discussions Faraday Soc.*, **9**, 235 (1950).
51. W. M. D. Bryant and R. C. Voter, *J. Am. Chem. Soc.*, **75**, 6113 (1953).
52. J. B. Nichols, *J. Appl. Phys.*, **25**, 840 (1954).
53. F. M. Rugg, J. J. Smith, and R. C. Bacon, *J. Polymer Sci.*, **13**, 535 (1954).
54. S. L. Aggarwal and O. J. Sweeting, *Chem. Revs.*, **57**, 665 (1957).
55. C. W. Bunn, *Chemical Crystallography*, Clarendon Press, Oxford, 1946, p. 233.
56. G. Natta, *J. Polymer Sci.*, **16**, 143 (1955).

5

MECHANISMS
AND KINETICS
OF POLYMERIZATION

In the initial stages of the development of polymer chemistry, it was generally believed that in a polymerization reaction, the reactivity of the molecules involved became low as the polymerization reaction proceeded. There were several reasons for this belief. First, it was assumed that large molecules should have retarded molecular motion and so should react at a low rate. The collision rate should be low since the large molecules would have a low kinetic velocity and the medium in which the reaction was taking place, as it became more viscous, would further slow down the motion. Secondly, it was held that certain steric factors were involved in that the reactive group would be shielded by burying its head in its own chain. These ideas have been proven totally false. The influence of size, fortunately, may be disregarded and the principles of reaction kinetics which are applicable for small molecules can be applied to polymerization reactions.

5.1 CONDENSATION POLYMERIZATION

There are several distinct features found in the reactions involved in condensation polymerization on one hand and addition polymerization on the other. These features have been employed as a basis for the classification of polymers into condensation and addition polymers (Chapter 2). These differences will be pointed out in the following sections.

Chemical reactions of monomeric compounds. The reaction kinetics of certain reaction systems in a homologous series give a good insight into condensation polymerization reactions and have given to polymer chemistry a workable theory for polymerization reactions. These results have shown that within a homologous series, the velocity constants approach an asymptotic limit as the chain length increases. Two reactions are especially worthy of mention.[1]

$$CH_3(CH_2)_nCO_2H + C_2H_5OH \xrightarrow{\text{HCl}} CH_3(CH_2)_nCO_2C_2H_5 + H_2O \quad (5.1)$$

$$(CH_2)_n(CO_2H)_2 + C_2H_5OH \xrightarrow{\text{HCl}} (CH_2)_n \begin{matrix} \diagup CO_2C_2H_5 \\ \diagdown CO_2H \end{matrix} + H_2O$$

$$\xrightarrow{\text{C}_2\text{H}_5\text{OH}} (CH_2)^n \begin{matrix} \diagup CO_2C_2H_5 \\ \diagdown CO_2C_2H_5 \end{matrix} + H_2O \quad (5.2)$$

Both esterification reactions were carried out in an excess of methanol. The results are recorded in Table 5.1. It is clearly shown that as the chain

TABLE 5.1

Velocity constants for acid esterfication

Chain Length (n)	$K_{5.1} \times 10^4$, 25°	$K_{5.2} \times 10^4$, 25°
1	22.1	
2	15.3	6.0
3	7.5	8.7
4	7.4	8.4
5	7.4	7.8
6		7.3
7		
8	7.5	
9	7.4	
Higher	7.6	

Velocity constants, K in (gram equivalents/liter)$^{-1}$ sec.$^{-1}$.

length increases, the velocity constant approaches an asymptotic limit. Furthermore, the constants for the dibasic and monobasic acids approach the same limit. In addition, the same rate constant can be applied to each of the consecutive steps in the case of the dibasic acid, and the reaction rates for these steps are written as shown:

$$d[\text{monoester}]/dt = k_1[CO_2H]''[H^{\oplus}]$$
$$d[\text{diester}]/dt = k_2[CO_2H]'[H^{\oplus}]$$

where $[CO_2H]''$ and $[CO_2H]'$ are the concentrations of carboxyl groups in the diacid and monoacid respectively. The alcohol, which is present in large excess, does not enter into the rate expression. At larger values of n, the reactivity of one carboxyl group is unaffected by the other esterified end so that $k_1 = k_2$ and d[ester groups]$/dt = k[CO_2H][H^{\oplus}]$, where $[CO_2H]$ is the total carboxyl group concentration.

The same conclusions can be drawn from studying the rates of the reverse reactions, either acid- or base-catalyzed hydrolysis. The same conclusions must be reached with a homologous series of diols. Again it must be stressed that in the case of small members of the homologous series where the insulating chain is small there will be electronic effects transmitted from one group to the other. This is true with the diol ethylene glycol. With glycerin this is complicated by the fact that there are two different types of hydroxyl groups, primary and secondary.

Large molecules. Extensions of these results to polymerization reactions would seem logical. At least one important point is known with certainty. The reactivity of a functional group is independent of the molecular size, at least in all but smaller molecules.

The earlier interpretation of polymerization mechanisms supported the idea that polymerization reactions were unique because of such factors as retarded molecular motion, collision rate, viscosity of reaction medium, and shielding. Large molecules do diffuse slowly, but this does not affect the collision rate of the functional groups. The diffusion rate of a molecule as a whole ties down the reacting group somewhat; but this group can still wander over a considerable region by means of changes in configuration of the molecular chain. Its collisions with another functional group are at a rate comparable to that of smaller molecules so that a reaction which is determined by collision frequencies within sets of the same types of functional groups differing only in molecular size of the rest of the chain will occur at the same rate.

It is well known that functional groups may collide many times before diffusing apart. The lower the diffusion rate, the greater number of collisions before diffusion. Several series of collisions and diffusions will take place before a reaction actually takes place, but in the case of the large molecule, the period of collisions will be lengthened even though the period of diffusion may be lengthened (i.e., the time before the group starts a series of collisions with a different group). The collision rate over a period of time should therefore be about the same for large molecules as for small molecules and the viscosity will not play an important part in the overall rate of reaction.

There will be exceptions to this when the mobility is extremely low, and especially when the mobility is low and the reaction rate constant is high (when a high percentage of collisions result in reaction). Here the diffusion will become the rate-controlling step. Usually in condensation reactions only one reaction occurs in 10^{13} collisions, so the exceptions are not often found.

Here we can see a difference in condensation and addition polymerization. In condensation polymerization, many small molecules react immediately to form dimers, trimers, etc., so that even in the initial stages there is *nearly complete conversion* to *low molecular weight* polymer. Few monomer molecules remain in the reaction mixture. As the reaction progresses over a period of time the molecular weight is increasing by reaction of the dimers, trimers, and tetramers with each other. Thus, a considerable period of time is taken for the production of high molecular weight polymer as the concentration of the reactants (available functional groups) decreases rapidly. By one reaction of all the molecules in the system initially, the concentration of functional groups is cut in half.

In addition polymerization, the reaction proceeds by the addition of monomer to the ends of a relatively small but fixed number of growing (active) chains. The concentration of the monomers which can react does not change so rapidly and the rate of reaction is dependent on the number of active growing centers (chain ends). Thus, in this rapid reaction (one reaction in every 10^9 collisions) there is initially a *low conversion* to *high molecular weight* molecules. Here the monomer is affected very little by the surrounding polymer molecules and the concentration of monomers in the vicinity of active centers is constant. Diffusion is not a rate-controlling factor at all.

Does shielding play an important role in condensation polymerization? In dilute solutions, where the polymer molecules can exist independently of one another, this is a possible argument. In concentrated solutions, the polymer molecules are entangled and the functional group should show no preference for its own chain over those of surrounding molecules.

Kinetics of condensation polymerization. For an example of condensation polymerization, the reaction of a dialcohol and dibasic acid can be taken as typical. The polyesterification reaction can be followed by titrating the unreacted carboxyl groups in the mixture.

In practical polymerizations, this reaction is catalyzed by a strong acid. When none is present, the carboxylic acid itself acts as the catalyst and the rate expression $-d[CO_2H]/dt = k[CO_2H]^2[OH]$ holds, if it is assumed that k is the same for all the functional groups and does not change with molecular weight as previously discussed. In practice, when the carboxyl and hydroxyl concentrations are equal, then $2kt = 1/C^2 -$ constant.

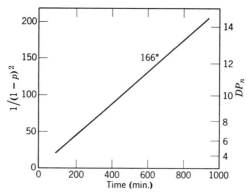

Fig. 5.1. Reaction of diethylene glycol with adipic acid.[2]

Usually C is expressed in terms of the *extent of the reaction*, p, at time t where $C = (1 - p)C_0$ so that $2C_0^2 kt = 1/(1 - p)^2 -$ constant. Using this equation, a typical third-order plot is shown in Fig. 5.1.[2] In this reaction system, the number of unreacted carboxyl groups will equal the number of molecules in the system and the number of molecules in moles per unit volume is equal to $C_0(1 - p)$. If the structural unit of the polymer is taken both as a diol unit and a dibasic acid unit, the number of structural units will equal the initial number of monomers employed and the number average D.P. is expressed as $DP_n =$ No. of units/No. of molecules $= 1/(1 - p)$, so that $M_n = M_0/(1 - p)$ where M_0 is the average of the molecular weights of diol and diacid. Figure 5.1 shows that the rate is at least unaffected by DP_n up to 14. This further shows that DP_n is proportional, approximately, to the square root of the time of the reaction (third order). This means the rate of increase in molecular weight is slowing down as the reaction proceeds and the molecules get larger, and in order to obtain high molecular weights the reaction is not practical. This is a characteristic of this third-order reaction and is *not* due to the loss of reactivity of the reacting species.

This problem in practical application is solved by employing a strong acid catalyst. Since the catalyst concentration is fixed, the following equations can be written:

$$-d[CO_2H]/dt = k[CO_2H][-OH][H^{\oplus}]$$
$$-d[CO_2H]/dt = k'[CO_2H][-OH]$$

For the second order expression:

$$-dC/dt = k'C^2$$
$$C_0 k't = 1/(1 - p) -\text{ constant}$$

The effect is shown in Fig. 5.2.[2,3] This reaction order usually holds at least to a degree of polymerization of 90 ($M_n = 10{,}000$). Other condensation polymerizations, for example the formation of polyamides, conform to reaction schemes based on the reactions of monofunctional acids and amines.

In the experiments described, care was taken to remove the water as rapidly as it was formed in order to prevent the reverse reaction from occurring. In practice, in bulk polymerizations of this type, the kinetics described begin to fail in the high molecular weight range since, as the viscosity increases, the removal of the water becomes an important and difficult problem.[4]

The importance of monomer purity and perfect balance to the attainment of high molecular weight polymers can now be readily understood. Under perfect conditions, in theory, a single chain of infinite length should be obtained. Impurities in a mixture not only may come with the sample of reactants, but may be formed during the reaction.

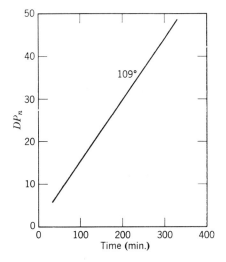

Fig. 5.2. Decamethylene glycol–adipic acid.[2,3]

If this impurity is designated as B+B, and the reacting monomer(s) as A—B or A—A and B—B, B+B can act as an overbalance of B—B or an impurity. It can be shown that DP_n = No. of units/No. of molecules = $[1 + r]/[2r(1 - p) + 1 - r]$, where r = ratio of the number of groups of A to B initially (N_A/N_B) and p = the fraction of groups which have reacted at any given time. When $r = 1$, $DP_n = 1/(1 - p)$, or when the reaction is complete, $p = 1$ and (moles of bifunctional units exclusive of B+B)/(moles of B+B) + 1 = $DP_n = (1 + r)/(1 - r)$. The same equation is applicable to an impurity B+ if r is defined as $N_A/(N_A + 2N_{B+})$.[5]

Sometimes it is desirable to use an unbalanced system by adding calculated extra amounts of A—A or B—B so that the molecular weight is limited or controlled to the exact point desired. The same effect is obtained by adding B+.

In the case of a monomer A—B, an intramolecular reaction can occur, sometimes to the exclusion of polymerization. For example, hydroxy acids may form lactides, α,β-unsaturated acids, or lactones. An α,β-unsaturated acid is an impurity formed during the reaction, the consequences of which are discussed above. The formation of a lactide, a reaction characteristic of α-hydroxy acids and the formation of a lactone, a reaction of γ- and δ-hydroxy acids in the formation of five and six-membered rings respectively, exclude the chance of polymerization. Similarly, amino acids may form diketo piperazines and lactams. Whether or not ring formation will take place depends on the strain in the ring which is formed. This is governed by the size of the ring, the substituents on the ring, and the hetero atom present in the ring. Generally, five- and six-membered rings are readily formed in preference to polymerization. Six- and seven-membered rings seem to be borderline cases, while sizes below four and above seven usually give polymers, although there are quite a few examples of five-membered rings which can be opened up in polymerization reactions.

The mechanisms by which rings such as lactams and lactones can be opened up to form polymers, even in the cases where apparently strainless rings exist, will be discussed in the section on condensation polymers, where this particular type of polymer is described.

Gelation in condensation polymers.[6]   Three-dimensional condensation polymers that gain a crosslinked network from at least one trifunctional or greater unit are complex in structure. Since in this type of polymerization reaction an extremely high molecular weight molecule is rapidly formed, the polymer becomes insoluble in its reaction medium or any other solvent and the polymer *gels* at a well-defined point in the course of the polymerization reaction.

In order to define the point of gelation in any polymerization reaction, the same assumptions which have been substantiated in the case of a linear polymer are made. The branching coefficient, α, is defined as the probability that a functional group on a branch unit, which has a functionality of three or more, is joined to another branch unit. If we consider a

trifunctional monomer $A\!-\!\!\!\diagdown\!\!\!\begin{smallmatrix} A \\ \\ A \end{smallmatrix}$ and the bifunctional monomer $A\!-\!\!A$

which can react with $B\!-\!\!B$, a three-dimensional structure will be formed

in which any linear chain of $A\!-\!\!A$ and $B\!-\!\!B$ is terminated by $A\!-\!\!\!\diagdown\!\!\!\begin{smallmatrix} A \\ \\ A \end{smallmatrix}$,

which gives rise to two more linear chains, each one terminated by $A\!-\!\!\!\diagdown\!\!\!\begin{smallmatrix} A \\ \\ A \end{smallmatrix}$, and so on. If α is 0.5, there is an even chance that each linear chain will lead to a branch unit and an even chance that it will end in a bifunctional unit. When α is less than 0.5, the network cannot continue indefinitely and a finite molecule will be realized; when α is greater than 0.5, a gel will be produced. With the trifunctional unit $A{\overset{A}{\underset{A}{-\!\!<}}}$, α_{cr} equals $1/(3-1)$, or in the general case α_{cr} equals $1/(f-1)$ where f is the functionality of the unit responsible for branching.

In a theoretical calculation α is related to the extent of the reaction p. When only trifunctional units $A{\overset{A}{\underset{A}{-\!\!<}}}$ and $B{\overset{B}{\underset{B}{-\!\!<}}}$ are reacting, then α equals p. When the reaction occurs between $A{\overset{A}{\underset{A}{-\!\!<}}}$ and B—B only, with the number of A groups equal to the number of B groups, the probability is the product of the probabilities of the reaction of A with B and B with A; $\alpha = p^2$. In the general case of $A{\overset{A}{\underset{A}{-\!\!<}}}$, A—A, and B—B, where the initial ratio of A groups to B groups is r and the ratio of A units on the trifunctional molecules to A units on the bifunctional molecules is ρ, the following equation describes the situation:

$$\alpha = \frac{rp_A{}^2\rho}{1 - rp_A{}^2(1-\rho)} = \frac{p_B{}^2\rho}{r - p_B{}^2(1-\rho)}$$

Interfacial condensation polymerization.[7-17] The condensation polymerization of two monomers at the interface of two immiscible liquids, one of which contains monomer A and the other monomer B has been shown to produce high molecular weight polymers. Reactions of this type take place in the organic phase at the interface and the transfer of one monomer into this phase from the aqueous phase controls the rate of polymerization. The molecular weight buildup is characteristic of condensation reactions and molecular weights as high as 500,000 have been obtained. Reactive monomers must be used for rapid conversion to high molecular weight. The particular advantages of this polymerization are the rapid reaction, the low temperatures, simple equipment, and the absence of a necessity for precise monomer balance or purity.

5.2 FREE RADICAL ADDITION POLYMERIZATION[18-21]

The mechanisms by which vinyl monomers produce high molecular weight polymers are characteristic of chain reactions. In these polymerizations the active center of polymerization is retained on the end of the growing chain throughout its growth process. The reaction may be represented as follows:

$$n CH_2{=}CHX \longrightarrow \left[\begin{array}{c} CH_2{-}CH \\ | \\ X \end{array} \right]_n$$

Some of the features which are characteristic of this type of polymerization, in contrast to condensation polymerization, have already been pointed out.

The free radical mechanism. The process of free radical polymerization has three rather distinct steps. (1) Chain *initiation* involves a decomposition of an initiator to yield a pair of free radicals and the subsequent addition of the free radical to a monomer molecule.

Initiation:

$$I \rightarrow 2R\cdot; \qquad R\cdot + CH_2{=}CHX \longrightarrow R{-}CH_2{-}CHX\cdot$$

(2) *Propagation* involves the successive addition of monomers to the radical formed. This is the growth step in which the active free radical is maintained at the end of the chain in the successive addition and thus, once the initiation step has generated a free radical, the active center remains alive until its death.

Propagation:

$$RCH_2{-}CHX\cdot + CH_2{=}CHX \longrightarrow RCH_2{-}CHX{-}CH_2{-}CHX\cdot$$

$$RCH_2{-}CHX{-}CH_2{-}CHX\cdot \xrightarrow{CH_2{=}CHX} \xrightarrow{etc.}$$

$$R(CH_2{-}CHX)_n CH_2{-}CHX\cdot$$

(3) *Termination* can occur in any one of three ways: (*a*) *bimolecular coupling* of two growing chains, (*b*) *disproportionation* through transfer of a hydrogen atom (free radical) from one growing chain to another, and (*c*) *chain transfer* through transfer of a hydrogen atom (free radical) or other atom of the solvent or other molecule foreign to the growing chain.

Termination:

(*a*) $R(CH_2{-}CHX)_n CH_2{-}CHX\cdot + R(CH_2{-}CHX)_m CH_2 CHX\cdot \longrightarrow$
$R(CH_2 CHX)_n CH_2{-}CHX{-}CHX{-}CH_2(CHX{-}CH_2)_m R$

(*b*) $R(CH_2{-}CHX)_n CH_2 CHX\cdot + R(CH_2 CHX)_m CH_2 CHX\cdot \longrightarrow$
$R(CH_2{-}CHX)_n CH{=}CHX + R(CH_2{-}CHX)_m CH_2{-}CH_2 X$

(*c*) $R(CH_2 CHX)_n CH_2 CHX\cdot + RSH \longrightarrow$
$R(CH_2 CHX)_n CH_2 CH_2 X + RS\cdot$

Often such chain transfer agents are intentionally added to a polymerization reaction for the purpose of regulating the molecular weight. Of all the chain transfer agents, mercaptans are the most widely employed. The free radical RS·, generated in this reaction, can now serve to initiate another chain or couple with a growing chain or other radical source.

Initiators. Some polymerizations can be initiated by heat or ultraviolet irradiation where the monomer itself acts as a radical initiator. One thousand monomer molecules may be polymerized by one quantum of light. Usually the initiation is by another added, unstable molecule which generates free radicals. Under certain conditions, oxygen will act as an initiator, but generally the initiator is a peroxide, hydroperoxide, or azonitrile. Water soluble inorganic initiators include hydrogen peroxide, persulfates, perborates, and permanganates. Organic peroxides such as benzoylperoxide decompose to give free radicals at about 80°C.

$$(C_6H_5CO_2)_2 \longrightarrow 2C_6H_5COO· \longrightarrow 2C_6H_5· + 2CO_2$$

Organic hydroperoxides (e.g., *t*-butylhydroperoxide) may decompose spontaneously without activation or a reducing agent activator may be necessary. These latter-mentioned redox systems consist of alkyl or aryl hydroperoxides along with a metal in a reduced state.

$$ROOH + Fe^{+2} \longrightarrow RO· + OH^- + Fe^{+3}$$

This same redox method has been employed with hydrogen peroxide. Azo compounds lose nitrogen on decomposition to free radicals. Most important of these is azo-bis-isobutyronitrile (AIBN).

$$(CH_3)_2C—N{=}N—C(CH_3)_2 \longrightarrow 2(CH_3)_2C· + N_2$$
$$\underset{CN}{|} \qquad \underset{CN}{|} \qquad\qquad \underset{CN}{|}$$

One piece of evidence for the free radical polymerization mechanism is provided by end group studies where the polymer is found to contain initiator fragments. Polymers of methyl methacrylate and styrene initiated by peroxides which carry tagged atoms or other identifiable groups show the presence of these groups on the chain.[22-25] When two initiator fragments are found per chain, it can be assumed that the coupling method of termination occurs exclusively, and on the other hand, if one is found, disproportionation must predominate. However, the amount of initiator on the chain seems to vary with the conditions of the polymerization.[26] The most quantitatively reliable results come from radioactive isotope studies. Azo-bis-isobutyronitrile containing C^{14} yields polymers containing C^{14}.[27]

By using tagging techniques it has been shown that the disproportionation mode of termination in styrene polymerization at ordinary temperatures is not important but in the methyl methacrylate polymerization, a good portion of the chains terminate in this manner.[28] In some studies with C^{14}-labeled benzoyl peroxide initiation of methyl methacrylate, 43% of the initiation by benzoyl peroxide was by phenyl radicals and 57% by benzoyl radicals.[29] In this polymerization, the initiator fragment average per molecule was found to be 1.27, indicating that 57.5% of the termination takes place by disproportionation and 42.5% by coupling.

Polymers prepared in aqueous media with a hydrogen peroxide–Fe(II) redox initiator contain two hydroxy end groups per molecule, indicating that coupling was the exclusive mode of termination.[30-32]

Chain transfer agents. Most of the chain transfer agents in use are mercaptans or disulfides. Dodecyl mercaptan is widely employed in soap emulsion systems since it has the correct balance of solubility in the water and oil phase to give the desired transfer rate to the polymerization reaction. Disulfides such as diphenyl disulfide are inactive to chain transfer, while a more sterically hindered disulfide where sulfur–sulfur bond breaking is enhanced is active.[4]

$$CH_3-\underset{CH_3}{\overset{CH_3}{\bigcirc}}-S-S-\underset{CH_3}{\overset{CH_3}{\bigcirc}}-CH_3 + R(CH_2-CHX)_nCH_2CHX\cdot \longrightarrow$$

$$R(CH_2CHX)_nCH_2CHX-S-\underset{CH_3}{\overset{CH_3}{\bigcirc}}-CH_3 + CH_3-\underset{CH_3}{\overset{CH_3}{\bigcirc}}-S\cdot$$

Either the reaction is initiated by attack by the growing chain on the —S—S— link or the growing chain reacts with a sulfide radical subsequent to —S—S— bond breaking. In either case, excessive hindrance where the methyl groups are replaced by isopropyl groups renders the disulfide or sulfide radical inactive.

Chain transfer through reaction of the growing molecule with solvent was proposed[33] to explain the presence of chlorine in polystyrene polymerized in the presence of carbon tetrachloride.[34] In the polymerization of ethylene in carbontetrachloride, where the products were intentionally limited to low molecular weight polymers, hydrolysis gave various aliphatic acids which were suitably identified.[35]

$$R\cdot + CCl_4 \longrightarrow RCl + \cdot CCl_3$$

$$\cdot CCl_3 + nCH_2{=}CHC_6H_5 \longrightarrow Cl_3C(CH_2{-}\underset{\underset{C_6H_5}{|}}{CH})_n CH_2{-}\underset{\underset{C_6H_5}{|}}{CH}\cdot$$

$$Cl_3C(CH_2{-}\underset{\underset{C_6H_5}{|}}{CH})_n{-}CH_2{-}\underset{\underset{C_6H_5}{|}}{CH}\cdot + CCl_4 \longrightarrow$$

$$Cl_3C(CH_2{-}\underset{\underset{C_6H_5}{|}}{CH}){-}CH_2{-}\underset{\underset{C_6H_5}{|}}{CHCl} + \cdot CCl_3$$

Kinetics.[36] Employing simplified notation with the initiation, propagation, and termination steps in the mechanism for free radical polymerization previously discussed, the following equations can be written:

Initiation:

$$I \xrightarrow{k_d} 2R\cdot$$

$$R\cdot + M \xrightarrow{k_i} M_1\cdot$$

Propagation:

$$M_1\cdot + M \xrightarrow{k_p} M_2\cdot$$

$$M_2\cdot + M \xrightarrow{k_p} M_3\cdot$$

In general,

$$M_x\cdot + M \xrightarrow{k_p} M_{x+1}\cdot$$

Termination:

$$M_x\cdot + M_y\cdot \xrightarrow{k_{tc}} M_{xy} \qquad \text{(coupling)}$$

$$M_x\cdot + M_y\cdot \xrightarrow{k_{td}} M_x + M_y \quad \text{(disproportionation)}$$

The rate equations for these three steps are shown below:
Initiation:

$$d[M\cdot]/dt = 2fk_d[I]$$

Termination:

$$-d[M\cdot]/dt = 2k_t[M\cdot]^2$$

In the initiation equation f equals the fraction of radicals formed by the decomposition of the initiator that are successful in initiating the polymerization. The concentration of free radicals, $M\cdot$, becomes constant in the early moments of the polymerization reaction, and the radicals are destroyed and formed at identical rates. Thus a steady state condition is reached in which the rate of initiation equals the rate of termination, $d[M\cdot]/dt = -d[M\cdot]/dt$:

$$2fk_d[I] = 2k_t[M\cdot]^2$$

$$[M\cdot] = \left(\frac{fk_d[I]}{k_t}\right)^{1/2}$$

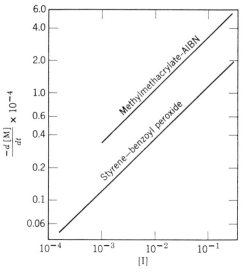

Fig. 5.3.

The rate of propagation is the same as the rate of disappearance of the monomer. If the number of monomers employed in the initiation step is small compared to the number used in the propagation step, the following equations can be written when high molecular weight polymer is to be obtained:

Propagation:

$$-d[M]/dt = k_p[M][M\cdot]$$

$$-d[M]/dt = k_p[M](fk_d[I]/k_t)^{1/2}$$

From this it can be seen that in the early stages of the polymerization reaction, the rate of polymerization should be proportional to the square root of the initiator concentration and to the first power of the monomer concentration, if the initiator efficiency f is high. If the efficiency is low, f could be proportional to [M] and thus the rate would be proportional to $[M]^{3/2}$. Experimental data bear out these rate equations for free radical polymerization[36,37] (Fig. 5.3).

Chain branching in polyethylene.[38-40] The infrared spectrum of polyethylene prepared by free radical initiation at high pressure and temperature is quite different from the spectrum of a linear polyethylene in that there are more methyl groups than can be accounted for by considering end groups alone (Chapter 4). Two types of branches are found, the long-chain and short-chain branches.

The long-chain branches may arise through the reaction of a growing chain with another polymer chain by a hydrogen extraction:

$$\sim\!CH_2\!-\!CH_2\!\cdot \ + \ \sim\!CH_2\!-\!CH_2\!-\!CH_2\!-\!CH_2\!\sim \ \longrightarrow$$

$$\sim\!CH_2\!-\!CH_3 \ + \ \sim\!CH_2\!-\!\overset{\cdot}{C}H\!-\!CH_2\!-\!CH_2\!\sim$$

The product free radical, which may appear at any position along the polymer chain that was attacked, can now act as a new site (initiator) for the propagation of a branched chain. This mechanism does not, however, account for all the chain branching in polyethylene.

A second mechanism which involves an intramolecular chain transfer was also postulated, since it was observed that most of the branches contained four carbons in the abundance of 0.2 to 4.6 such branches per 100 carbon atoms. Both types of chain transfer reactions, intermolecular and intramolecular, are believed to occur.

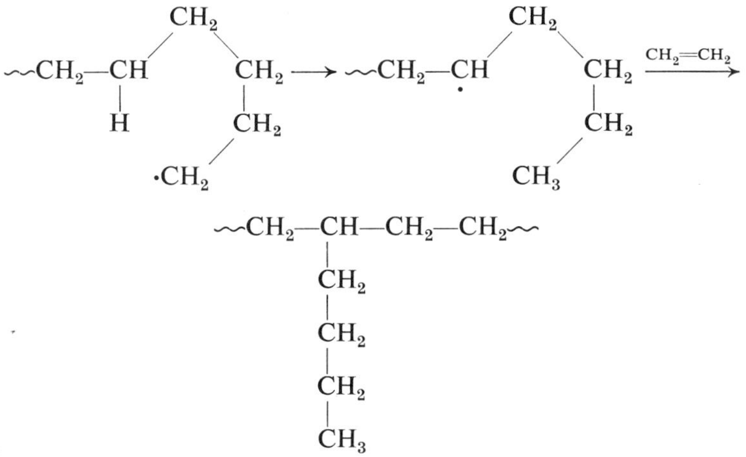

Copolymerization.[41] There is a wide variety of monomers which will enter into a copolymerization reaction with another monomer. Some monomers which will not homopolymerize will form copolymers. The physical properties of the copolymers are quite different from the properties of either homopolymer but approach the properties of either homopolymer as the composition of copolymer approaches the composition of either homopolymer.

If it is assumed that the rate of addition of any monomer to the free radical end on the chain depends only on the nature of the end group bearing the radical, that is, where monomers M_1 and M_2 give M_1 and M_2

ends, the following set of equations can be written for the various types of addition reactions possible:

$$M_1\cdot + M_1 \longrightarrow M_1\cdot \qquad \text{rate} = k_{11}[M_1\cdot][M_1]$$
$$M_1\cdot + M_2 \longrightarrow M_2\cdot \qquad \text{rate} = k_{12}[M_1\cdot][M_2]$$
$$M_2\cdot + M_1 \longrightarrow M_1\cdot \qquad \text{rate} = k_{21}[M_2\cdot][M_1]$$
$$M_2\cdot + M_2 \longrightarrow M_2\cdot \qquad \text{rate} = k_{22}[M_2\cdot][M_2]$$

If a steady state is reached instantly after the polymerization is started, then the total concentrations of $M_1\cdot$ and $M_2\cdot$ will remain constant, and the rate of conversion of $M_1\cdot$ to $M_2\cdot$ will equal the rate of conversion of $M_2\cdot$ to $M_1\cdot$:

$$k_{21}[M_2\cdot][M_1] = k_{12}[M_1\cdot][M_2]$$

The rates of disappearance of the two different monomer types can be expressed as:

$$-d[M_1]/dt = k_{11}[M_1\cdot][M_1] + k_{21}[M_2\cdot][M_1]$$
$$-d[M_2]/dt = k_{12}[M_1\cdot][M_2] + k_{22}[M_2\cdot][M_2]$$

If k_{11}/k_{12} and k_{22}/k_{21} are defined as r_1 and r_2 respectively, then

$$\frac{d[M_1]}{d[M_2]} = \frac{k_{11}[M_1\cdot][M_1] + k_{21}[M_2\cdot][M_1]}{k_{12}[M_1\cdot][M_2] + k_{22}[M_2\cdot][M_2]}$$

$$= \frac{[M_1]}{[M_2]}\left(\frac{k_{11}[M_1\cdot] + k_{21}[M_2\cdot]}{k_{12}[M_1\cdot] + k_{22}[M_2\cdot]}\right)$$

Multiplying through by $\dfrac{1}{k_{21}}\dfrac{[M_2]}{[M_2\cdot]}$,

$$\frac{d[M_1]}{d[M_2]} = \frac{[M_1]}{[M_2]}\left(\frac{\dfrac{k_{11}}{k_{21}}\dfrac{[M_1\cdot][M_2]}{[M_2\cdot]} + [M_2]}{\dfrac{k_{12}}{k_{21}}\dfrac{[M_1\cdot][M_2]}{[M_2\cdot]} + \dfrac{k_{22}}{k_{21}}[M_2]}\right)$$

Since $[M_1] = \dfrac{k_{12}}{k_{21}}\dfrac{[M_1\cdot][M_2]}{[M_2\cdot]}$, then

$$\frac{d[M_1]}{d[M_2]} = \frac{[M_1]}{[M_2]}\left(\frac{r_1[M_1] + [M_2]}{[M_1] + r_2[M_2]}\right) \qquad (5.3)$$

The *monomer reactivity ratios* r_1 and r_2 are the ratios of the rate constant for a radical adding to its own monomer to that of its addition to another. It is a measure of preference for its own kind of monomer to that of another. If $r_1 > 1$, the radical $M_1\cdot$ on the growing end of the chain prefers to add M_1. If $r_1 < 1$, the radical $M_1\cdot$ prefers to add M_2. In Table 5.2, reactivity ratios for various pairs of monomers are given. When $r_1r_2 = 1$,

TABLE 5.2

M_1	M_2	r_1	r_2	r_1r_2
Styrene	Butadiene	0.78	1.39	1.08
Styrene	p-Methoxystyrene	1.16	0.82	0.95
Styrene	Methyl methacrylate	0.52	0.46	0.24
Styrene	Vinyl acetate	55.0	0.01	—
Vinyl acetate	Vinyl chloride	0.23	1.68	0.39
Vinyl acetate	Diethyl maleate	0.17	0.043	0.007
Maleic anhydride	Isopropenyl acetate	0.002	0.032	—
Methyl acrylate	Vinyl chloride	9.0	0.083	0.75

the ideal situation results, in which the two monomer units are arranged at random along the chain in the relative amounts determined by the reactivities and concentrations of the monomer. An alternating copolymer in which the composition will be 1:1 is formed when $r_1 = r_2 = 0$. This copolymer is formed independently of the monomer concentrations. The case in which r_1 and r_2 are both greater than 1 and the monomers simultaneously homopolymerize is not known, even where $r_1r_2 > 1$. Most monomer pairs polymerize according to $0 < r_1r_2 < 1$.

In practical situations the concentrations of the monomers do not remain constant, so that the composition of the polymer chains will vary as the polymerization reaction takes place. If F_1 and F_2 are defined as the mole fractions of monomers 1 and 2 respectively in the polymer at any instant during the polymerization:

$$F_1 = 1 - F_2 = d[M_1]/d([M_1] + [M_2])$$

and f_1 and f_2 are the mole fractions of monomer feed:

$$f_1 = 1 - f_2 = [M_1]/[M_1] + [M_2]$$

then from the differential eq. 5.3,

$$F_1 = r_1f_1^2 + f_1f_2/r_1f_1^2 + 2f_1f_2 + r_2f_2^2 \qquad (5.4)$$

In general $F_1 \neq f_1$ and F_1 and f_1 will change as the polymerization reaction proceeds. Thus, over a range of conversion, the polymer will consist of chains differing in composition. From eq. 5.4 is obtained the polymer composition for the feed curves. Figure 5.4 shows the curves for an ideal copolymer, $r_1r_2 = 1$. When one monomer (M_1) is much more reactive than the other (M_2), the polymer chains formed early in the reaction

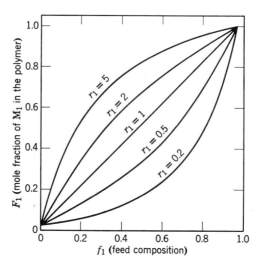

Fig. 5.4. Copolymer curves, $r_1 r_2 = 1$.

will have a large amount of M_1. As the reaction proceeds, for example to the halfway point, the concentration of M_1 will be low compared to M_2 by virtue of its greater reactivity, and the composition of the chains formed will begin to shift in favor of a higher amount of M_2, until at the end of the polymerization reaction the polymer chains will consist mostly of M_2. This case is exemplified by the styrene (M_1) vinyl acetate (M_2) system.

When both r_1 and r_2 are less than 1, the polymer-feed composition curves at some point during the polymerization cross the line $F_1 = f_1$ due to the fact that each radical end prefers the other type of monomer for addition, and at this point, where $F_1 = f_1$, the polymerization proceeds without change in composition or feed. This is the so-called *azeotropic copolymerization*.

Experimentally, r_1 and r_2 can be determined by varying the concentrations of M_1 and M_2 in several polymerizations which are taken to low conversion (so that the monomer concentrations do not change appreciably) and determining the composition of the polymer formed. Thus, the ratio or r_1 to r_2 can be plotted in any given series where a given feed gives a straight line. Practically, these values will allow one to obtain a copolymer of a desired composition by regulating the feed charge.

Monomer and radical reactivity. The reactivity of unsaturated monomers with free radicals depends on the structure of both the olefin and the radical. The reactivity of any substituted ethylene towards a free radical is dependent on the substituent group. From copolymerization studies it is observed that the order of reactivity is $-C_6H_5 > -CH=CH_2 > -COCH_3 > -CN > -CO_2R > -Cl > -CH_2X > -OCOCH_3 > -OR$. A second substituent on the same carbon atom usually increases the reactivity, for example, methyl methacrylate is more reactive than methyl acrylate. This order of reactivity can be correlated to the stability of the radical formed from the addition. Olefins with substituent groups which stabilize the product radical are also stable monomers, but in the case of the monomer the stabilization by the substituent group is small in comparison to the stabilization given to the radical. Thus, the overall effect is a greater reactivity where a radical which is stabilized through delocalization can be formed.

Resonance stabilization on the other hand depresses the reactivity of the radical toward a monomer and the reverse order previously given holds for radical reactivity. The effect of a substituent on the radical, however, is much greater for depressing its reactivity than enhancing the activity of the monomer. The styrene radical, for example, is 10^3 times less reactive than the vinyl acetate radical to any given monomer, but the styrene monomer (by virtue of the greater effect of the substituent in stabilizing the resulting radical after addition over stabilization of the monomer) is only 50 times as active as vinyl acetate to a given radical.

The relative reactivities of monomers have been expressed in terms of polarity.[42]

$$K_{12} = P_1 Q_2 e^{-e_1 e_2}$$

P_1 is the reactivity of the radical M_1, Q_2 is the reactivity of the monomer M_2, and e_1 (radical) and e_2 (monomer) are proportional to the interaction of the charges of the substituents attached to the double bond. A further assumption equates e_1 and e_2.

Styrene is a monomer which will copolymerize with most other monomers and it has been widely used to test the copolymerizability of other monomers. Monomers which do not homopolymerize, but will copolymerize, are usually 1,2-disubstituted olefins, exemplified by maleic and fumaric acid derivatives. In addition, the *trans* isomers of the following compounds will copolymerize but not homopolymerize:[4]

$C_6H_5CH=CHCN$, $C_6H_5CH=CH-CO_2CH_3$,

$C_6H_5CH=CH-COCH_3$ $C_6H_5CH=CH-COC_6H_5$,

$C_6H_5COCH=CHCOC_6H_5$, $C_6H_5COCH=CHCO_2CH_3$,

Polymerization systems and the theory of emulsion systems.[43] The polymerization of olefins by free radical mechanisms can be carried out in bulk, solution, suspension, or emulsion systems. In bulk polymerization, the initiator decomposes to give free radicals at a rapid rate and the system is fairly simple. The technique is employed mainly to cast where the casting of the preformed polymer at elevated temperatures cannot be accomplished. The most serious problem in this system is the transfer of heat from the system rapidly enough to maintain control of the reaction and prevent decomposition of the reactants.

Solution polymerization allows better heat transfer but offers several disadvantages. The mixture becomes more viscous as the reaction proceeds, the solvent is difficult to remove, and chain transfer with the solvent may be a serious problem.

Emulsion polymerization and suspension polymerization in aqueous media overcome the problems of heat transfer, chain transfer, and viscosity. These two techniques have become industrially important because of these practical advantages. Very high molecular weights can be obtained with emulsion systems. Suspension polymerization is essentially a bulk polymerization in a suspending medium where each colloidal monomer particle acts as an individual bulk polymerization, and the initiator is in the monomer droplet.

An emulsion system contains the initiator in the water phase and the free radicals generated migrate to the monomer phase, which may be suspended in solution by an emulsifier. Here it is very simple to control the molecular weight by varying the amounts of emulsifying agent, initiator, and chain transfer agent. The initiator may be a redox system such as previously described, and the modifier (chain transfer agent), a mercaptan. The emulsifier is usually a soap or synthetic detergent which is free from unsaturation, such as is found in linoleic and linolenic salts.

Kinetics of emulsion polymerization. In an emulsion system containing monomer, water, emulsifier, and a water-soluble initiator, the emulsifier, if present in the correct concentration, will exist as micelles which contain perhaps 50 to 100 soap molecules. Some of the monomer in the system enters the soap micelles but the larger portion exists in the form of droplets about 1 μ in diameter.

In this system, no polymer is formed in the monomer droplets. In the early stages of the polymerization, polymer is formed in the soap micelles. The micelles offer an abundance of monomer and a high surface-to-volume ratio to the free radicals in the water which initiate polymerization at the micelle surface. As the polymerization proceeds in the micelle, monomer from the aqueous phase enters the micelle to feed the growing polymer chain.

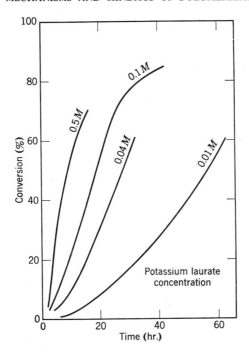

Fig. 5.5. Effect of soap concentration on rate of polymerization.[44]

At about 2-3% conversion, the polymer particles have grown much larger than the original micelle and have absorbed the soap. Micelles which have not been subjected to attack by initiator disappear and polymerization now takes place within the polymer particles which contain absorbed monomer. *No polymerization takes place in the monomer droplets which feed the polymer particles.*

In a typical emulsion system, free radicals are generated at the rate of about 10^{13} cc.$^{-1}$ sec.$^{-1}$, and there are approximately 10^{14} polymer particles per cubic centimeter. Termination of radicals in the aqueous phase is negligible and diffusion of the radicals is rapid enough to permit all the radicals to reach the polymer particles. This means that one radical gets to a particle every 10 sec. Two radicals in the same polymer particle terminate by coupling instantly so that at any given instant, a particle contains one or no free radicals, or half the particles will contain one radical and the other half none. The rate of polymerization can then be expressed as rate $= k_p[\mathrm{M}](N/2)$, where N is the number of particles per cubic centimeter. Since the monomer concentration in the particles (but not in the system overall) remains constant, the rate depends primarily on the number of particles present as does the D.P.:

$$\text{D.P.} = k_p N[\text{M}]/\rho$$

In this equation, ρ is the rate of generation of free radicals. The D.P. is a function of free radical formation. In bulk polymerization, increasing the rate of initiation increases the rate of polymerization. This, however, causes a decrease in D.P. In emulsion polymerization, the rate of polymerization can be increased by increasing the number of polymer particles, and if the initiation rate is held steady, D.P. will increase. Therefore, by increasing the amount of soap, which increases the number of micelles and in turn the number of polymer particles, both the D.P. and polymerization rate are increased (Fig. 5.5).[44]

5.3 IONIC ADDITION POLYMERIZATION[45]

Vinyl polymers can be obtained from a variety of substituted ethylenes by initiation either with anions or cations. For cationic polymerization, catalysts include most strong Lewis acids, while most anionic polymerization catalysts are strong bases such as sodium amide or organometallic bases. Here the term catalyst and not initiator is used since the catalysts exert their influence throughout the course of the polymerization reaction.

The polymerizations are characterized by high rates and low temperatures. A polymerization may proceed so rapidly that the liberation of heat becomes a problem and a low-boiling diluent is employed to dissipate the heat of reaction through its vaporization. The reactivity ratios observed in copolymerization by free radical means are usually quite different from ionic reactivity ratios. In many cases, only one of the two monomers will polymerize. There are few ionic 1:1 copolymers.

The polarity of the monomer double bond can be directly related to its susceptibility to polymerization by free radical, cationic, or anionic means. Monomers which contain electron-donating substituents attached to the double bond and will promote the formation of a stable carbonium ion are susceptible to cationic polymerization. Those which have electron-withdrawing groups and thus stabilize the carbanion will undergo anionic polymerization (Table 5.3). Olefins which are strongly activated for cationic polymerization such as isopropenyl alkyl ethers and vinylidine ethers can be polymerized by weak acids, while those which are weakly activated, such as isobutylene, alkyl vinyl ethers, and α-methylstyrene, require a strong Lewis acid as typified by BF_3. On the other hand, olefins which are strongly activated for anionic polymerization (vinylidine cyanide) are susceptible to catalysis by weak bases. Most others in the anionic class need strong bases, for example, lithium amide, sodium methoxide, or butyl lithium. Between these two extremes lie the substituted ethylenes which

TABLE 5.3[45]

Cationic (Acidic) $CH_2=C{\nearrow}^{G}$	Free Radical $CH_2=C{\nearrow}^{G}$	Anionic (Base) $CH_2=C{\nearrow}^{G}$
$CH_2=\overset{OR}{\underset{\vert}{C}}-CH_3 \qquad CH_2=C(CH_3)_2$	$CH_2=CHBr \qquad CH_2=CHCl$	$CH_2=C(CN)_2$
$CH_2=C(OR)_2 \qquad CH_2=\overset{R}{\underset{\vert}{C}}-CH_3$	$CH_2=CCl_2 \qquad CF_2=CCl_2$	$CH_2=\overset{CO_2R}{\underset{\vert}{C}}-CN$
$CH_2=C-CH_2$ (cyclic O–CH_2–O ketal) $\qquad CH_2=CHOR$	$CF_2=CF_2 \qquad CF_2=CFCl$	$CH_2=\overset{SO_2R}{\underset{\vert}{C}}-CN$
$CH_2=\overset{CH_3}{\underset{\vert}{C}}-C_6H_4-OR$	$CH_2=CHF \qquad CH_2=CF_2$	$CH_2=\overset{SO_2R}{\underset{\vert}{C}}-CO_2R$
$CH_2=$ (cubane)	$CH_2=CFCl \qquad CH_2=\overset{Cl}{\underset{\vert}{C}}-CO_2R$	$CH_2=\overset{CN}{\underset{\vert}{C}}-CF_3$
$CH_3-CH=CHOCH_3$	$CH_2=\overset{Cl}{\underset{\vert}{C}}-CH=CH_2$	$CH_2=CHNO_2$
(indene)	$CH_2=CH-O-COCH_3$	$CH_2=\overset{CH_3}{\underset{\vert}{C}}-NO_2$
(benzofuran)	$CH_2=CHOCOR$	$CH_2=\overset{Cl}{\underset{\vert}{C}}-NO_2$
(dihydrofuran)	$CH_2=CH-OCOCH_2Cl$	$CH_3-CH=CH-CH=\overset{CO_2R}{\underset{\vert}{C}}-CN$
	$CH_2=CHO\overset{O}{\overset{\|}{C}}-C_6H_5$	
	$CH_2=CH-CO_2R$	$CH_2=CHCONR_2$
	$CH_2=\overset{CH_3}{\underset{\vert}{C}}-CO_2R$	$CH_2=\overset{CH_3}{\underset{\vert}{C}}-CONR_2$
		$CH_2=CH-CN$
	$CH_2=C{\overset{CO_2R}{\underset{CO_2R}{}}}$	$CH_2=\overset{CH_3}{\underset{\vert}{C}}-CN$

Cationic (Acidic)	Free Radical	Anionic (Base)
(N-vinylcarbazole, N–$CH=CH_2$) (N-vinylpyrrolidone, N–$CH=CH_2$, ring with $=O$)	(dibenzofuran with $CH=CH_2$)	(two dihydronaphthalene structures)

Cationic (Acidic)	Free Radical	Anionic (Base)
$CH_2=CH_2$		$CH_2=CH-CH_3$
		$CH_2=CH-COCH_3$
$CH_2=CHC_6H_5 \qquad CH_2=\overset{CH_3}{\underset{\vert}{C}}-C_6H_5$	$CH_2=\overset{CH_3}{\underset{\vert}{C}}-CH=CH_2$	$CH_2=CH-CH=CH_2$

have at most a weakly electron-withdrawing group and are polymerized by free radical initiators. There are some monomers, however, which are polymerized by all three methods.

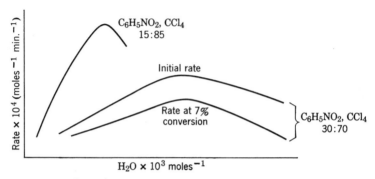

Fig. 5.6. Effect of water on the polymerization of styrene with $SnCl^4$.[46]

Cationic mechanisms. In addition to the generalizations made about ionic polymerizations there are several other observations which support cationic mechanisms for vinyl polymerization. It is known, for example, that polymerization takes place in a system in which carbonium ions have been proven to exist, and that a cocatalyst is necessary for the polymerization which involves a Lewis acid. Since a suitable cocatalyst is necessary to produce ions where a Lewis acid cannot alone, the effect of cocatalyst concentration in polymerization is observed[46-51] (Fig. 5.6). The propagation step may then be assumed to consist of the addition of monomer to carbonium ion. Whether or not the anionic species is closely associated with the carbonium ion as an ion pair either in the original catalyst or in the subsequent propagation steps may depend strongly on the solvent medium and the particular catalyst as well as on the nature of the polymer chain end. Certainly it can be seen from Fig. 5.6 that the solvent does affect the rate of polymerization. In some cases, however, a cocatalyst is not needed but in this case the acid would be capable of generating its own cations. The polymerization steps are then analogous to a free radical mechanism. The polymerization of isobutylene with boron fluoride and a small amount of water is representative.

Initiation:

$$BF_3 + HOH \longrightarrow BF_3\overset{\ominus}{O}H H^{\oplus}$$

$$BF_3\overset{\ominus}{O}H H^{\oplus} + CH_2\!\!=\!\!C(CH_3)_2 \longrightarrow CH_3\!\!-\!\!\overset{\overset{\displaystyle CH_3}{|}}{\underset{\underset{\displaystyle CH_3}{|}}{C}}{}^{\oplus} BF_3\overset{\ominus}{O}H$$

Propagation:

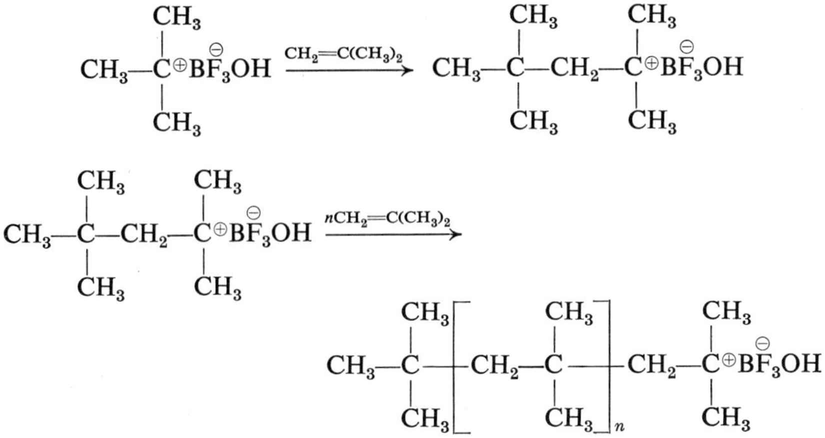

$$CH_3-\underset{\underset{CH_3}{|}}{\overset{\overset{CH_3}{|}}{C}}{}^{\oplus}B\bar{F}_3OH \xrightarrow{CH_2=C(CH_3)_2} CH_3-\underset{\underset{CH_3}{|}}{\overset{\overset{CH_3}{|}}{C}}-CH_2-\underset{\underset{CH_3}{|}}{\overset{\overset{CH_3}{|}}{C}}{}^{\oplus}B\bar{F}_3OH$$

$$CH_3-\underset{\underset{CH_3}{|}}{\overset{\overset{CH_3}{|}}{C}}-CH_2-\underset{\underset{CH_3}{|}}{\overset{\overset{CH_3}{|}}{C}}{}^{\oplus}B\bar{F}_3OH \xrightarrow{nCH_2=C(CH_3)_2}$$

$$CH_3-\underset{\underset{CH_3}{|}}{\overset{\overset{CH_3}{|}}{C}}\left[-CH_2-\underset{\underset{CH_3}{|}}{\overset{\overset{CH_3}{|}}{C}}-\right]_n CH_2-\underset{\underset{CH_3}{|}}{\overset{\overset{CH_3}{|}}{C}}{}^{\oplus}B\bar{F}_3OH$$

It can be seen here that in contrast to free radical mechanisms there is another species associated with the active end. There are three probable mechanisms for termination:

Kinetic termination:

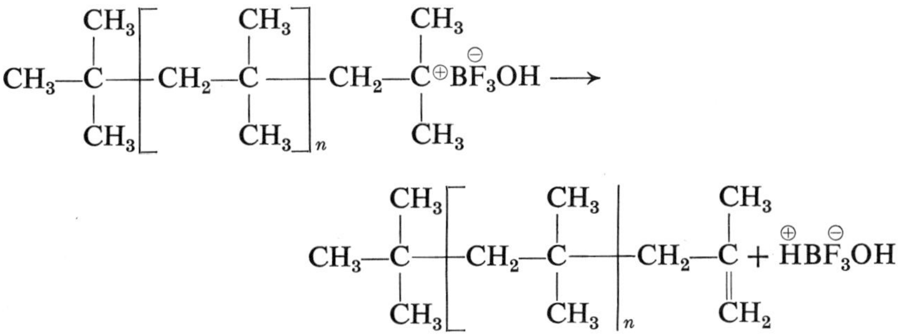

$$CH_3-\underset{\underset{CH_3}{|}}{\overset{\overset{CH_3}{|}}{C}}\left[-CH_2-\underset{\underset{CH_3}{|}}{\overset{\overset{CH_3}{|}}{C}}-\right]_n CH_2-\underset{\underset{CH_3}{|}}{\overset{\overset{CH_3}{|}}{C}}{}^{\oplus}B\bar{F}_3OH \longrightarrow$$

$$CH_3-\underset{\underset{CH_3}{|}}{\overset{\overset{CH_3}{|}}{C}}\left[-CH_2-\underset{\underset{CH_3}{|}}{\overset{\overset{CH_3}{|}}{C}}-\right]_n CH_2-\underset{\underset{CH_2}{\|}}{\overset{\overset{CH_3}{|}}{C}} + \overset{\oplus}{H}\overset{\ominus}{B}F_3OH$$

Monomer chain transfer:

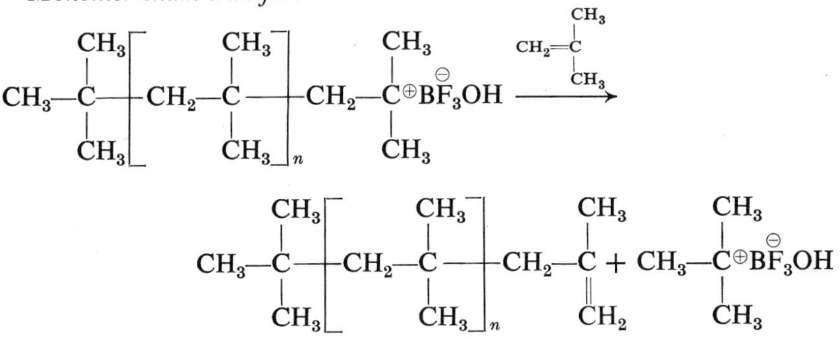

$$CH_3-\underset{\underset{CH_3}{|}}{\overset{\overset{CH_3}{|}}{C}}\left[-CH_2-\underset{\underset{CH_3}{|}}{\overset{\overset{CH_3}{|}}{C}}-\right]_n CH_2-\underset{\underset{CH_3}{|}}{\overset{\overset{CH_3}{|}}{C}}{}^{\oplus}B\bar{F}_3OH \xrightarrow{CH_2=\underset{\underset{CH_3}{|}}{\overset{\overset{CH_3}{|}}{C}}}$$

$$CH_3-\underset{\underset{CH_3}{|}}{\overset{\overset{CH_3}{|}}{C}}\left[-CH_2-\underset{\underset{CH_3}{|}}{\overset{\overset{CH_3}{|}}{C}}-\right]_n CH_2-\underset{\underset{CH_2}{\|}}{\overset{\overset{CH_3}{|}}{C}} + CH_3-\underset{\underset{CH_3}{|}}{\overset{\overset{CH_3}{|}}{C}}{}^{\oplus}B\bar{F}_3OH$$

Combination:

$$CH_3-\underset{\underset{CH_3}{|}}{\overset{\overset{CH_3}{|}}{C}}\left[CH_2-\underset{\underset{CH_3}{|}}{\overset{\overset{CH_3}{|}}{C}}\right]_n CH_2-\underset{\underset{CH_3}{|}}{\overset{\overset{CH_3}{|}}{C}}{}^{\oplus}BF_3\overset{\ominus}{O}H \longrightarrow$$

$$CH_3-\underset{\underset{CH_3}{|}}{\overset{\overset{CH_3}{|}}{C}}\left[CH_2-\underset{\underset{CH_3}{|}}{\overset{\overset{CH_3}{|}}{C}}\right]_n CH_2-\underset{\underset{CH_3}{|}}{\overset{\overset{CH_3}{|}}{C}}-OH + BF_3$$

In the example cited here, either kinetic termination or monomer chain transfer is involved since no hydroxyl end groups are detected. The end groups of the polymer which has been taken to low conversion are methyl and vinyl.[49,52] When deuterium oxide was employed as a cocatalyst, the methyl groups were found to contain deuterium. In certain other systems, combination takes place to an appreciable extent. Where titanium tetrachloride (catalyst) and trichloroacetic acid (cocatalyst) are the catalysts for the polymerization of isobutylene, trichloracetate end groups are found.[53] In the polymerization of styrene with trifluoroacetic acid alone, the polymer contains trifluoroacetate groups.[54]

$$TiCl_4 + Cl_3C-CO_2H \longrightarrow TiCl_4Cl_3C-\overset{\ominus}{C}O_2H{}^{\oplus}$$

$$\sim\!CH_2\underset{\underset{CH_3}{|}}{\overset{\overset{CH_3}{|}}{C}}{}^{\oplus}TiCl_4CCl_3\overset{\ominus}{C}O_2 \longrightarrow \sim\!CH_2-\underset{\underset{CH_3}{|}}{\overset{\overset{CH_3}{|}}{C}}-O-\overset{\overset{O}{\|}}{C}-CCl_3 + TiCl_4$$

$$\sim\!CH_2-\underset{\underset{CH_3}{|}}{\overset{\overset{CH_3}{|}}{C}}{}^{\oplus}\overset{\ominus}{O}COCF_3 \longrightarrow \sim\!CH_2-\underset{\underset{CH_3}{|}}{\overset{\overset{CH_3}{|}}{C}}-O-\overset{\overset{O}{\|}}{C}-CF_3$$

For a cationic polymerization, the general steps may be written:

$$A{\cdot}BH \rightleftharpoons AB^{\ominus}H^{\oplus}$$

$$AB^{\ominus}H^{\oplus} + M \overset{k_i}{\longrightarrow} HM^{\oplus}AB^{\ominus}$$

$$M_n{}^{\oplus}AB^{\ominus} + M \overset{k_p}{\longrightarrow} M_{n+1}^{\oplus}AB^{\ominus}$$

$$M_n{}^{\oplus}AB^{\ominus} \overset{k_t}{\longrightarrow} M_n + AB^{\ominus}H^{\oplus}$$

or

$$M_n{}^{\oplus}AB^{\ominus} + M \overset{k_{mt}}{\longrightarrow} M_n + HM^{\oplus}AB^{\ominus}$$

In a homogeneous system, the initiation rate should depend on the catalyst ($AB^{\ominus}H^{\oplus}$) concentration and the concentration of the monomer. Usually neither the concentration nor the nature of the catalyst is known and the rate must be expressed either as the Lewis acid concentration or the cocatalyst concentration [C]. The rate of initiation should then be either $k_i[C]$ or $k_i[C][M]$, depending on whether the propagation step is largely complete. The termination step should be first-order if an ion pair exists throughout the reaction. The concentration of active centers is then expressed by $[M^{\oplus}AB^{\ominus}] = (k_i/k_t)[C][M]^{a-1}$, where a is 1 or 2, depending on the kinetics discussed.

$$\text{Propagation rate} = k_p[M^{\oplus}AB^{\ominus}][M] = (k_i k_p/k_t)[C][M]^a$$

When kinetic termination is the dominate mode of termination, then the degree of polymerization is expressed by

$$\text{D.P.} = \frac{\text{rate of propagation}}{\text{rate of termination}} = \frac{k_p}{k_t}[M]$$

When chain transfer is the terminating step, D.P. $= k_p/k_{mt}$. These equations have been found to be valid for styrene polymerization with stannic chloride[55] where rate $= K[C][M]^2$. The polymerization of α-methylstyrene with boronfluoride-etherate and excess water in a methylene chloride solvent follows the equation rate $= k_i[C][M]\left(2\dfrac{k_p}{k_t}[M]\right)$, where kinetic termination seems to be the most probable mode of termination and the catalyst which best accounts for the variation of rate with water concentration is $H^{\oplus}(BF_3^{\ominus}OH)$.[47]

Anionic mechanisms.[6,56] There are many examples of polymerization initiated by anionic catalysts, but the mechanisms of these polymerizations are not all exactly the same. There are, however, several similar features in anionic polymerizations. Many of the polymerization reactions take place at a low temperature, but many are not as sensitive to temperature as are cationic polymerizations. There are a number of polymerizations that proceed well at room temperature and above. Many of the polymerizations have some degree of stereospecificity connected with them, especially when the catalyst is heterogeneous, not only in regard to tactic order in simple olefins but also with regard to 1,4-(cis or trans) and 1,2-addition in butadienes.

It has been reported that sodium in liquid ammonia will polymerize methacrylonitrile, acrylonitrile, and methyl methacrylate whereas butadiene and isobutylene do not polymerize to any appreciable extent. Other anionic catalysts such as Grignard reagents and triphenylmethyl sodium are also effective catalysts in the polymerization of acrylics. Styrene yields low polymers with amide ion initiation but neither butadiene nor α-methylstyrene will polymerize.

On the contrary, butadiene and styrene polymerize readily in the presence of dispersions of alkali metals. From a variety of reports which were often conflicting, much confusion evolved concerning the nature of these polymerizations. Anionic mechanisms were accepted on the basis of (a) the nature of the catalyst, (b) the colors which developed during polymerization, (c) the termination of the reaction on the introduction of carbon dioxide, (d) the conversion of triphenylmethane to triphenylmethyl sodium in the sodium-initiated butadiene polymerization, (e) the structures of the diene polymers obtained, which differed from either the radical or cationic processes, and (f) the difference in the copolymer ratios from radical or cationic polymerizations.

Conventional anionic polymerization. In the polymerization of styrene by potassium amide in liquid ammonia, an anionic mechanism is postulated for the following reasons:[57]

1. The polymer contains one nitrogen atom per mole.
2. The polymer chain is free from unsaturation.
3. The molecular weight of the polymer is independent of the amide ion concentration and the potassium amide concentration.
4. The molecular weight at constant conversion is dependent on the potassium ion concentration.
5. The molecular weight depends on the initial styrene concentration.
6. The molecular weight declines slightly with increasing conversion of monomer to polymer.
7. The molecular weight increases with decreasing temperature.
8. $-d[\text{styrene}]/dt = k[\text{styrene}]^2[\text{KNH}_2]^{1/2} = k'[\text{styrene}]^2[\text{NH}_2^{\ominus}]$
9. No potassium amide is consumed.
10. The rate of the reaction increases with decreasing temperature.

Of several possible mechanisms, the one best suited to these observations is the following:

Initiation:

$$K^{\oplus}NH_2^{\ominus} + C_6H_5CH{=}CH_2 \longrightarrow NH_2{-}CH_2{-}\overset{\ominus}{C}HC_6H_5 + K^{\oplus}$$

Propagation:

$$NH_2{-}CH_2{-}\overset{\ominus}{C}HC_6H_5 + CH_2{=}CHC_6H_5 \longrightarrow$$

$$NH_2{-}CH_2{-}\underset{\underset{C_6H_5}{|}}{CH}{-}CH_2{-}\underset{\underset{C_6H_5}{|}}{CH}^{\ominus}$$

Termination:

$$NH_2CH_2—CH—(CH_2—CH)_n—CH_2—CH^\ominus + NH_3 \longrightarrow$$
$$\overset{|}{C_6H_5} \quad \overset{|}{C_6H_5} \quad \overset{|}{C_6H_5}$$

$$NH_2—(CH_2—CH)_n—CH_2—CH_2—C_6H_5 + NH_2^\ominus$$
$$\overset{|}{C_6H_5}$$

In general, for this type of system, the following mechanism can be written:

$$CA \rightleftharpoons C^\oplus + A^\ominus$$
$$A^\ominus + M \longrightarrow A—M^\ominus$$
$$A—M_{x-1}{}^\ominus + M \longrightarrow A—M_x{}^\ominus$$
$$A—M_x{}^\ominus + HA \longrightarrow A—M_x—H + A^\ominus$$

Where potassium in liquid ammonia is employed, potassium amide is generated through a reduction of a molecule of styrene, thereby furnishing the same catalyst.[58]

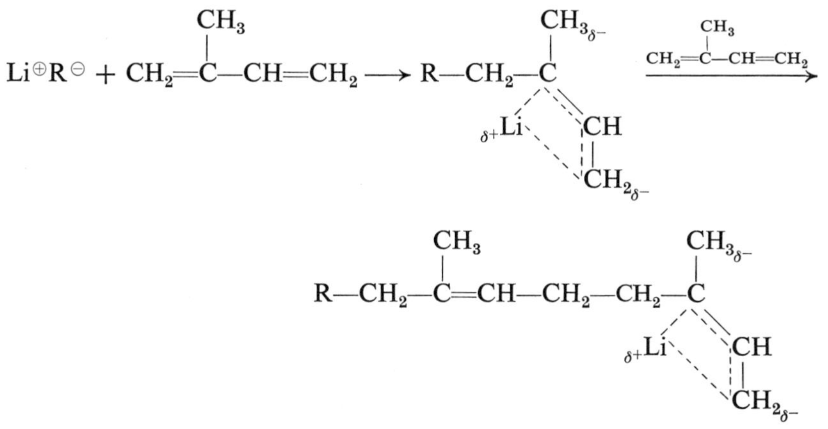

Metal alkyls also act as anionic catalysts for the polymerization of olefins. The polymerization of isoprene with butyl lithium, phenyl lithium, phenyl sodium, and benzyl sodium gives a different polymer depending on the catalyst and the solvent.[59-61] A nearly all *cis*-1,4-polyisoprene is obtained with butyl lithium in a heptane or benzene solvent but in a tetrahydrofuran solvent, a mixture of 3,4-, 1,2-, and *trans*-1,4-isoprene units are formed. Even when phenyl lithium, phenyl sodium, or benzyl sodium is the catalyst in a solvent like heptane and a heterogeneous system is obtained, a mixture of structural units is obtained. The mechanism in all cases is undoubtedly ionic, but in the case of butyl lithium in a solvent of low dielectric constant, there is apparently an intimate ion pair association or a more covalent-type bonding between the growing carbanion end and the metal ion. Methyl methacrylate and acrylonitrile are also particularly susceptible to polymerization by butyl lithium in a heptane solvent.[62]

The rate of polymerization of styrene with butyl lithium in benzene is independent of the butyl lithium concentration over a hundredfold range, while in tetrahydrofuran, the rate is proportional to the butyl lithium concentration.[63]

This is explained by the fact that in benzene the butyl lithium is associated so that the unimolecular concentration in solution is low while tetrahydrofuran complexes the butyl lithium as individual molecules. The following mechanism for the benzene butyl lithium system is proposed:

$$(BuLi)_n \rightleftharpoons \overset{\delta^- \ \delta^+}{BuLi} + (BuLi)_{n-1}$$

$$\overset{\delta^- \ \delta^+}{BuLi} + M \xrightarrow{k_1} Bu\overset{\ominus}{M}Li^{\oplus}$$

$$Bu\overset{\ominus}{M}Li^{\oplus} + M \xrightarrow{k_2} \cdots \xrightarrow{k_2} BuM_x\overset{\ominus}{}Li^{\oplus}$$

$$BuM_x\overset{\ominus}{}Li^{\oplus} + (BuLi)_n \xrightarrow{k_3} BuM_x\overset{\ominus}{}Li^{\oplus} \cdot (BuLi)_n$$

Radical ion mechanisms. Styrene is rapidly polymerized by sodium in the presence of an aromatic hydrocarbon where the molecular weight of the polystyrene depends on the monomer-to-catalyst ratio.[64–68] This polymerization shows typical anionic characteristics, yet in certain respects is different from conventional types. The system produces bright colors which have been shown to be characteristic of the reaction of sodium with certain aromatic hydrocarbons. The remarkable thing about this system is that it stays alive after all the monomer has been used up, and days later, when more monomer is added, the chain starts growing again. These and other observations support the proposed radical ion mechanism:

Catalyst formation
(one-electron transfer):

$$Naphthalene^{\ominus} + C_6H_5CH{=}CH_2 \longrightarrow C_6H_5\overset{\cdot}{C}H{-}CH_2^{\ominus} + Naphthalene$$

$$\updownarrow$$

$$C_6H_5CH{-}CH_2\cdot$$
$$\underset{\ominus}{}$$

$$C_6H_5\overset{\cdot}{C}H\!\!-\!\!CH_2{}^\ominus$$

$$C_6H_5\overset{\ominus}{C}H\!\!-\!\!CH_2\cdot \xrightarrow{\;C_6H_5CH=CH_2\;} \overset{\ominus}{C}H\!\!-\!\!CH_2\!\!-\!\!CH\!\!-\!\!CH_2\cdot$$
$$\qquad\qquad\qquad\qquad\qquad\qquad\underset{\displaystyle C_6H_5}{|}\quad\underset{\displaystyle C_6H_5}{|}$$

$$\cdot CH\!\!-\!\!CH_2\!\!-\!\!CH_2\!\!-\!\!CH^\ominus$$
$$\text{or}\qquad \underset{\displaystyle C_6H_5}{|}\qquad\qquad\underset{\displaystyle C_6H_5}{|}$$

Dimerization (initiation):

$$\overset{\ominus}{C}H\!\!-\!\!CH_2\cdot \longrightarrow \overset{\ominus}{C}H\!\!-\!\!CH_2\!\!-\!\!CH_2\!\!-\!\!CH^\ominus$$
$$\underset{\displaystyle C_6H_5}{|}\qquad\quad\underset{\displaystyle C_6H_5}{|}\qquad\qquad\underset{\displaystyle C_6H_5}{|}$$

Propagation:

$$\overset{\ominus}{C}H\!\!-\!\!CH_2\!\!-\!\!CH_2\!\!-\!\!CH^\ominus \xrightarrow{\;C_6H_5CH=CH_2\;}$$
$$\underset{\displaystyle C_6H_5}{|}\qquad\quad\underset{\displaystyle C_6H_5}{|}$$

$$\overset{\ominus}{C}H\!\!-\!\!CH_2\!\!-\!\!CH\!\!-\!\!CH_2\!\!-\!\!CH_2\!\!-\!\!CH^\ominus$$
$$\underset{\displaystyle C_6H_5}{|}\qquad\quad\underset{\displaystyle C_6H_5}{|}\qquad\qquad\qquad\underset{\displaystyle C_6H_5}{|}$$

In the propagation step the polymer can grow from both ends and is not terminated except by added acid (alcohol, water, etc.). This type of anionic polymerization has been observed with α-methylstyrene and sodium-naphthalene in a tetrahydrofuran solvent[69] and with methacrylonitrile and lithium in liquid ammonia.[70]

$$Li\cdot + NH_3 \longrightarrow Li^\oplus(NH_3) + e\overset{\ominus}{N}H_3$$

$$e\overset{\ominus}{N}H_3 + CH_2\!\!=\!\!\underset{\displaystyle |}{\overset{\displaystyle CH_3}{C}}\!\!-\!\!CN \longrightarrow \overset{\ominus}{C}H_2\!\!-\!\!\underset{\displaystyle \cdot}{\overset{\displaystyle CH_3}{C}}\!\!-\!\!CN + NH_3$$

$$2\overset{\ominus}{C}H_2\!\!-\!\!\underset{\displaystyle \cdot}{\overset{\displaystyle CH_3}{C}}\!\!-\!\!CN \longrightarrow \overset{\ominus}{C}H_2\!\!-\!\!\underset{\displaystyle CN}{\overset{\displaystyle CH_3}{C}}\!\!-\!\!\!\!-\!\!\underset{\displaystyle CN}{\overset{\displaystyle CH_3}{C}}\!\!-\!\!CH_2{}^\ominus$$

Whether the reaction follows this course, i.e., dimerization of the radical ion to give a dianion, or whether the radical ion adds monomer immediately to give both radical and ion growth, as shown in the following discussion, depends on the conditions of the polymerization.[68]

A lithium dispersion in petroleum jelly where the lithium particles have an average diameter of 20 μ is a system employed for the polymerization of isoprene (Coral Rubber).[71] The infrared structure of the polymer is nearly identical to *Hevea*. In this system, there is no aromatic solvent for the one-electron transfer reaction which produces the radical ion. The observations shown in Table 5.4, however, have led investigators to postulate a mechanism similar to the radical ion mechanism of Szwarc.[72-74]

TABLE 5.4
Lithium-initiated copolymerization

Solvent (in Order of Increasing Basicity)	Per Cent Styrene in the Copolymer	
	Styrene–Methyl Methacrylate	Styrene-Isoprene
None	28	—
Hydrocarbons	15	52 (benzene)
THF	7	80
Et_3N	3	>80
Et_2NH	1	>80
$NH_3(l)$	0	>80

In the sodium-catalyzed polymerizations, no styrene was present in the methyl methacrylate copolymer and an even higher percentage was present than shown in the table for the isoprene copolymer regardless of the solvent. Since $R^{\ominus}Na^{\oplus}$ is more ionic than $R^{\ominus}Li^{\oplus}$, and the degree of ionic character of these species is influenced by the solvent medium, it appears that a more ionic catalyst favors the polymerization of the monomer more susceptible to anionic polymerization; methyl methacrylate > styrene > isoprene.

In the polymerization of isoprene alone where a nonbasic solvent is present, a cyclic complex with the metal and isoprene (ion pair) would account for the formation of an all *cis*-1,4-polymer. In this system when the solvent becomes more basic, an ionic catalyst is predominant, giving rise to other structural units. Sodium- or potassium-catalyzed polymerizations of isoprene (more ionic) also result in mixtures of 1,2-, 3,4-, and 1,4-units. When the results in Table 5.4 (styrene-methyl methacrylate) are compared with the per cent styrene in a styrene-methyl methacrylate copolymer prepared by conventional cationic (>99%), free radical (51%), and anionic (<1%) systems, it appears that the mechanism for polymerization must have some of the features of both a radical and an ionic mechanism. Therefore, a mechanism has been proposed in which both an anionic and free radical propagation can take place, probably at unequal rates.

One-electron transfer:

$$R^{\ominus} + CH_2 = CXY \longrightarrow \cdot CH_2 - \overset{\ominus}{C}XY + R\cdot$$

Propagation:

Anionic $\cdot CH_2 - \overset{\ominus}{C}XY + CH_2 = CXY \xrightarrow{k_{pa}} \overset{\bullet}{C}H_2 - CXY - CH_2 - \overset{\ominus}{C}XY$

Radical $\cdot CH_2 - CXY^{\ominus} + CH_2 = CHZ \xrightarrow{k_{pr}} \overset{\bullet}{C}HZ - CH_2 - CH_2 - \overset{\ominus}{C}XY$

Thus addition of monomer to the radical ion to give a true radical end and a true anion end takes place at a faster rate than the coupling of the radical ion to give a dianion.[68]

Alfin catalyst.[75-78] The alfin catalyst is a solid-surface catalyst which is composed of allyl sodium or a benzyl sodium, sodium chloride, and sodium isopropoxide and is effective in the polymerization of olefins. The catalyst is prepared by converting amyl chloride to amyl sodium, destroying half or more of the amyl sodium with isopropylalcohol, thereby obtaining sodium isopropoxide, and finally passing in propene to destroy the remainder of the amyl sodium and obtain allyl sodium:

$$C_5H_{11}Cl + 2Na \longrightarrow C_5H_{11}Na + NaCl$$

$$\tfrac{1}{2}C_5H_{11}Na + \tfrac{1}{2}(CH_3)_2CHOH \longrightarrow \tfrac{1}{2}(CH_3)_2CHONa + \tfrac{1}{2}C_5H_{12}$$

$$\tfrac{1}{2}C_5H_{11}Na + \tfrac{1}{2}CH_3 - CH = CH_2 \longrightarrow C_5H_{12} + CH_2 = CH - CH_2Na$$

The catalyst has been employed primarily for the polymerization of butadiene and styrene and has the following features:

1. It is an extremely rapid reaction in which the faster the reaction, the higher the molecular weight.

2. The molecular weight is independent of the amount of catalyst, but a higher ratio of sodium isopropoxide to allyl sodium increases the molecular weight.

3. It is a solid-surface catalyst.

4. A narrow molecular weight range (1.5–2 million) is obtained[79] (Figs. 5.7 and 5.8).

5. The polymer has a high gel content.

6. G.R.S.-type copolymers are formed in a 1:1 ratio with equal amounts of styrene and butadiene.

Alfin polybutadiene is 70–80% 1,4-, similar to free-radical-initiated butadiene but unlike sodium-initiated, which is 70% 1,2-.[80-82] X-ray studies show a *trans* double bond and 25% 1,2-addition.[83]

The use of *m*-xylyl sodium in place of allyl sodium is not as good for the polymerization of butadiene but yields an isotactic polystyrene, a finding which is characteristic for polymerization at solid surfaces.[84] It has been

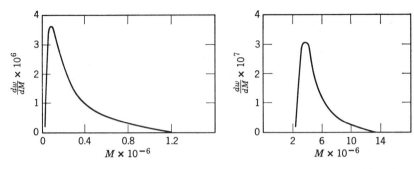

Fig. 5.7. Cold rubber.[79]   Fig. 5.8. Alfin rubber.[79]

found that the yield of polystyrene increases from 2.6% in 1 hr. at 0° to 92% in 10 min. at 60°,[85] but the low-temperature polymer has a higher degree of crystallinity. Table 5.5 shows the effect of the ratio of isopropyl

TABLE 5.5

Effect of catalyst on molecular weight

i-PrONa/Amyl Na	η
90/10	2.27
50/50	1.05
20/80	0.79

sodium to amyl sodium in the catalyst. The solid precipitate is responsible for the polymerization since the solution above the catalyst alone will not polymerize styrene. In complexing solvents, such as ether or amines, the system is homogeneous and a low degree of crystallinity is observed. This is similar to the butyl lithium polymerizations cited earlier in this chapter. The rate of the reaction is first-order with respect to monomer and proportional to the amount of initiator present.[86]

Coordinated (complexed) anionic catalysts.[56,87] There are a multitude of coordinated catalysts which will polymerize olefins. These catalysts might be divided into two classes: (1) those which are made up from a metal hydride or metal alkyl reducing and/or alkylating agent in combination with reducible metal halides and (2) reduced metal oxides, usually on supports. The most common catalysts of the first type are made up from aluminum alkyls such as aluminum triethyl, aluminum triisobutyl, or diethylaluminum chloride and a titanium or vanadium halide such as titanium tetrachloride, titanium trichloride, or vanadium chlorides. The most common catalysts of the second type are reduced nickel oxide on a charcoal support, reduced molybdenum oxide on an alumina support, and chromium oxide on a silica-alumina support. These two catalyst types undoubtedly have completely different mechanisms for olefin polymerization.

These catalysts in most cases are effective for the polymerization of 1-olefins which do not have branching any closer to the double bond than the 3 or 4 position,

$$
\underset{4}{R-\overset{\overset{\displaystyle R}{|}}{C}H}-\underset{3}{CH_2}-\underset{2}{CH}=\underset{1}{CH_2}
$$

with the exception of styrene, norbornene, and a few others. Almost any conjugated diene will polymerize, regardless of branching. One important difference between the 1-olefin and conjugated diene polymerizations with the catalysts of the first type is that the ratio of aluminum alkyl to titanium halide is quite different for the optimum polymerization conditions for each. This indicates a different catalyst and perhaps a different mechanism for each.

Most of the published work is on the catalyst systems of the first type. Most workers agree that the reaction of an aluminum alkyl and a titanium halide is one in which the titanium compound is alkylated by the aluminum alkyl and reduced to a lower valence state. The following equations seem to best describe these reactions:[88-89]

$$TiCl_4 + AlR_3 \longrightarrow TiCl_3R + AlR_2Cl$$
$$TiCl_3R \longrightarrow TiCl_3 + R\cdot$$

or

$$TiCl_4 + 2AlR_3 \longrightarrow TiCl_2R_2 + 2AlR_2Cl$$
$$TiCl_2R_2 \longrightarrow TiCl_2R + R\cdot$$
$$TiCl_3 + AlR_3 \longrightarrow TiCl_2R + AlR_2Cl$$
$$TiCl_2R \longrightarrow TiCl_2 + R\cdot$$
$$TiCl_2R + AlR_3 \longrightarrow TiClR_2 + AlClR_2$$
$$TiCl_2 + AlR_3 \longrightarrow TiClR + AlClR_2$$

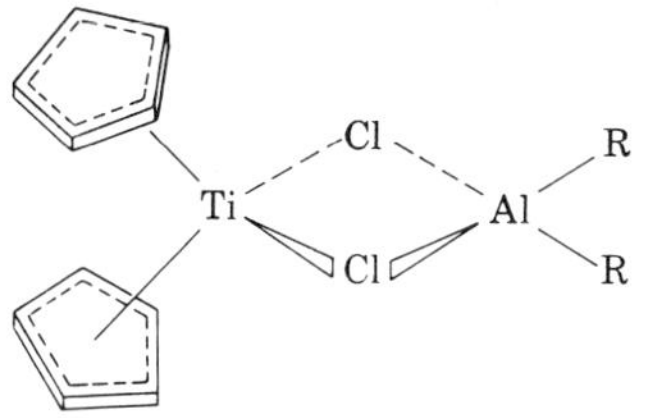

Support for the occurrence of at least some of these reactions is that maximum catalyst activity is obtained with a valence state of titanium of 2,[90] although other workers have evidence for a +3 state.[91,92] Bis(cyclopentadienyl)titanium dichloride aluminum dialkyls, whose structures are known, contain titanium in a $+3$ state, but are effective only for the polymerization of ethylene.[93-96] Most investigators agree, however, that the rate of polymerization is dependent on the concentration of titanium, and olefin, the nature of the alkylating agent, and the ratio of the alkylating agent to titanium tetrachloride. It is most probable that the true catalyst has the structure shown:[97-99]

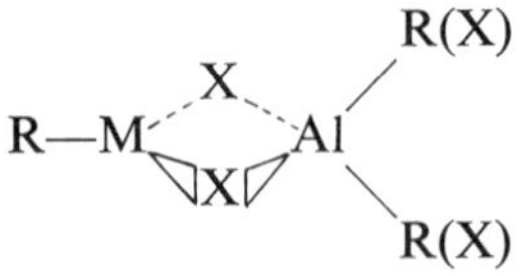

$$
\begin{array}{c}
\text{R(X)} \\
\text{X} \quad / \\
\text{R—M} \overset{\cdots}{\underset{\diagdown \text{X} \diagup}{}} \text{Al} \\
\diagdown \\
\text{R(X)}
\end{array}
$$

where $M = Ti^{+2}$ or V^{+2}

$R =$ alkyl

$X =$ halogen

There are several important features in this polymerization which must be accounted for in a mechanism:

1. The polymerization reaction is stereoselective in that isotactic polymers of 1-olefins are formed and all *cis*-1,4-, all *trans*-1,4-, or all 1,2-isotactic or syndiotactic polybutadienes can be formed, depending on the catalyst. In the case of polybutadienes, the catalyst is most likely a different one from that which polymerizes α-olefins.
2. The reaction has most of the characteristics of anionic polymerization reactions discussed earlier.
3. The reaction takes place on a solid surface.

Many mechanisms have been proposed for this polymerization reaction, but these are still theory and the true mechanism is not known for certain.[100,101] Indeed, those proposed for the catalysts of the reduced metal oxides or metal oxides on supports are justifiably different.[102-105]

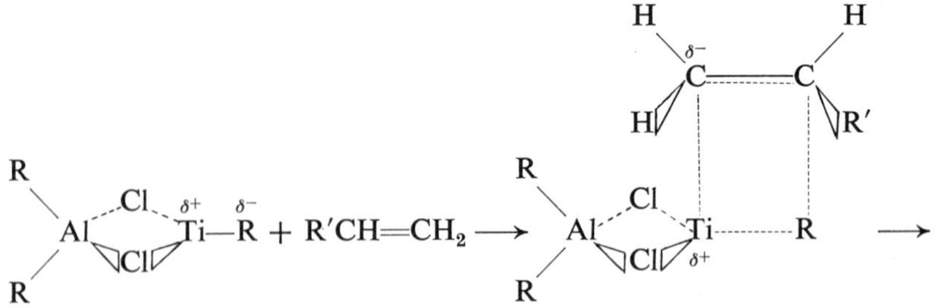

$$
\begin{array}{l}
\text{R} \\
\diagdown \\
\text{Al} \overset{\cdots\text{Cl}}{\underset{\diagdown \text{Cl} \diagup}{}} \overset{\delta+\quad\delta-}{\text{Ti—R}} + R'CH{=}CH_2 \longrightarrow \\
\diagup \\
\text{R}
\end{array}
\qquad
\begin{array}{l}
\text{H} \qquad\qquad \text{H} \\
\diagdown \overset{\delta-}{} \diagup \\
\text{C}\text{-----}\text{C} \\
\text{H} \diagup \quad | \qquad | \diagdown \text{R}' \\
\qquad | \qquad | \\
\text{R} \qquad\qquad \text{Cl} \quad | \\
\diagdown \qquad \overset{\cdots}{} \\
\text{Al} \overset{\cdots\text{Cl}}{\underset{\diagdown \text{Cl} \diagup \delta+}{}} \text{Ti}\text{-------}\text{R} \longrightarrow \\
\diagup \\
\text{R}
\end{array}
$$

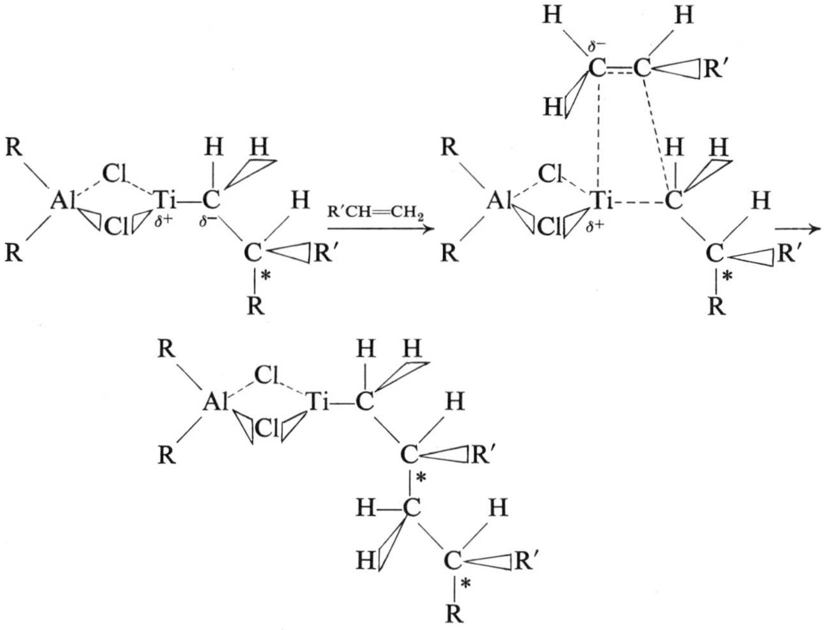

In the mechanism shown, the catalyst surface acts as a mold on which the polymer is absorbed. Whichever configuration is taken by the first monomer, d or l, influences the direction of addition of the next monomer. The particular catalyst site with which the first monomer molecule reacts makes that site an optically active one. The rapid polymerization even of gaseous olefins such as ethylene is due to the high concentration of the monomer in the proximity of the catalyst owing to the absorption of the monomer on the catalyst surface through metal-olefin π-bonding.

REFERENCES

1. B. V. Bhide and J. J. Sudborough, *J. Indian Inst. Sci.*, **8A**, 89 (1925).
2. P. J. Flory, *J. Am. Chem. Soc.*, **61**, 3334 (1939); **62**, 2261 (1940).
3. N. Ivanoff, *Bull. soc. chim.*, France, 5, **17**, 347 (1950).
4. C. S. Marvel, *An Introduction to the Organic Chemistry of High Polymers*, John Wiley and Sons, New York (1959).
5. D. D. Coffman, G. J. Berchet, W. R. Peterson, and E. W. Spanagel, *J. Polymer Sci.*, **2**, 306 (1947).
6. P. J. Flory, *Principles of Polymer Chemistry*, Cornell University Press, Ithaca, New York, 1953.
7. E. L. Wittbecker and P. W. Morgan, *J. Polymer Sci.*, **40**, 289 (1959).
8. P. W. Morgan and S. L. Kwolek, *J. Polymer Sci.*, **40**, 299 (1959).
9. R. G. Beaman, P. W. Morgan, C. R. Koller, E. L. Wittbecker, and E. E. Magat, *J. Polymer Sci.*, **40**, 329 (1959).

10. M. Katz, *J. Polymer Sci.*, **40**, 337 (1959).
11. V. E. Shashoua and W. M. Eareckson III, *J. Polymer Sci.*, **40**, 343 (1959).
12. C. W. Stephens, *J. Polymer Sci.*, **40**, 359 (1959).
13. E. L. Wittbecker and M. Katz, *J. Polymer Sci.*, **40**, 367 (1959).
14. J. R. Schaefgen, F. H. Koontz, and R. F. Tietz, *J. Polymer Sci.*, **40**, 377 (1959).
15. S. A. Sundet, W. A. Murphey, and S. B. Speck, *J. Polymer Sci.*, **40**, 389 (1959).
16. W. M. Eareckson III, *J. Polymer Sci.*, **40**, 399 (1959).
17. D. J. Lyman and S. L. Jung, *J. Polymer Sci.*, **40**, 407 (1959).
18. T. E. Ferington, *J. Chem. Ed.*, **36**, 174 (1959).
19. C. H. Bamford, W. G. Barb, A. D. Jenkins, and P. F. Onyon, *The Kinetics of Vinyl Polymerizations by Free Radical Mechanisms*, Academic Press, New York, 1958.
20. C. M. Burnett, *Mechanism of Polymer Reactions*, Interscience Publishers, New York, 1954.
21. F. R. Mayo, *J. Chem. Ed.*, **36**, 157 (1959).
22. C. C. Price, R. W. Kell and E. Krebs, *J. Am. Chem. Soc.*, **64**, 1103 (1942).
23. C. C. Price and B. E. Tate, *J. Am. Chem. Soc.*, **65**, 517 (1943).
24. J. W. Breitenbach and H. Schneider, *Ber.*, **76B**, 1088 (1943).
25. P. D. Bartlett and S. G. Cohen, *J. Am. Chem. Soc.*, **65**, 543 (1943).
26. S. G. Cohen, *J. Polymer Sci.*, **2**, 511 (1947).
27. L. M. Arnett and J. H. Peterson, *J. Am. Chem. Soc.*, **74**, 2031 (1952).
28. J. C. Bevington, H. W. Melville, and R. P. Taylor, *J. Polymer Sci.*, **12**, 449 (1954).
29. G. Avrey and C. G. Moore, *J. Polymer Sci.*, **36**, 41 (1959).
30. J. H. Baxendale, M. G. Evans, and G. S. Park, *Trans. Faraday Soc.*, **42**, 155 (1946).
31. J. H. Baxendale, S. Bywater, and M. G. Evans, *J. Polymer Sci.*, **1**, 237 (1946).
32. L. M. Arnett, *J. Am. Chem. Soc.*, **74**, 2027 (1952).
33. F. R. Mayo, *J. Am. Chem. Soc.*, **65**, 2324 (1943).
34. J. W. Breitenbach and A. Maschin, *Z. physik. Chem.*, **A187**, 175 (1940).
35. R. M. Joyce, W. E. Hanford, and J. Harmon, *J. Am. Chem. Soc.*, **76**, 2529 (1948).
36. T. E. Ferington, *J. Chem. Ed.*, **36**, 174 (1959).
37. L. M. Arnett, *J. Am. Chem. Soc.*, **74**, 2027 (1952).
38. S. L. Aggarwal and O. J. Sweeting, *Chem. Revs.*, **57**, 665 (1957).
39. M. J. Roedel, *J. Am. Chem. Soc.*, **75**, 6110 (1953).
40. A. H. Willbourn, *J. Polymer Sci.*, **34**, 569 (1959).
41. T. Alfrey, J. J. Bohrer and H. Mark, *Copolymerization*, Interscience Publishers, New York, 1952.
42. T. Alfrey, Jr. and C. C. Price, *J. Polymer Sci.*, **2**, 101 (1947).
43. F. A. Bovey, I. M. Kolthoff, A. I. Medalia, and E. J. Meehan, *Emulsion Polymerization*, Interscience Publishers, New York, 1955.
44. W. D. Harkins, *J. Am. Chem. Soc.*, **69**, 1428 (1947).
45. C. E. Schildknecht, *Ind. Eng. Chem.*, **50**, 107 (1958).
46. C. G. Overberger, R. J. Ehrig, and R. A. Marcus, *J. Am. Chem. Soc.*, **80**, 2456 (1958).
47. D. J. Worsfold and S. Bywater, *J. Am. Chem. Soc.*, **79**, 4917 (1957).
48. R. G. W. Norrish and K. E. Russel, *Trans. Faraday Soc.*, **48**, 91 (1952).
49. A. G. Evans and G. W. Meadows, *Trans. Faraday Soc.*, **46**, 327 (1950).
50. F. S. Dainton and G. B. B. M. Sutherland, *J. Polymer Sci.*, **4**, 37 (1949).
51. A. G. Evans and M. Polanyi, *J. Chem. Soc.*, **1947**, 252.
52. P. H. Plesch, *Cationic Polymerization and Related Complexes*, W. Heffer and Son, Cambridge, 1953.
53. M. S. C. Flett and P. H. Plesch, *J. Chem. Soc.*, **1952**, 3355.

54. J. J. Throssell, S. P. Sood, M. Szwarc, and V. Stannett, *J. Am. Chem. Soc.*, **78**, 1122 (1956).
55. D. C. Pepper, *Trans. Faraday Soc.*, **45**, 404 (1949).
56. N. G. Gaylord and H. F. Mark, *Linear and Stereoregular Addition Polymers: Polymerization with Controlled Propagation*, Interscience Publishers, New York, 1959.
57. W. C. E. Higginson and N. S. Wooding, *J. Chem. Soc.*, **1952**, 760.
58. N. S. Wooding and W. C. E. Higginson, *J. Chem. Soc.*, **1952**, 1178.
59. H. Hsieh, D. J. Kelley, and A. V. Tobolsky, *J. Polymer Sci.*, **26**, 240 (1957).
60. H. Hsieh and A. V. Tobolsky, *J. Polymer Sci.*, **25**, 245 (1957).
61. H. Morita and A. V. Tobolsky, *J. Am. Chem. Soc.*, **79**, 5853 (1957).
62. M. Frankel, A. Ottolenghi, M. Albeck, and A. Zilkha, *J. Chem. Soc.*, **1959**, 3858.
63. K. F. O'Driscoll and A. V. Tobolsky, *J. Polymer Sci.*, **35**, 259 (1959).
64. M. Szwarc, *Nature*, **178**, 1168 (1956).
65. H. Brody, M. Ladacki, R. Milkovich, and M. Szwarc, *J. Polymer Sci.*, **25**, 221 (1957).
66. M. Szwarc, M. Levy, and R. Milkovich, *J. Am. Chem. Soc.*, **78**, 2656 (1956).
67. R. Waak, A. Rembaum, J. D. Coombes, and M. Szwarc, *J. Am. Chem. Soc.*, **79**, 2026 (1957).
68. M. Levy and M. Szwarc, *J. Am. Chem. Soc.*, **82**, 521 (1960).
69. D. J. Worsfold and S. Bywater, *J. Polymer Sci.*, **26**, 299 (1957).
70. C. G. Overberger, E. M. Pearce, and N. Mayes, *J. Polymer Sci.*, **31**, 217 (1958); **34**, 109 (1959).
71. F. W. Stavely and Coworkers, *Ind. Eng. Chem.*, **48**, 778 (1956).
72. A. V. Tobolsky, D. J. Kelley, K. F. O'Driscoll, and C. E. Rogers, *J. Polymer Sci.*, **28**, 425 (1958).
73. K. F. O'Driscoll, R. J. Boudreau, and A. V. Tobolsky, *J. Polymer Sci.*, **31**, 115, 123 (1958).
74. A. V. Tobolsky and C. E. Rogers, *J. Polymer Sci.*, **40**, 73 (1959).
75. A. A. Morton, E. E. Magat, and R. L. Letsinger, *J. Am. Chem. Soc.*, **69**, 950 (1947).
76. A. A. Morton, *Ind. Eng. Chem.*, **42**, 1488 (1950).
77. A. A. Morton, F. H. Bolton, F. W. Collins, and E. F. Cluff, *Ind. Eng. Chem.*, **44**, 2876 (1952).
78. A. A. Morton and E. J. Lanpher, *J. Polymer Sci.*, **44**, 233 (1960).
79. A. A. Morton, *Rubber Age*, **72**, 473 (1953).
80. C. S. Marvel, W. J. Bailey, and G. E. Inskeep, *J. Polymer Sci.*, **1**, 275 (1946).
81. J. D. D'Ianni, *Ind. Eng. Chem.*, **40**, 253 (1948).
82. A. W. Meyer, R. R. Hampton, and J. A. Davidson, *J. Am. Chem. Soc.*, **74**, 2294 (1952).
83. J. D. D'Ianni, F. J. Naples, and J. E. Field, *Ind. Eng. Chem.*, **42**, 95 (1950).
84. A. A. Morton and L. D. Taylor, *J. Polymer Sci.*, **38**, 7 (1959).
85. J. L. R. Williams, J. van Den Berghe, W. J. Dulmage, and K. R. Dunham, *J. Am. Chem. Soc.*, **79**, 1716 (1957); **78**, 1260 (1956).
86. R. L. Cleland, R. L. Letsinger, E. E. Magat, and W. H. Stockmayer, *J. Polymer Sci.*, **39**, 249 (1959).
87. J. K. Stille, *Chem. Revs.*, **58**, 541 (1958).
88. W. M. Saltman, W. E. Gibbs, and J. Lal, *J. Am. Chem. Soc.*, **80**, 5615 (1958).
89. G. Natta, *J. Inorg. and Nuclear Chem.*, **8**, 589 (1958).
90. D. B. Ludlum, A. W. Anderson, and C. E. Ashby, *J. Am. Chem. Soc.*, **80**, 1380 (1958).

91. H. N. Frielander and K. Oita, *Ind. Eng. Chem.*, **49**, 1885 (1957).
92. G. Natta, P. Pino, G. Mazzanti, and P. Longi, *Gazz. Chim. Ital.*, **87**, 549 (1957).
93. G. Natta, P. Corradini, and I. W. Bassi, *J. Am. Chem. Soc.*, **80**, 755 (1958).
94. G. Natta, P. Pino, G. Mazzanti, and U. Giannini, *J. Inorg. and Nuclear Chem.*, **8**, 612 (1958).
95. D. S. Breslow and N. R. Newburg, *J. Am. Chem. Soc.*, **81**, 81 (1959).
96. J. C. W. Chien, *J. Am. Chem. Soc.*, **81**, 86 (1959).
97. W. L. Carrick, *J. Am. Chem. Soc.*, **80**, 6455 (1958).
98. W. L. Carrick, F. J. Karol, G. L. Karapinka, and J. J. Smith, *J. Am. Chem. Soc.*, **82**, 1502 (1960).
99. W. L. Carrick, A. G. Chasar, and J. J. Smith, *J. Am. Chem. Soc.*, **82**, 5319 (1960).
100. J. Furukawa and T. Tsuruta, *J. Polymer Sci.*, **36**, 275 (1959).
101. N. Gaylord and H. Mark, *Makromol. Chem.*, **44–46**, 448 (1961).
102. M. Feller and E. Field, *Ind. Eng. Chem.*, **51**, 155 (1959).
103. H. N. Frielander, *J. Polymer Sci.*, **38**, 91 (1959).
104. A. A. Harban, E. Field, and H. N. Frielander, *J. Polymer Sci.*, **41**, 157 (1959).
105. H. N. Frielander, W. E. Smith, and R. J. Ross, *J. Polymer Sci.*, **48**, 17 (1960).

6

CONVENTIONAL
CONDENSATION
POLYMERS

The treatment of condensation polymers and condensation polymerization has been divided into two separate chapters. The condensation polymerization reactions that occur with open-chain monomers are treated separately in this chapter from those condensation polymerizations that proceed by a ring-opening reaction (Chapter 7). Although the product polymers may be the same or similar, the general mechanisms of the two reaction types are dissimilar and the techniques employed for the polymerizations differ.

6.1 POLYESTERS

Nearly all the methods available for the formation of esters are suitable for polymerization reactions. Direct esterification between acid and an alcohol in the presence of a strongly acidic catalyst may very often not form a polymer with a high enough molecular weight because of the difficulty in water removal. Close temperature control is necessary to avoid ester pyrolysis, and ether formation from the alcohol must be prevented through the proper choice of catalyst.

Ester interchange provides an excellent practical method for producing high molecular weight polymers since the alcohol eliminated in the transesterification is usually more easily removed than water. Often the formation of the ester of an acid is necessary since the acid itself may not be soluble. Reactions of acid anhydrides and diols are widely employed in the formation of polyester resins.

An acid chloride–alcohol reaction has several drawbacks. On an industrial scale, the expense of acid chlorides with the exception of phosgene usually makes the reaction impractical. Replacement of the hydroxyl group on the alcohol with halogen becomes a serious problem in certain cases, thus destroying monomer balance, but a base acceptor helps to eliminate this problem and the general utility of this reaction at the interface of two immiscible layers has been demonstrated. The following examples will serve to illustrate these methods.

Poly(ethylene terephthalate). The most commercially important linear polyester, poly(ethylene terephthalate), is produced through an ester interchange reaction.[1,2,3] The reaction between dimethyl terephthalate and ethylene glycol takes place in two stages, and a weak base, calcium acetate or antimony oxide, is employed as a catalyst.

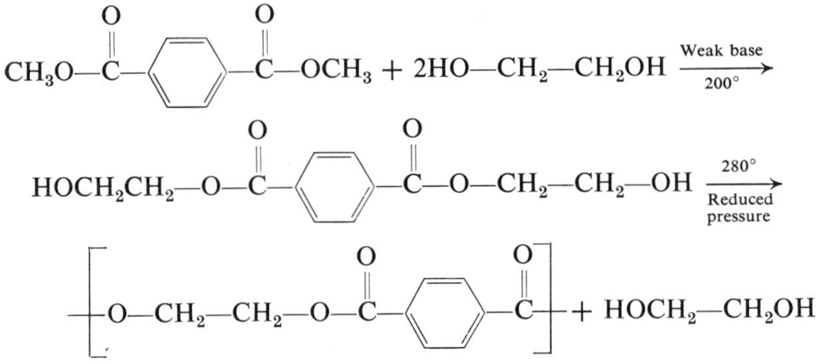

The first step consists of the interchange of two molecules of methanol for two of ethylene glycol at about 200°C. in the formation of a new monomer. This monomer then enters into a self-transesterification reaction at a higher temperature (280°C.) under reduced pressure to eliminate one mole of ethylene glycol per monomer.

The resulting crystalline polymer is marketed mainly in the form of a film (Mylar, Cronar) which has a tensile strength of about 25,000 p.s.i. (about three times as strong as cellulosic products) and a fiber (Dacron, Teron, Terylene). The polymer has a high resistance to flex failure, has excellent tear strength, impact strength, and a crystalline melting point near 260°C. The polymer is melt-spun through a spinneret at temperatures of 270°C. to afford a fiber, the major portion of which is used in textile fabrics and blends.

Polycarbonates.[4-11] A polycarbonate which can be prepared either through the reaction of the diacid chloride, phosgene, or the ester interchange of diphenyl carbonate with 2,2-bis(4-hydroxyphenyl)propane (bisphenol A) has become commercially available under the name Lexan.

In the phosgenation of bisphenol A at room temperatures either a pyridine acceptor solvent or a two-phase system containing a methylene chloride–aqueous sodium hydroxide medium is employed:

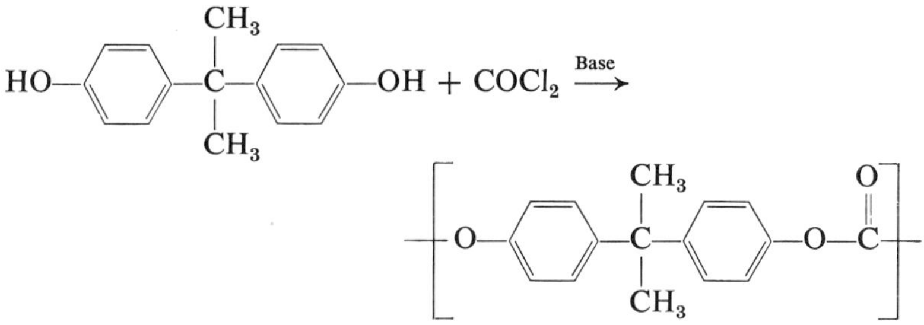

$$HO \underset{}{\overset{CH_3}{\underset{CH_3}{-C-}}} OH + COCl_2 \xrightarrow{\text{Base}}$$

$$\left[-O \underset{}{\overset{CH_3}{\underset{CH_3}{-C-}}} O \underset{}{\overset{O}{\overset{\|}{C}}} \right]$$

The ester interchange reaction takes place to the extent of 90% at 200–230°C. at 20–30 mm. in the absence of a solvent. The polymerization reaction is finished at a temperature of 290–300°C. at 1 mm.

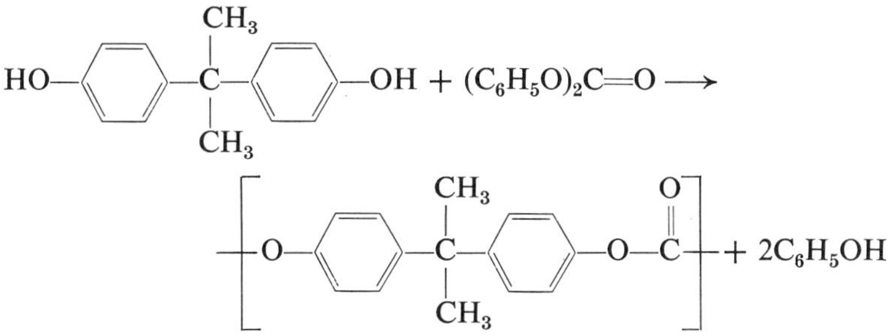

$$HO \underset{}{\overset{CH_3}{\underset{CH_3}{-C-}}} OH + (C_6H_5O)_2C{=}O \longrightarrow$$

$$\left[-O \underset{}{\overset{CH_3}{\underset{CH_3}{-C-}}} O \underset{}{\overset{O}{\overset{\|}{C}}} \right] + 2C_6H_5OH$$

Higher molecular weights are produced by the first method although polymer purification is more difficult.

The product polymer is a clear plastic material but possesses a slight yellow discoloration. It has excellent electrical properties, a high impact strength, a tensile strength of 9000–10,000 p.s.i., a crystalline melting point of 270°C., and a second-order transition temperature at 145–150°C. The polymer shows 20–40% crystallinity and molecular weights of 800,000 ($\bar{M}_n$) have been achieved. This is perhaps the highest molecular weight linear condensation polymer (by elimination) ever produced.

The product polymer has found use mainly as a molding compound by injection, transfer, or compression.

Polyesters through reaction at the interface. The preparation of the polycarbonate by the reaction of phosgene and bisphenol A in the two-phase methylene chloride—aqueous sodium hydroxide system described is an example of a polymerization reaction which takes place at the interface of two immiscible liquids. Several other examples of the formation of polyesters by the reaction of a diacid chloride with a diphenol have been described.[12-14] Some examples of this reaction are given below:

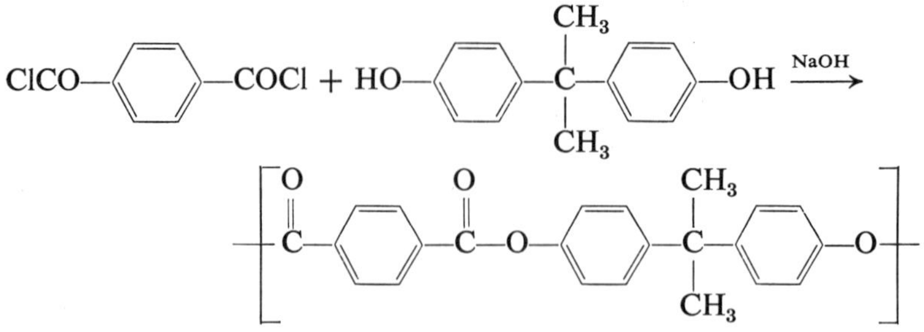

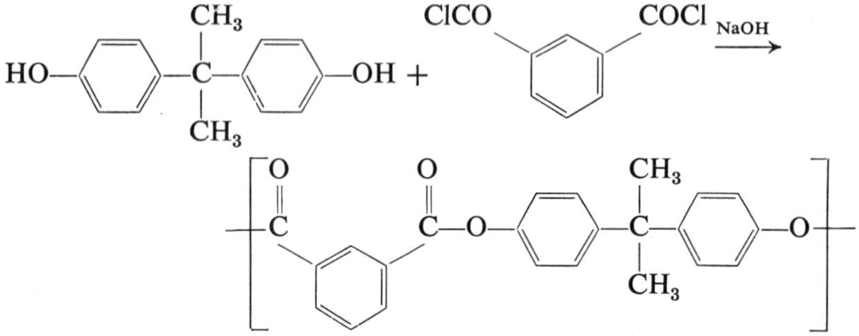

Aromatic polysulfone esters have also been synthesized by the reaction of a disulfonyl chloride on a phenol.[15] The polymer shown is crystalline and has a melting point of 160–165°C.

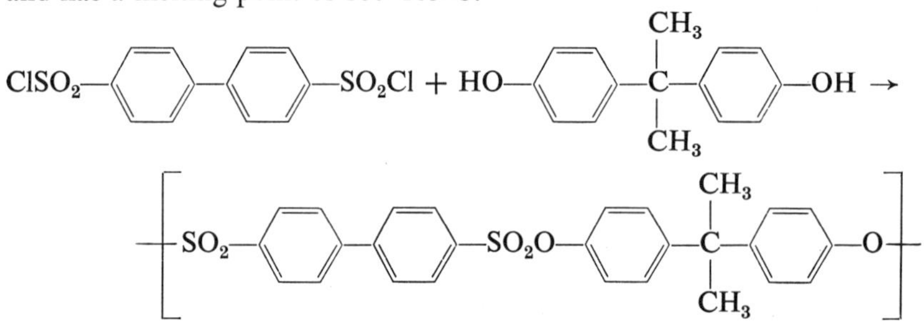

Three-dimensional or crosslinked polyester resins.[16,17] There are primarily two ways in which a three-dimensional polyester can be formed. The polymerization reaction can be run with monomers in which the functionality of one monomer is at least two and the functionality of the other is more than two. The second method involves the formation of a linear polyester from a dibasic acid or dibasic acid derivative and a diol with a subsequent crosslinking reaction which does not involve ester or acid functions. The term resin can refer to any polymer, crosslinked or not, but any three-dimensional network polymer is a resin, regardless of its application.

There is a wide variety of polyester resins which fulfill the different requirements for different applications. Only two examples of polyester resins which illustrate each of the two methods are given.

Polyester resins[18] formed from triols and dibasic acids or dibasic acid derivatives are given the name alkyd. In the polymerization of glycerin with phthalic anhydride the product resin is commonly called a glyptal resin. The reaction of these two monomers is usually taken to a point where the polymer has not gelled, so that it may be poured. Once in the mold, the polymerization is finished off by further heating, thus setting up the polymer.

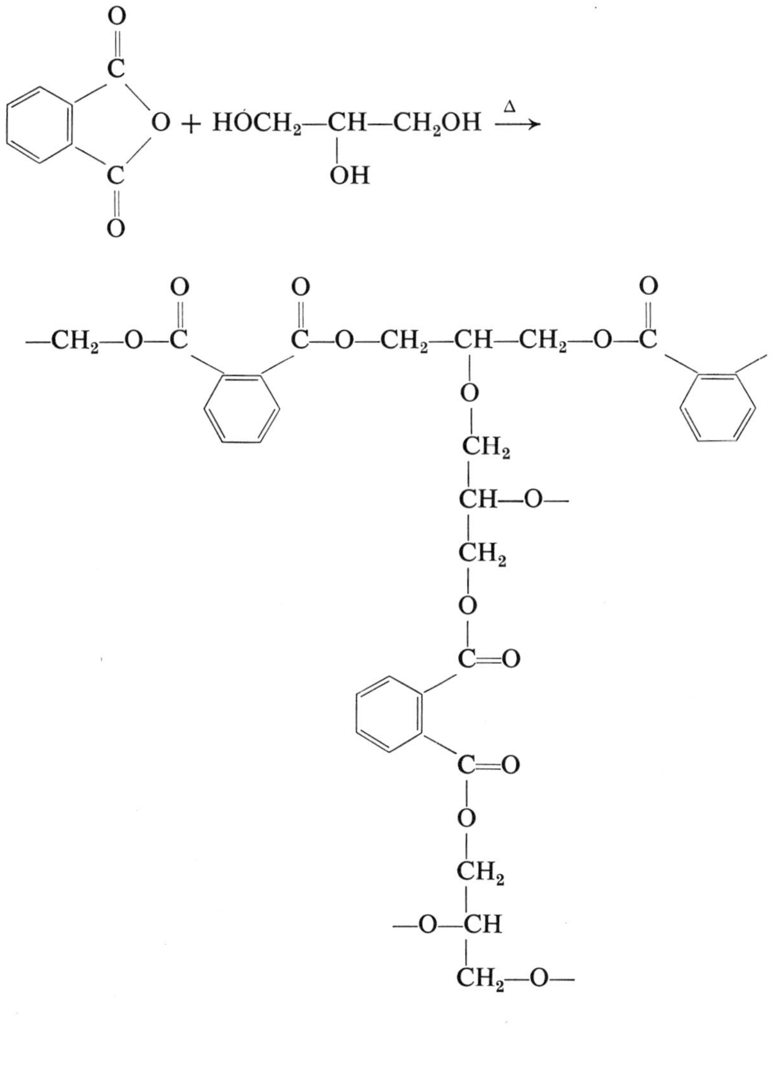

$$\text{phthalic anhydride} + HOCH_2\text{—}CH\text{—}CH_2OH \xrightarrow{\Delta}$$

with glycerin having an OH on the central carbon.

In practice, some diol or monobasic acid may be added to obtain a tractable product. The properties of the polymer can be modified over a wide range by the proper monomer balance.

A linear polyester formed from a diol and a diacid which contains unsaturation can be crosslinked in drying by oxidation of the carbon-carbon double bond or crosslinked by a copolymerization reaction (graft) with a vinyl monomer such as styrene. The unsaturated acid may be dibasic acid itself[19] or an added monobasic acid.

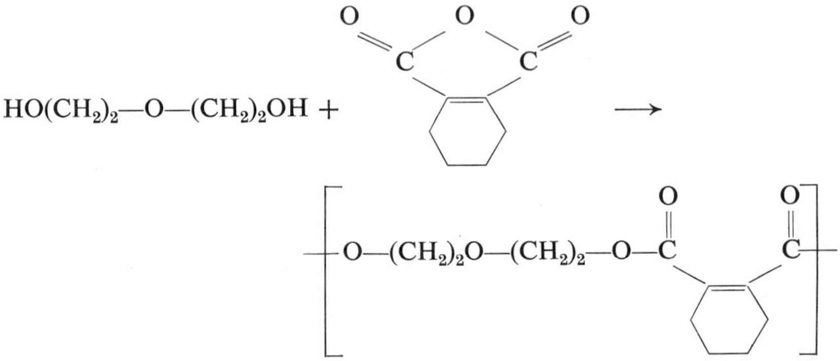

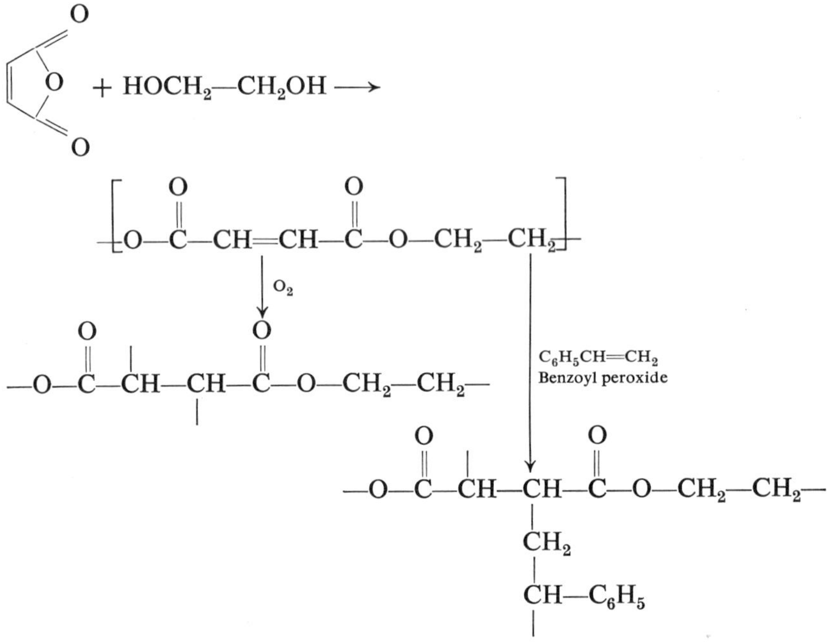

If the monobasic acid is unsaturated, another dibasic acid and diol or triol form the polyester, which will contain unsaturated monobasic acid end groups. The unsaturated acid portion serves to crosslink the polymer during drying.

Resins of this type are used for enamel-, lacquer-, and varnish-type coatings, drying oils, and molding compounds.

6.2 POLYAMIDES AND RELATED POLYMERS

The conventional methods of preparing polyamides are much the same as those employed in polyester preparation. These methods include the reaction of a diamine and a dibasic acid, the reaction of an acid chloride or anhydride with an amine, and the aminolysis of a diester with a diamine. There are several other rather unique methods for polyamide formation which will be covered in later chapters. In addition, the reaction of a diisocyanate and a dibasic acid forms a polyamide. Especially suited to polyamide formation are the reactions of ω-amino acids and their derivatives. In general, these same reaction types are employed in the syntheses of the polymers related to polyamides such as the polyimides, polyimidazoles, polytriazoles, polyureas, and polyurethanes.

Nylon 66.[20] The most industrially important polyamides are those made from diamines and dibasic acids. Nylon was developed primarily by a group of chemists led by W. H. Carothers in a program of fundamental research on polymers started in 1928. Two years after the beginning of the fundamental investigations on polymers and polymer-forming reactions, the cold-drawing discovery on one of Carothers' "superpolymers" was made. At this time, nylon was found to have the best fiber-forming properties, and in April 1937, the first experimental stockings were knit from nylon 66, then designated Fiber 66. In 1938 the announcement of the new fiber, nylon ("synthesized"), was made. The first nylon hosiery was put on trial sale in Wilmington in October 1939 and became generally available in the United States on May 18, 1940. The history of the development of this fiber is a classic story of the worth of fundamental research. The word nylon through its common usage is now not a trade name, but describes all fiber-forming polyamides.

Nylon 66 is formed from the reaction of adipic acid (a six-carbon dibasic acid) and hexamethylenediamine (a six-carbon diamine).[21,22] Most of the adipic acid is prepared by the air oxidation of cyclohexane to cyclohexanol and cyclohexanone or the reduction of phenol to cyclohexanol followed by the nitric acid oxidation to adipic acid. Hexamethylenediamine is made from adipic acid by going through the amide and the nitrile. Alternatively, it is prepared from butadiene.

A perfect stoichiometric balance in the polymerization reaction is achieved by forming and purifying the 1:1 salt. The salt is polymerized

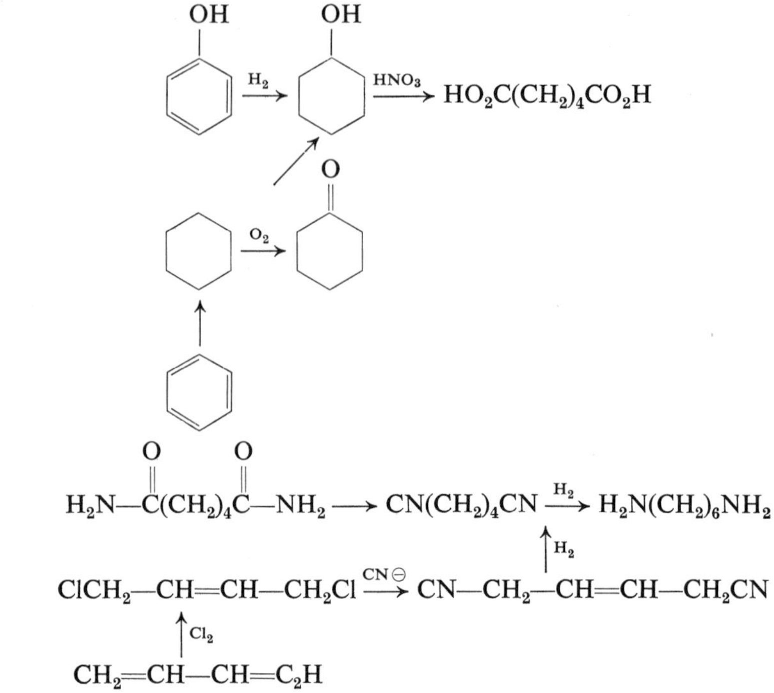

$$
\begin{array}{ccc}
\text{OH} & \text{OH} & \\
\text{(benzene ring)} \xrightarrow{H_2} \text{(cyclohexanol)} \xrightarrow{HNO_3} & HO_2C(CH_2)_4CO_2H
\end{array}
$$

$$
\text{(cyclohexanone, } O\text{)} \xleftarrow{O_2} \text{(cyclohexane)} \xleftarrow{} \text{(benzene)}
$$

$$
\underset{H_2N-\overset{\overset{O}{\|}}{C}(CH_2)_4\overset{\overset{O}{\|}}{C}-NH_2}{} \longrightarrow CN(CH_2)_4CN \xrightarrow{H_2} H_2N(CH_2)_6NH_2
$$

$$
ClCH_2-CH{=}CH-CH_2Cl \xrightarrow{CN^{\ominus}} CN-CH_2-CH{=}CH-CH_2CN \uparrow H_2
$$

$$
\uparrow Cl_2
$$

$$
CH_2{=}CH-CH{=}C_2H
$$

in two stages; first, the temperature is raised to 280°C. at 250 p.s.i. in an oxygen-free atmosphere, after which time the pressure is released and the mixture is heated for several hours under reduced pressure.[23-25]

$$
H_2N(CH_2)_6NH_2 + HO_2C(CH_2)_4CO_2H \longrightarrow
$$

$$
[H_3N(CH_2)_6NH_3]^{+2}[OCO(CH_2)_4CO_2]^{-2} \xrightarrow{\Delta}
$$

$$
\left[-NH-(CH_2)_6-NH-\overset{\overset{O}{\|}}{C}-(CH_2)_4-\overset{\overset{O}{\|}}{C}\right] + 2H_2O
$$

Nylon 610 is made from hexamethylenediamine and sebacic acid under essentially the same reaction conditions as those applied for the preparation of nylon 66.

The nylons are some of the strongest condensation polymers known. Nylon 66 has a tensile strength (drawn) of about 60,000 p.s.i., a melting point of 250°C., and is soluble in formic acid. In general, the nylons are characterized by excellent impact strength, toughness, flexibility, abrasion, resistance, and a high degree of crystallinity (Table 6.1).

Several grades of Nylon 66 are available for molding and extrusion. Because of its excellent properties, it is well suited for cast machine parts such as gears and bearings where no lubrication is required.[26] Its utility as a melt-spun fiber for fabrics, tire cord, rope, etc. is well known. In addition to the desirable physical properties cited, its low sensitivity to moisture and its ability to take a permanent set in preshaping and pleating increase its desirability as a fabric material.

TABLE 6.1
Melting points of nylons (°C)[23]

Dibasic Acids	Diamines, No. of Carbons								
	4	5	6	7	8	9	10	11	12
Adipic 6	278	223	250	226	235	205	230		209
Pimelic 7	233	183	202	196					
Suberic 8	250	202	215		200				
Azeleic 9	223	178	185			165			
Sebacic 10	239	195	209	187	197	174	194	168	172

Other methods of polyamide preparation. Condensation reactions of the type described for nylon are always subject to some large ring formation (Chapter 2). The formation of rings and other side reactions are of course enhanced in the reactions of α-, β-, γ-, and δ-amino acids. It is quite difficult to polymerize these amino acids directly, although once a lactam has been formed, it may be opened up in a polymerization reaction to give a polyamide (Chapter 7). If the amino group is placed far enough down the carboxylic acid chain so that the possibility of ring formation is minimized, a polyamide can be formed.

$$\overset{\oplus}{H_3N}-(CH_2)_n-C\overset{O}{\underset{O^{\ominus}}{\big<}} \xrightarrow[n \geq 5]{} \left[-NH-(CH_2)_n-\overset{O}{\overset{\|}{C}}-\right] + H_2O$$

The action of a diacid chloride on a diamine is a fast reaction and is especially suited to the formation of polyamides by the interfacial technique.[12,13,27-32] The reaction of a variety of acid chlorides with amines gives successful polymerization reactions.

In this reaction, excess amine can take up the evolved hydrogen chloride but it is preferable to add an inorganic base to the aqueous phase for this purpose. Most of these reactions are run with the acid chloride in the carbon tetrachloride phase and the amine in the water phase. Either the polymer can be pulled from the interface of the two layers or high speed stirring can be employed until the polymerization reaction is complete.

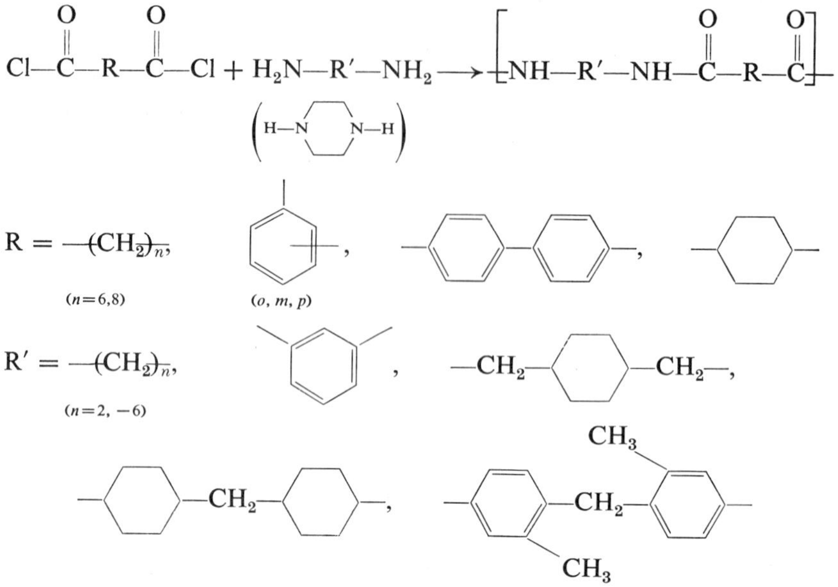

$$\underset{O}{\overset{O}{\underset{\parallel}{Cl-C}}}-R-\underset{O}{\overset{O}{\underset{\parallel}{C}}}-Cl + H_2N-R'-NH_2 \longrightarrow \left[NH-R'-NH-\underset{O}{\overset{O}{\underset{\parallel}{C}}}-R-\underset{O}{\overset{O}{\underset{\parallel}{C}}} \right]$$

$$\left(H-N \underset{\smile}{\overset{\frown}{}} N-H \right)$$

$R =$ —(CH$_2$)$_n$,

($n=6,8$)

(o, m, p)

$R' =$ —(CH$_2$)$_n$,

($n=2,-6$)

—CH$_2$—⬡—CH$_2$—,

—⬡—CH$_2$—⬡—,

—⬡—CH$_2$—⬡— with CH$_3$ groups

Polysulfone amides are readily prepared from disulfonyl chlorides and diamines with this technique.[33]

$$ClSO_2-R-SO_2Cl + H_2N-R'NH_2 \longrightarrow$$

$$\{NH-R'-NH-SO_2-R-SO_2\}$$

Aminolysis of a dibasic ester with a diamine produces a polymer through the elimination of the alcohol portion. Phenyl esters, because of their greater reactivity compared to alkyl esters, are particularly adaptable to this reaction.[34] It is not necessary to distill the phenol from the reaction mixture as the reverse reaction is not serious and the phenol can later be washed from the polymer.

$$H_2N(CH_2)_6NH_2 + (C_4H_9)_2C \underset{CO_2C_6H_5}{\overset{CO_2C_6H_5}{<}} \longrightarrow$$

$$\left[NH-(CH_2)_6-NH-\underset{O}{\overset{O}{\underset{\parallel}{C}}}-\underset{C_4H_9}{\overset{C_4H_9}{\underset{\mid}{C}}}-\underset{O}{\overset{O}{\underset{\parallel}{C}}} \right] + 2C_2H_5OH$$

In addition, methyl esters and esters of oxalic acid have an enhanced reactivity.

The reaction of an isocyanate with a carboxylic acid to produce an amide has also been employed in a polymer-forming reaction.[35]

$$OCN—R—NCO + HO_2C—R'—CO_2H \longrightarrow$$

$$\left[\begin{array}{c} O \\ \| \\ C—NH—R—NH—C—R' \\ \| \\ O \end{array} \right] + 2CO_2$$

Polyimides, imidazoles, and triazoles. Polyimides are primarily formed from the reaction of a primary amine with either the free acid, the ester, or the anhydride. Success in this reaction has been found primarily where the resultant imide forms a five-membered ring. This reaction usually requires a tetrafunctional acid or one carboxylic group for each amino hydrogen. The facile formation of the five-membered ring limits the reaction to the production of a linear rather than a three-dimensional polymer.[36]

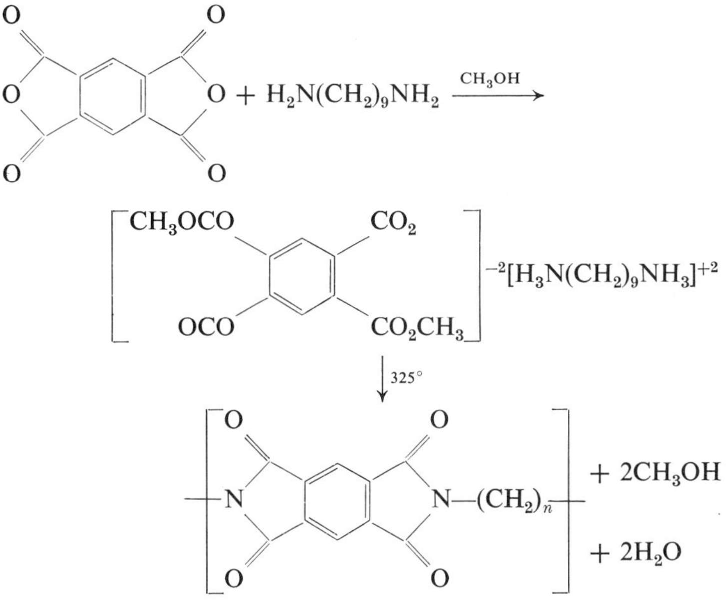

When the functionality of the two monomers are reversed and five-membered rings can be formed, a linear imidazole is formed rather than a crosslinked polymer.[37-39]

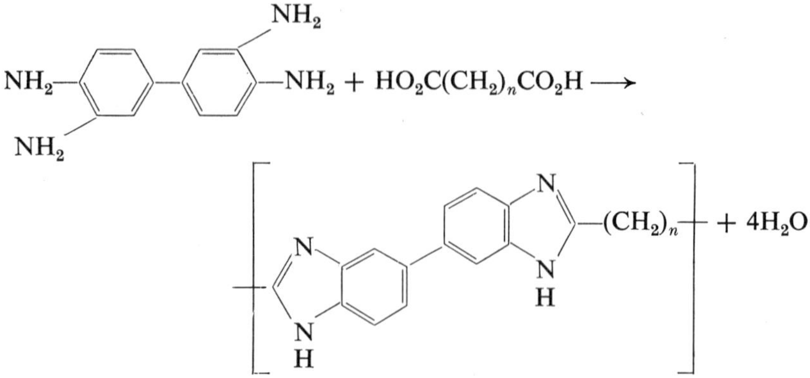

$$\text{NH}_2\text{-}\underset{\overset{|}{\text{NH}_2}}{\bigcirc}\text{-}\bigcirc\text{-NH}_2 + \text{HO}_2\text{C(CH}_2)_n\text{CO}_2\text{H} \longrightarrow$$

(with an NH$_2$ substituent on the first ring)

$$\left[\text{benzimidazole polymer} \text{-(CH}_2)_n\text{-}\right] + 4\text{H}_2\text{O}$$

Polymers containing recurring thiazole rings have been formed from a bis-α-bromoketone and several thioamides.[40]

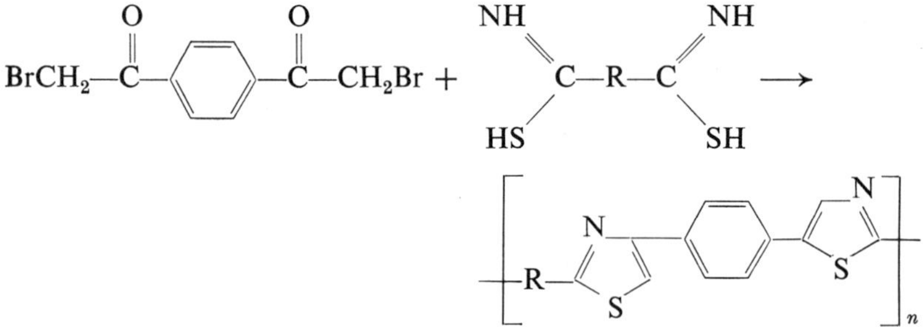

$$\text{BrCH}_2\text{-}\overset{\text{O}}{\overset{\|}{\text{C}}}\text{-}\bigcirc\text{-}\overset{\text{O}}{\overset{\|}{\text{C}}}\text{-CH}_2\text{Br} + \underset{\text{HS}}{\overset{\text{NH}}{\diagdown}}\text{C-R-C}\underset{\text{SH}}{\overset{\text{NH}}{\diagup}} \longrightarrow$$

$$\left[\text{-R-}\underset{\text{S}}{\overset{\text{N}}{\diagup}}\bigcirc\underset{\text{S}}{\overset{\text{N}}{\diagup}}\right]_n$$

Hydrazides of dibasic acids react at elevated temperatures to form amino triazoles. The reaction is run under pressure and the purging of water from the system during polymerization is not necessary in order to obtain high molecular weight polymers.[41,42] The products all have high melting points, and can be melt-spun into fibers of high tensile strength and excellent dyeability.

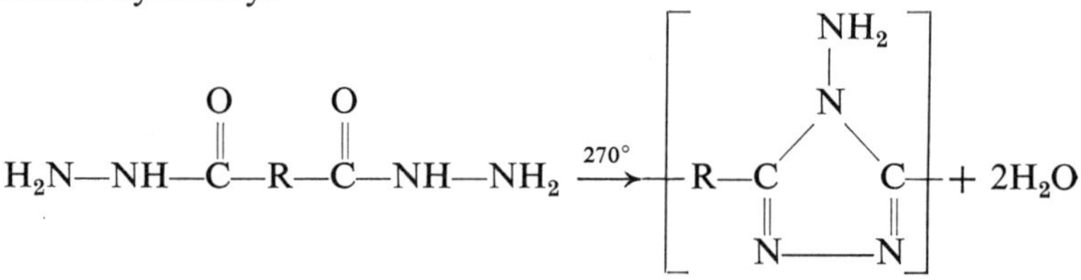

$$\text{H}_2\text{N-NH-}\overset{\text{O}}{\overset{\|}{\text{C}}}\text{-R-}\overset{\text{O}}{\overset{\|}{\text{C}}}\text{-NH-NH}_2 \xrightarrow{270°} \left[\text{-R-C}\underset{\overset{\|}{\text{N}}}{}\underset{\overset{\|}{\text{N}}}{}\text{C-}\overset{\overset{\text{NH}_2}{|}}{\text{N}}\right] + 2\text{H}_2\text{O}$$

Polyureas. Several methods are available for the formation of polyureas. The reaction of a diamine with urea itself to form a polymer by the elimination of ammonia has limited application.[43]

$$\text{H}_2\text{N-R-NH}_2 + \text{H}_2\text{N-}\overset{\text{O}}{\overset{\|}{\text{C}}}\text{-NH}_2 \xrightarrow{250°} \left[\text{-R-NH-}\overset{\text{O}}{\overset{\|}{\text{C}}}\text{-NH-}\right] + 2\text{NH}_3$$

An analogous reaction to the aminolysis of an ester in the formation of a polyamide is the aminolysis of a diurethane with a diamine.[44]

$$H_2N-R-NH_2 + C_2H_5-O-\overset{\overset{\displaystyle O}{\|}}{C}-NH-R'-NH-\overset{\overset{\displaystyle O}{\|}}{C}-O-C_2H_5 \xrightarrow{200°}$$

$$\left[R-NH-\overset{\overset{\displaystyle O}{\|}}{C}-NH-R'-NH-\overset{\overset{\displaystyle O}{\|}}{C}-NH\right] + 2C_2H_5OH$$

The reaction of a diacid chloride with a diamine by interfacial techniques, which has been discussed in the preparation of polyamides, can be employed for polyurea formation when the diacid chloride is phosgene.[27]

$$H_2N(CH_2)_6NH_2 + COCl_2 \xrightarrow{Base} \left[(CH_2)_6-NH-\overset{\overset{\displaystyle O}{\|}}{C}-NH\right]$$

The most extensively investigated polyurea-forming reaction is the addition of amines to isocyanates. This reaction can be carried out in solution, thus avoiding the decomposition and discoloration which accompanies the manufacture of polyureas at high temperatures.[45]

$$H_2N(CH_2)_{10}-NH_2 + OCN(CH_2)_{10}NCO \longrightarrow$$

$$\left[(CH_2)_{10}-NH-\overset{\overset{\displaystyle O}{\|}}{C}-NH-(CH_2)_{10}-NH-\overset{\overset{\displaystyle O}{\|}}{C}-NH\right]$$

Hydrazine and dihydrazides also react with diisocyanates to afford polymers containing a semicarbizide recurring unit.[46]

The reaction of a diamine with carbon oxysulfide to form a thiocarbamate salt which loses hydrogen sulfide on heating, offers a unique method for the formation of polyureas. The salt is not heated above its melting point initially in the formation of the intermediate polymer, where polymerization takes place in the solid state. A second heating cycle at a higher temperature completes the conversion.[47]

$$H_2N-R-NH_2 + COS \longrightarrow \overset{\oplus}{H_3N}-R-NH-\overset{\overset{\displaystyle O}{\|}}{C}-S^{\ominus} \xrightarrow{\Delta}$$

$$\left[R-NH-\overset{\overset{\displaystyle O}{\|}}{C}-NH\right] + H_2S$$

These polyureas are higher melting and less soluble than the polyamides (Chapter 3), but more susceptible to degradation.

Polyurethanes.[48] Extensive work on polyurethanes was undertaken in Germany shortly after the discovery of the nylon polymers, in order to synthesize polymers similar to nylon without infringing on the nylon patents. For example, the polyurethane prepared from tetramethylene glycol and hexamethylenediisocyanate has a structure which differs from nylon only in that there are two additional oxygens in the adipic acid portion.[49,50] The polymer, Perlon U is similar to nylon in all respects except one. Its main disadvantage is its somewhat low melting point, 185°C.

$$HO(CH_2)_4OH + ONC(CH_2)_6NCO \longrightarrow$$

$$\left[O(CH_2)_4-O-\overset{\displaystyle O}{\overset{\displaystyle \|}{C}}-NH(CH_2)_6-NH-\overset{\displaystyle O}{\overset{\displaystyle \|}{C}} \right]$$

Two rather unique examples of polyurethane formation from the reaction of a bischloroformate and a diamine have been made possible by interfacial polycondensation. The bischloroformate formed from the reaction of phosgene on ethylene glycol reacts with various diamines to form polyurethanes.[51]

$$Cl-\overset{\displaystyle O}{\overset{\displaystyle \|}{C}}-O-CH_2-CH_2-O-\overset{\displaystyle O}{\overset{\displaystyle \|}{C}}-Cl + H_2N-R-NH_2 \overset{Base}{\longrightarrow}$$

$$\left[NH-R-NH-\overset{\displaystyle O}{\overset{\displaystyle \|}{C}}-O-CH_2-CH_2-O-\overset{\displaystyle O}{\overset{\displaystyle \|}{C}} \right]$$

This same reaction can be employed where the amino group and the chloroformate group are on the same molecule if the amino group is first blocked to prevent premature reaction with the acid chloride. Subsequent treatment with a basic solution polymerizes the ω-aminochloroformate.[52]

$$A^{\ominus} \overset{\oplus}{N}H_3-R-O-\overset{\displaystyle O}{\overset{\displaystyle \|}{C}}-Cl \overset{Base}{\longrightarrow} \left[R-O-\overset{\displaystyle O}{\overset{\displaystyle \|}{C}}-NH \right]$$

$$A^{\ominus} = Cl^{\ominus} \quad or \quad \overset{\ominus}{S}O_3-\!\!\left\langle\!\!\bigcirc\!\!\right\rangle\!\!-CH_3$$

In practice, the salt which is dissolved in chloroform, is washed with aqueous base.

A reaction which involves the action of dioximes on diisocyanates to produce polyurethane-like polymers has been reported.[53] The diisocyanate and dioxime are polymerized in a dimethyl sulfoxide solvent with a triethylamine catalyst at 80–100°C. for 2 hr. The resulting polymers have inherent viscosities of 0.8–1.3.

$$OCN-\!\langle\bigcirc\rangle\text{-}\langle\bigcirc\rangle\!-NCO + HON\!\!=\!\!R\!\!=\!\!NOH \longrightarrow$$

$$\left[\!\langle\bigcirc\rangle\text{-}\langle\bigcirc\rangle\!-NH-\overset{\overset{\text{O}}{\|}}{C}-O-N\!\!=\!\!R\!\!=\!\!N-O-\overset{\overset{\text{O}}{\|}}{C}-NH\!\right]$$

$$R = \;=\!\langle\bigcirc\rangle\!=\;,\quad \overset{\quad CH_3\; CH_3}{=\!\!C\!\!-\!\!C\!\!=}\;,$$

$$=\!CH-\!\langle\bigcirc\rangle\!-CH\!=\;,$$

$$=\!CH\underset{N}{\langle\bigcirc\rangle}CH\!=$$

By far the largest use of diisocyanates is in the formation of polyurethane rubbers, foams, and coatings. The reaction of low molecular weight polyesters which have alcohol end groups with diisocyanates produces a polyester elastomer with urethane linkages.[54,55] For example, a low molecular weight polyethylene adipate in which an excess of ethylene glycol has been added to ensure alcohol end groups can be extended with *m*-toluenediisocyanate or biphenylenediisocyanate.

$$HO\!\left[\!CH_2\!-\!CH_2\!-\!O\!-\!\overset{\overset{\text{O}}{\|}}{C}\!-\!(CH_2)_4\!-\!\overset{\overset{\text{O}}{\|}}{C}\!-\!O\!\right]_{\!x}\!\!CH_2\!-\!CH_2OH + OCN\!-\!\langle\bigcirc\rangle\!-\!\langle\bigcirc\rangle\!-\!NCO \rightarrow$$

$$\left[\!(CH_2\!-\!CH_2\!-\!O\!-\!\overset{\overset{\text{O}}{\|}}{C}\!-\!(CH_2)_4\!-\!\overset{\overset{\text{O}}{\|}}{C}\!-\!O)_{\!x}CH_2\!-\!CH_2\!-\!O\!-\!\overset{\overset{\text{O}}{\|}}{C}\!-\!NH\!-\!\langle\bigcirc\rangle\!-\!\langle\bigcirc\rangle\!-\!NH\!-\!\overset{\overset{\text{O}}{\|}}{C}\!-\!O\!\right]_{\!y}$$

The largest amount of diisocyanates produced goes into the manufacture of urethane foams. The condensation of glycerin and adipic acid is first carried out with enough adipic acid to ensure some carboxylic acid

$$HO\!-\!\overset{\overset{\text{O}}{\|}}{C}\!-\!(\text{Polyester})\!-\!\overset{\overset{\text{O}}{\|}}{C}\!-\!OH + \underset{NCO}{\overset{CH_3}{\langle\bigcirc\rangle}\!\!\!\!\!^{NCO}} \longrightarrow$$

$$\left[\!(\text{Polyester})\!-\!\overset{\overset{\text{O}}{\|}}{C}\!-\!NH\!-\!\langle\bigcirc\rangle\!-\!NH\!-\!\overset{\overset{\text{O}}{\|}}{C}\!\right] + 2CO_2$$

end groups.[56] The polyesters have acid values from 14 to 40. A typical recipe combines 3.8 moles of glycerin, 2.5 moles of adipic acid, and 0.5 moles of phthalic anhydride. The polyester, which has an acid value of 40 and 1.3–1.8% water content, is treated with the diisocyanate. The carbon dioxide evolved in the reaction with the carboxylic acid and water serves to foam the polymer as it is being formed.

By varying the amounts of reagents in the recipe and adding plasticizers to the mixture either a rigid or a flexible foam can be obtained. The flexible foam rubbers have found use in cushions, upholstery, and pillows, while the rigid foams are primarily used for insulating and lightweight structural material.

6.3   FORMALDEHYDE RESINS[16]

Phenol-formaldehyde resins.[57–59] The first important synthetic polymer was Bakelite and this resin is still produced today in greater amounts than any other synthetic resin. At the time the resin was first patented by Baekeland, very little was known about its structure. Even though there have been many contributions of many workers in the past sixty years, there are still some unanswered questions about the structure of the polymer and the mechanism of its formation.

The reaction of phenol with formaldehyde is catalyzed either by acid or base and the structures of the resulting products are different. Base catalysis seems to involve condensation of formaldehyde with phenol in the ortho and para positions since substitution in any one position, either ortho or para, by a blocking group allows formaldehyde reaction in only two positions and a linear polymer is obtained. Little or no linkage occurs through the phenolic-OH since the low molecular weight resins are alkali soluble. In the acid catalyzed reaction, however, there is a reaction between the phenolic-OH and the aldehyde since the low molecular weight resins are insoluble. Either acetal or ether formation is involved.

The reaction of phenol and formaldehyde under basic conditions is usually carried to a point where the intermediate low molecular weight (300–700) polymer is still soluble. At this stage the products, known as *resoles*, are formed with excess formaldehyde present.

They contain hydroxymethyl groups and possibly some ether linkages. The resoles can condense on further heating to high molecular weight crosslinked polymers.

In the acid catalyzed reaction of formaldehyde with phenol, there are no hydroxymethyl groups formed and, with the correct formaldehyde-phenol ratio, a linear polymer of about 1000–1500 molecular weight, which will not crosslink without the addition of more formaldehyde in a basic medium, may be prepared. The intermediate *novolac* may be set up by the addition of hexamethylenetetramine, which provides both the base and the formaldehyde.

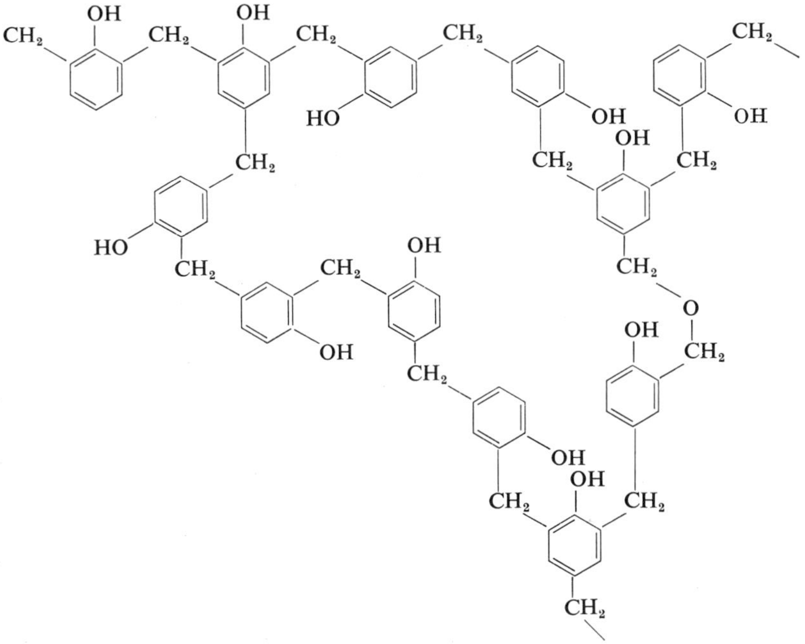

In practice, a molding resin is prepared by forming a resole at a temperature of about 90°C. The resole is mixed with fillers and pigments and ground into a molding powder. During the molding, the polymer thermosets to the final product. During the molding of novolacs, the hexamethylenetetramine is added as a crosslinking agent in the final stage.

Urea-formaldehyde resins.[16] The mechanism of formation of the urea-formaldehyde resins as well as the structure of the polymer are not known with certainty. Many investigators have made suggestions concerning both the mechanism and the structure. Indeed, the structure of the polymer could well be a mixture of types of structures resulting from different reactions.

The reaction of urea with formaldehyde and base can produce, under certain conditions, either of two crystalline compounds, methylol urea or dimethylol urea.

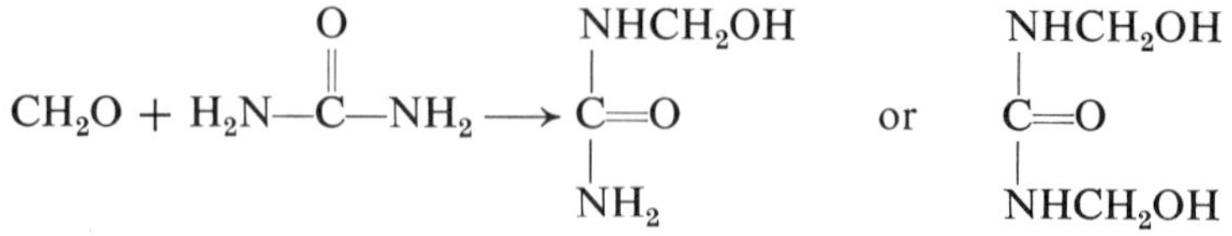

$$CH_2O + H_2N-\overset{\overset{\displaystyle O}{\|}}{C}-NH_2 \longrightarrow \underset{\underset{\displaystyle NH_2}{|}}{\overset{\overset{\displaystyle NHCH_2OH}{|}}{C}}=O \quad \text{or} \quad \underset{\underset{\displaystyle NHCH_2OH}{|}}{\overset{\overset{\displaystyle NHCH_2OH}{|}}{C}}=O$$

The polymerization of urea and formaldehyde could conceivably result from this condensation reaction. A simple amide will react with formaldehyde to form a bismethylene amide, which will condense with another mole of formaldehyde to form a methylol derivative. A polymer from this type of reaction could be represented as shown:

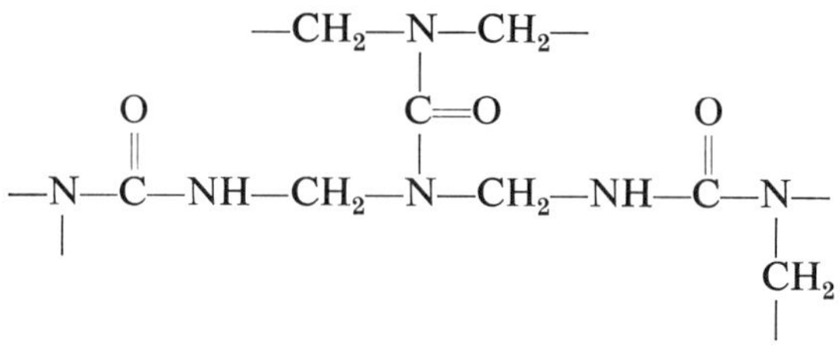

$$-CH_2-N-CH_2-$$

$$-N-\overset{\overset{\displaystyle O}{\|}}{C}-NH-CH_2-\underset{|}{\overset{\overset{\displaystyle C}{|}}{N}}=O \quad CH_2-NH-\overset{\overset{\displaystyle O}{\|}}{C}-N-$$
$$\qquad\qquad\qquad\qquad\qquad\qquad\qquad\qquad\qquad\qquad CH_2$$

This mechanism is not supported by the fact that monosubstituted and symmetrically substituted ureas do not give polymers.

Another suggested mechanism involves the formation of an intermediate which could react with itself to produce a polymer:

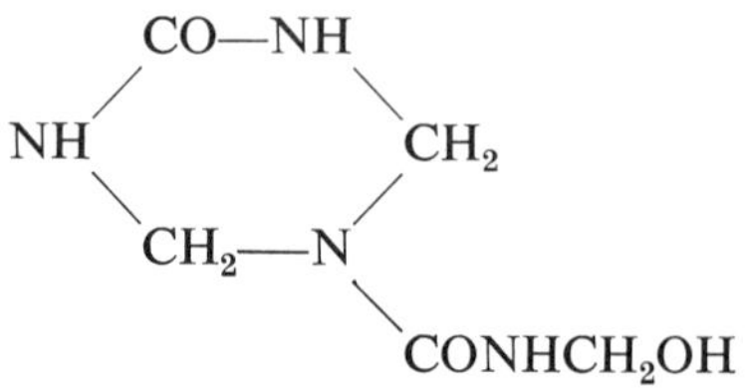

$$\begin{array}{ccc} & CO-NH & \\ NH & & CH_2 \\ & CH_2-N & \\ & & CONHCH_2OH \end{array}$$

Such an intermediate is known, but the ratios of formaldehyde to urea in this formation are actually higher than that which is needed to produce a polymer. A more favorable postulate is based on the formation of a trimer of the Schiff's base which could form from methylol urea. The free amide groups present in the trimer could then react with more formaldehyde to form a crosslinked polymer.[60]

This proposal is supported by the fact that the monomethylamide of glycine reacts with formaldehyde to give a trimer bearing three free amide groups. This trimer will polymerize with formaldehyde. The trimer postulate is also in accord with the ratio of urea and formaldehyde used in the formation of the best commercial resins.

The preparation of a resin involves the reaction of urea and formaldehyde in a 1:1.5 or 1:2 molar ratio in an aqueous medium with a base catalyst. Heating and removal of the water will eventually produce a hard crosslinked resin.

$$
\begin{array}{c}
\text{CONH}_2 \\
|\\
\text{N} \\
\diagup \quad \diagdown \\
\text{CH}_2 \qquad \text{CH}_2 \\
|\qquad\qquad | \\
\text{N} \qquad \text{N} \\
\diagup \quad \diagdown \diagup \quad \diagdown \\
\text{NH}_2\text{CO} \quad \text{CH}_2 \quad \text{CONH}_2
\end{array}
\longrightarrow
$$

$$
\begin{array}{c}
\text{CONH—CH}_2\text{—NH—CO} \\
|\qquad\qquad\qquad\qquad | \\
\text{N} \qquad\qquad\qquad \text{N} \\
\diagup \; \diagdown \qquad\qquad \diagup \; \diagdown \\
\text{CH}_2 \quad \text{CH}_2 \qquad \text{CH}_2 \quad \text{CH}_2 \\
|\qquad\quad | \qquad\qquad |\qquad\quad | \\
\text{N} \qquad \text{N} \qquad \text{N} \qquad \text{N—CONH—} \\
\diagup\;\diagdown\diagup\;\diagdown \quad |\;\diagdown\diagup \\
\text{CO} \quad \text{CH}_2 \quad \text{CONH} \quad \text{CO CH}_2 \\
|\qquad\qquad\qquad\qquad\qquad |\qquad\quad | \\
\text{NH} \qquad\qquad\qquad\qquad \text{CH}_2 \; \text{NH—CH}_2\text{—} \\
|\qquad\qquad\qquad\qquad\qquad\quad |
\end{array}
$$

In the formation of a molding powder, cellulose is added to the solution after acidifying the mixture and the water is removed leaving the powder. Pigments, lubricants, latent catalysts, and plasticizers can be added at this point. The powder can be molded in a thermosetting reaction under pressure at temperatures from 130 to 160°C.

The molded resins are light in color (translucent white) and can be converted to brilliantly colored resins by the use of pigments. They are not too resistant to water, acid, or base but can be used for a variety of molded objects. A recent innovation is the application of the soluble condensates to textiles where thermosetting will take place in ironing, thus giving crease resistant wash-and-wear fabrics.

A similar resin is made from the reaction of melamine with formaldehyde. Melamine will react with formaldehyde to form methylol derivatives. At 60–70°C. a mixture of polymethylol melamines is obtained. Both tri- and hexamethylol melamine will yield resins on heating at 80°C. with acid or base catalysis.

A controlled solution polymerization will produce a low molecular weight polymer that can be compounded in the form of a molding powder which will set up on heating. A variety of modified melamine polymers can be formed from reactions of the resins with phthalic anhydride, aryl amines, and phenols.

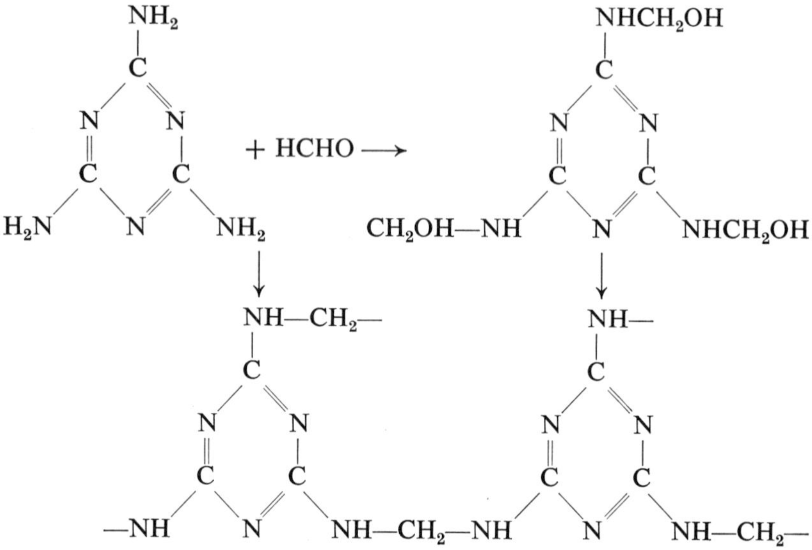

The melamine resins have been used on textiles for water resistance, as binders for paper to impart wet strength, and as adhesives, in addition to being used in the production of various molded objects.

6.4   THIOKOLS AND POLYTHIOETHERS

There are several synthetic methods which lead to polymers containing a sulfur linkage along the backbone of a polymer chain. Three of these will be discussed here, while the polymer-forming reactions involving the addition of a mercaptan to an aldehyde or a ketone and to an olefin will be discussed elsewhere.

Polythioethers are formed by the reaction of the disodium salt of a dimercaptan on a dihalide.[61] This reaction gives a poor yield of polymer which is usually low melting, at least in the aliphatic series.

$$Na—S—R—S—Na + X—R'—X \longrightarrow \text{-}[S—R—S—R'\text{]-} + 2NaX$$

In a similar reaction, the dihalide is treated with sodium polysulfide to produce a polymer having multiple sulfur links between hydrocarbon backbone portions.[62] Commercially, ethylene chloride is used as the dihalide portion.

$$Cl\text{—}CH_2\text{—}CH_2\text{—}Cl + Na_2S_x \longrightarrow \text{—}[CH_2\text{—}CH_2\text{—}S_x]\text{—} + 2NaCl$$

These thiokol polymers are rubbery and have good resistance to oil. The conversion to polymer is much better and the melting point higher than the dithiol-dihalide polymer.

Aromatic dihalides undergo a reaction with sulfur in the presence of sodium carbonate to form poly(arylene sulfides).[63-66] The reaction which takes place in the melt can also be run with a mixture of aryl halides, in which case copolymers are formed. This reaction with *p*-dichlorobenzene affords a quantitative yield of polymer which has a 193–204°C. melting point and the structure shown:

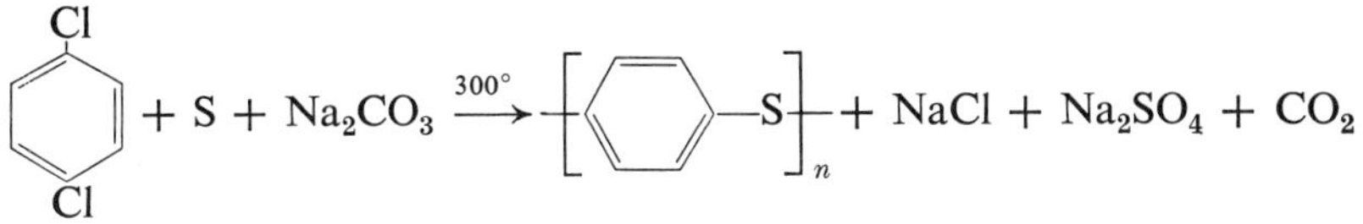

The oxidation of alkylenedithiols creates a disulfide link in a polymerization reaction which yields relatively high molecular weight thiokols.[67] The dimercaptan is dispersed in a soap emulsion and oxidized by air in the presence of trace amounts of selenous acid. With a variety of dithiols, polymers having inherent viscosities as high as 1.0 can be produced and the softening points range from 40 to 130°C.

$$H\text{—}S\text{—}R\text{—}S\text{—}H \xrightarrow{\frac{1}{2}O_2} \text{—}[R\text{—}S\text{—}S]\text{—} + H_2O$$

Dithols which contain silicon-oxygen linkages in the molecule give disulfide polymers which have properties not unlike the simple alkylene disulfides.[68]

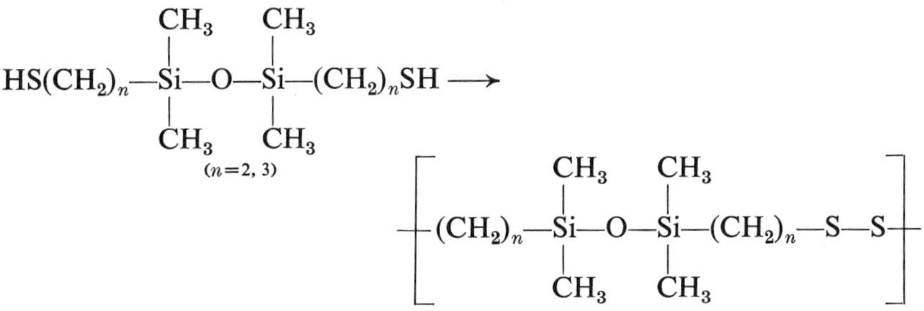

6.5 SILICONES[69-71]

The hydrolysis of chlorosilanes leads to hydroxysilanes which will undergo condensation reactions to yield silicones. Methyltrichlorosilane will yield crosslinked networks, while dimethyldichlorosilane yields low molecular weight linear polymers and cyclic silicones.

$$n(CH_3)_2SiCl_2 \xrightarrow{H_2O} \begin{bmatrix} CH_3 \\ | \\ Si-O \\ | \\ CH_3 \end{bmatrix}_n$$

Depending upon the method of hydrolysis, the variety and amounts of products from this reaction can be varied to some extent. The low molecular weight linear polymers are known as silicone oils and the cyclic silicones which make up more than half of the product have ring sizes where n varies from 3 to 9. Most of the cyclic product is the tetrasiloxane ($n = 4$). Part of the product from such a reaction is moderately high molecular weight linear silicones which can be converted to cyclic trimers and tetramers by pyrolysis. It is obvious that such a polymer would be undesirable for certain uses since pyrolysis breaks it down rather readily. This is due to the fact that the hydroxyl ends are free and these ends must be capped in order to produce a stable polymer, at least in this moderate molecular weight range.

This hydrolysis method at best yields only low-viscosity fluids. The viscosity can be increased by treating the low polymer with a strong acid catalyst to further the condensation of hydroxyl end groups. Very high molecular weight silicone polymers are not made directly from the monomers by the hydrolysis reaction, but are prepared by a ring opening of the cyclic silicones. Even the lower molecular weight silicones in which the molecular weight has been controlled by the addition of calculated amounts of trimethylchlorosilane, $(CH_3)_3SiCl$ (which caps the chain), can be prepared by a ring-opening reaction.

The hydrolysis reaction never achieves the high molecular weights observed in the ring-opening since there is a tendency to form cyclic compounds under the hydrolysis conditions and there are invariably impurities which stop the chain. The cyclic silicones produce high molecular weight polymers because the cyclic monomers can be highly purified. This polymerization by ring opening as well as the properties and uses of the silicones are discussed in Chapter 7.

There are three important chlorosilanes in the manufacture of silicones.[70] Trimethylchlorosilane is hydrolyzed by water to hexamethyldisiloxane, which is employed as a chain cap in the equilibration process.

$$(CH_3)_2SiCl \xrightarrow{H_2O} [(CH_3)_3SiOH] \longrightarrow (CH_3)_3Si-O-Si(CH_3)_3$$

Dimethyldichlorosilane hydrolyzes to dimethylsilanediol, an unstable intermediate which has been isolated, but the intermediate yields silicones which are linear and cyclic.

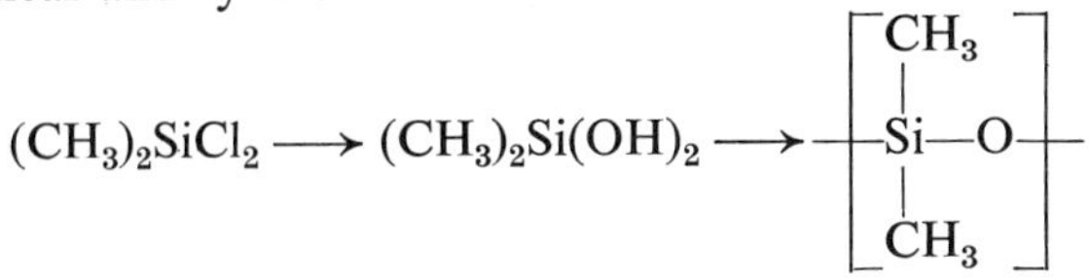

$$(CH_3)_2SiCl_2 \longrightarrow (CH_3)_2Si(OH)_2 \longrightarrow \left[\begin{array}{c} CH_3 \\ | \\ -Si-O- \\ | \\ CH_3 \end{array} \right]$$

Dichlorodimethylsilane always contains some trichloromethylsilane, which gives rise to some trifunctional monomeric units, and thus some crosslinking will occur. The hydrolysis of dichlorodimethylsilane can be carried out in a batch process where the silane is added to water or in a continuous process in which two streams are fed into a pipe through a pump.

The crude silicone thus produced is subjected to an equilibrium process in the presence of hexamethyldisiloxane and a strong acidic catalyst, usually sulfuric acid. During the equilibration process, condensation of silanols to form higher molecular weight oils and rearrangement reactions which involve breaking of silicon-oxygen bonds in both the linear and cyclic silicones with subsequent reforming of these bonds take place. In the rearrangement process, the bond breaking involves the formation of siliconates. Water hydrolyzes the siliconates to silanols and dehydration of silanol ends produces silicon-oxygen bonds again.

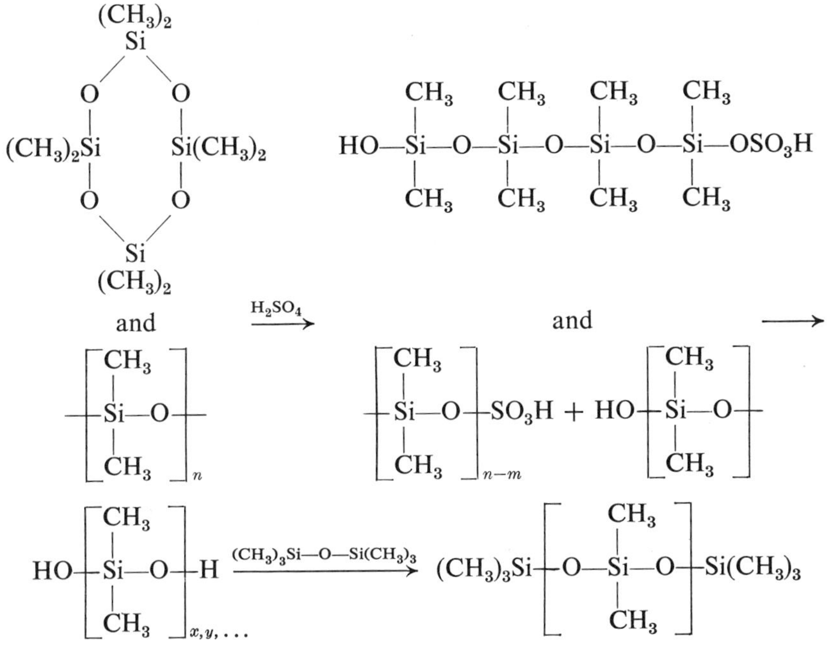

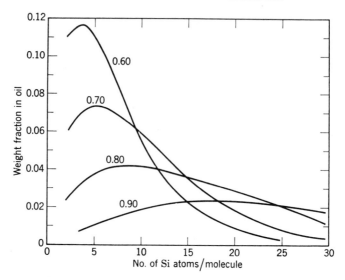

Fig. 6.1. Silicone oil equilibration molecular distribution at various mole fractions (0.6–0.9) of $-(CH_3)_2SiO-$ in the oil.[72]

Hexamethyldisiloxane is added to this reaction to provide terminal groups. The amount of this chain terminator regulates the molecular weight and the amount added must also account for the trifunctional units formed from the trichloromethylsilane impurity (Fig. 6.1). The low molecular weight oils are then removed under reduced pressure.

6.6 POLYMERIC ANHYDRIDES

Early investigations by Carothers[73] demonstrated the fact that polymeric anhydrides could be formed only when the anhydride will not form a stable ring. Thus malonic, suberic, and higher dicarboxylic acids form polymers, while succinic and glutaric acids form cyclic anhydrides. Adipic acid yields both a cycle and polymer. Sebacic acid reacts with acetic anhydride to form a mixed anhydride which on further heating yields a polymeric anhydride with a melting point 79–80°C. and a molecular weight of 5000.

$$HO_2C(CH_2)_8CO_2H + (CH_3-CO)_2O \longrightarrow$$

$$\left[O-\overset{\overset{\displaystyle O}{\|}}{C}-(CH_2)_8-\overset{\overset{\displaystyle O}{\|}}{C} \right] + 2CH_3CO_2H$$

This polymer can be converted to higher molecular weight polymers by heating at 200°C. in a molecular still to obtain a residue of 15,000–30,000 molecular weight and a 22-membered cyclic anhydride distillate. The cyclic anhydride is polymerized to a high molecular weight polymer at its melting point. Although these higher molecular weight anhydrides will form fibers, they are extremely unstable and traces of moisture will rapidly destroy the high molecular weight.

Aromatic dicarboxylic acids, on the other hand, form more stable polymeric anhydrides.[74] For example, 1,3-bis-(p-carboxyphenoxy) propane reacts with acetic anhydride to form the mixed anhydride. The product is then heated to 280°C. under reduced pressure to eliminate acetic anhydride and form the polymer.

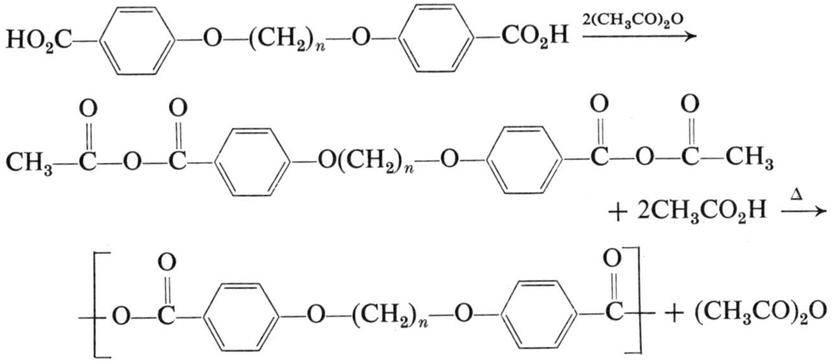

$$HO_2C - \langle \rangle - O - (CH_2)_n - O - \langle \rangle - CO_2H \xrightarrow{2(CH_3CO)_2O}$$

$$CH_3 - \overset{O}{\overset{||}{C}} - O - \overset{O}{\overset{||}{C}} - \langle \rangle - O(CH_2)_n - O - \langle \rangle - \overset{O}{\overset{||}{C}} - O - \overset{O}{\overset{||}{C}} - CH_3$$

$$+ \; 2CH_3CO_2H \xrightarrow{\Delta}$$

$$\left[O - \overset{O}{\overset{||}{C}} - \langle \rangle - O - (CH_2)_n - O - \langle \rangle - \overset{O}{\overset{||}{C}} \right] + (CH_3CO)_2O$$

The melting points of these polymers range from $Tm = 260°C.$ ($n = 4$) to greater than 340°C. ($n = 2$). Where $n = 3$, the polymer is about as stable as Dacron to moisture and base and is fiber forming.

6.7 POLYACETALS AND MERCAPTALS[75]

The formation of an acetal from a glycol and aldehyde leads to cyclic acetals in the cases where five- and six-membered rings are formed. Thus ethylene and trimethylene glycols yield cycles while tetramethylene glycol gives both rings and polymer. Larger glycols yield polymer of low molecular weight.[76] For example, a polyacetal formed from benzaldehyde and diethylene glycol by alcohol interchange yields a low molecular weight acetal.

$$C_6H_5 - CH(OC_2H_5)_2 + HO - CH_2 - CH_2 - O - CH_2 - CH_2OH \xrightarrow{Acid}$$

$$\left[O - \underset{\underset{C_6H_5}{|}}{CH} - O - CH_2 - CH_2 - O - CH_2 - CH_2 \right] + 2C_2H_5OH$$

This alcohol interchange has proven to afford high molecular weight polymers in certain cases. Acetals of a number of dialdehydes will react with tetraalcohols to form linear polycycloacetals.[77]

$$(C_2H_5O)_2CH(CH_2)_nCH(OC_2H_5)_2 \ + \quad \begin{array}{c} HOCH_2 \qquad CH_2OH \\ \diagdown \qquad \diagup \\ C \\ \diagup \qquad \diagdown \\ HOCH_2 \qquad CH_2OH \end{array} \quad \longrightarrow$$

$$(n = 3\text{–}10)$$

or

$$+ \ (HOCH_2)_2CH-(CH_2)_mCH(CH_2OH)_2 \longrightarrow$$

$$(m = 6 \text{ or } 10)$$

The reaction is run by heating stoichiometric amounts of the two monomers to 170°C. during which time the ethanol distills and the mixture is finally heated to 250°C. under reduced pressure. The acetal has film and fiber forming properties. The polymer from pentaerythritol and 1,1,8,8-tetraethoxyoctane ($n = 6$) has a melting point of 190–210°C. and a second-order transition temperature of 53°C.

Similarly, a dithiol will react with an aldehyde or a ketone to form a cyclic dimercaptal or a polymer.[78–80] In general pentamethylenedithiol yields a cyclic dimercaptal while hexamethylenedithiol with benzaldehyde gives a polymercaptal which has an inherent viscosity of 1.37.

$$C_6H_5CHO + HS(CH_2)_6SH \xrightarrow{HCl} \begin{array}{c} \Big[S-CH-S-(CH_2)_6 \Big] \\ \quad\ | \\ \quad C_6H_5 \end{array}$$

Heptamethylene- and nonamethylenedithiol yield macrocycles.

REFERENCES

1. J. R. Whinfield, *Nature*, **158**, 930 (1946).
2. J. R. Whinfield and J. T. Dickson, British Pat. 578,079 (June 14, 1946); *C. A.*, **41**, 1495c (1947).
3. P. A. Koch, *Mod. Textiles Mag.*, **36**, 38 (1958).
4. Belgian Patents 546,376 and 546,377 (March 1956).
5. H. Schnell, *Angew. Chem.*, **68**, 633 (1956).
6. D. W. Fox and E. P. Goldberg, Papers Presented at the Gordon Research Conference on Polymers, New London, N. H., July 1957.

7. R. J. Thompson and K. B. Goldblum, *Modern Plastics*, **35**, 131 (1958).
8. H. Schnell and G. Fritz, German Pat. 1,031,512, June 4 (1958); *Zentr.*, **130**, 18826 (1959).
9. L. Bottenburch and H. Schnell, German Patent 1,046,311, Dec. 11 (1958); *Zentr.*, **130**, 17516 (1959).
10. H. Schnell, *Ind. Eng. Chem.*, **51**, 157 (1959).
11. H. Schnell, *Trans. Plastics Inst.*, **28**, 143 (1960).
12. E. L. Wittbecker and P. S. Morgan, *J. Polymer Sci.*, **40**, 289 (1959).
13. P. W. Morgan and S. L. Kwolek, *J. Polymer Sci.*, **40**, 299 (1959).
14. W. M. Eareckson, III, *J. Polymer Sci.*, **40**, 399 (1959).
15. A. Conix and U. Laridon, IUPAC Symposium on Macromolecules, Wiesbaden, Oct. 12–17 (1959).
16. R. S. Morrell (ed.), *Synthetic Resins and Allied Plastics*, Oxford University Press, London, 1951.
17. Bjorksten Research Laboratories, Inc., *Polyesters and Their Applications*, Reinhold Publishing Co., New York, 1956.
18. J. R. Lawrence, *Polyester Resins*, Reinhold Publishing Co., New York, 1960.
19. S. O. Greenlee, J. W. Pearce, and J. Kawa, *Ind. Eng. Chem.*, **49**, 1085 (1957).
20. H. Mark and G. S. Whitby (eds.), *Collected Papers by Wallace Hume Carothers*, Interscience Publishers, New York, 1940.
21. K. H. Inderfurth, *Nylon Technology*, McGraw-Hill Book Co., New York, 1953.
22. R. Hill, *Fibres From Synthetic Polymers*, Elsevier Publishing Co., Amsterdam, 1953.
23. D. D. Coffman, G. J. Berchet, W. R. Peterson, and E. W. Spanagel, *J. Polymer Sci.*, **2**, 306 (1947).
24. R. G. Beaman and F. B. Cramer, *J. Polymer Sci.*, **21**, 223 (1956).
25. E. F. Carlston and F. G. Lum, *Ind. Eng. Chem.*, **49**, 1239 (1957).
26. J. F. Kohlwey and C. Maters, *Modern Plastics*, **33**, 158 (Sept. 1955).
27. R. G. Beaman, P. W. Morgan, C. R. Koller, E. L. Wittbecker, and E. E. Magat, *J. Polymer Sci.*, **40**, 329 (1959).
28. M. Katz, *J. Polymer Sci.*, **40**, 337 (1959).
29. V. E. Shashoua and W. M. Eareckson III, *J. Polymer Sci.*, **40**, 343 (1959).
30. P. W. Morgan and S. L. Kwolek, *J. Chem. Ed.*, **36**, 182 (1959).
31. C. W. Stephens, *J. Polymer Sci.*, **40**, 359 (1959).
32. D. J. Lyman and S. L. Jung, *J. Polymer Sci.*, **40**, 407 (1959).
33. S. A. Sundet, W. A. Murphey, and S. P. Speck, *J. Polymer Sci.*, **40**, 389 (1959).
34. S. B. Speck, *J. Am. Chem. Soc.*, **74**, 2876 (1952).
35. British Patent 543,297 (Feb. 18, 1942).
36. W. M. Edwards and I. M. Robinson, U.S. Patent 2,710,853 (June 14, 1955); *C. A.*, **50**, 5753d (1956).
37. K. C. Brinker and I. M. Robinson, German Patent 1,038,280 (Sept. 4, 1958); Canadian Patent 575,411 (May 1959); U.S. Patent 2,895,948 (July 21, 1959); *C. A.*, **53**, 18552f (1959).
38. H. Vogel and C. S. Marvel, *J. Polymer Sci.*, **50**, 511 (1961).
39. J. E. Mulvaney and C. S. Marvel, *J. Polymer Sci.*, **50**, 541 (1961).
40. J. E. Mulvaney and C. S. Marvel, *J. Org. Chem.*, **26**, 95 (1961).
41. R. C. Moncrieff, U.S. Patent 2,512,667 (June 27, 1950); *C. A.*, **44**, 10377c (1950).
42. J. W. Fisher, *Chem. and Ind.*, **71**, 244 (1952).
43. E. I. du Pont de Nemours and Co., British Patent 530,267 (Dec. 9, 1940); *C. A.*, **35**, 8160[1] (1941).
44. E. I. du Pont de Nemours and Co., British Patent 528,437 (Oct. 29, 1940); *C. A.*, **35**, 7148[7] (1941).

45. E. I. du Pont de Nemours and Co., British Patent 535,139 (March 31, 1941); *C. A.,* **36**, 1413[7] (1942).

46. T. W. Campbell, V. S. Foldi, and J. Farago, *J. Appl. Polymer Sci.,* **2**, 155 (1959).

47. G. J. M. Van der Kerk, H. G. J. Overmars, and G. M. Van der Want, *Rec. trav. chim.,* **74**, 1301 (1955).

48. O. Bayer and E. Muller, *Angew. Chem.,* **72**, 934 (1960).

49. W. E. Oatlin, U.S. Patent 2,284,637 (June 2, 1942); *C. A.,* **36**, 6707[1] (1942).

50. O. Bayer, *Angew. Chem.,* **A59**, 257 (1947).

51. E. L. Wittbecker and M. Katz, *J. Polymer Sci.,* **40**, 367 (1959).

52. J. R. Schaefgen, F. H. Koontz, and R. F. Tietz, *J. Polymer Sci.,* **40**, 377 (1959).

53. T. W. Campbell, V. S. Foldi, and R. G. Parrish, *J. Appl. Polymer Sci.,* **2**, 81 (1959).

54. J. H. Saunders and R. J. Slocombe, *Chem. Revs.,* **43**, 203 (1948).

55. H. L. Heiss, J. H. Saunders, M. R. Morris, B. R. Davis, and E. E. Hardy, *Ind. Eng. Chem.,* **46**, 1498 (1954).

56. B. A. Dombrow, *Polyurethanes,* Reinhold Publishing Co., New York, 1957.

57. D. F. Gould, *Phenolic Resins,* Reinhold Publishing Co., New York, 1959.

58. R. W. Martin, *The Chemistry of Phenolic Resins,* John Wiley and Sons, New York, 1956.

59. T. S. Carswell, *Phenoplasts,* Interscience Publishers, New York, 1947.

60. C. S. Marvel, J. R. Elliot, F. E. Boettner, and H. Yuska, *J. Am. Chem. Soc.,* **68**, 1681 (1946).

61. C. S. Marvel and A. Kotch, *J. Am. Chem. Soc.,* **73**, 481 (1951).

62. J. D. D'Ianni, *Ind. Eng. Chem.,* **40**, 253 (1948).

63. A. D. Macallum, *J. Org. Chem.,* **13**, 154 (1948).

64. A. D. Macallum, U.S. Patent 2,513,188, June 27 (1950); *C. A.,* **44**, 8165a (1950); 2,538,941 Jan. 23 (1951); *C. A.,* **45**, 5193c (1951).

65. R. W. Lenz and W. K. Carrington, *J. Polymer Sci.,* **41**, 333 (1959).

66. R. W. Lenz and C. E. Handlovits, *J. Polymer Sci.,* **43**, 167 (1960).

67. C. S. Marvel and L. E. Olson, *J. Am. Chem. Soc.,* **79**, 3089 (1957).

68. P. V. Bonsignore, C. S. Marvel, and S. Banerjee, *J. Org. Chem.,* **25**, 237 (1960).

69. E. G. Rochow, *An Introduction to the Chemistry of the Silicones,* John Wiley and Sons, New York, 1951.

70. R. R. McGregor, *Silicones and Their Uses,* McGraw-Hill Book Co., New York, 1954.

71. R. N. Meals and F. M. Lewis, *Silicones,* Reinhold Publishing Co., New York, 1959.

72. R. Gutoff, *Ind. Eng. Chem.,* **49**, 1807 (1957).

73. J. W. Hill and W. H. Carothers, *J. Am. Chem. Soc.,* **54**, 1569 (1932).

74. A. Conix, *J. Polymer Sci.,* **29**, 343 (1958).

75. W. H. Linton, *Trans. Plastics Inst.,* **28**, 131 (1960).

76. W. Carothers, *Chem. Revs.,* **8**, 353 (1931).

77. A. Schors and O. E. van Lohuizen, IUAPC Symposium on Macromolecules, Wiesbaden, Oct. 12–17 (1959).

78. C. S. Marvel, E. H. H. Shen, and R. R. Chambers, *J. Am. Chem. Soc.,* **72**, 2106 (1950).

79. C. S. Marvel, E. A. Sienicki, M. Passer, and C. N. Robinson, *J. Am. Chem. Soc.,* **76**, 933 (1954).

80. C. S. Marvel and R. C. Farrar, Jr., *J. Am. Chem. Soc.,* **79**, 986 (1957).

7

POLYMERIZATION
BY RING-OPENING
REACTIONS

The conversion of a cyclic monomer to polymer may be accomplished in many cases by a ring-opening reaction. In all of these reactions the cyclic monomer contains at least one heteroatom and the opening is accomplished usually by a catalyst of the anionic or cationic type. In a few cases, the ring-opening reaction is the only way to obtain high molecular weight polymer of a given structural unit.

This type of reaction may be classed as a condensation reaction, since the polymer formed has the structural features of a condensation polymer and the polymer can be prepared, at least in theory, by a typical condensation reaction in which a small molecule is eliminated. On the other hand, the polymer in most examples has the same composition as the monomer and the polymerization reaction takes place by a chain mechanism.

7.1 CYCLIC ESTERS

Cyclic esters which are four-, seven-, or eight-membered ring compounds in general tend to polymerize.[1] In the aliphatic lactone series, the five-membered lactones fail to yield polymers, while the six-membered lactones, except for those substituted by at least one n-propyl group or two methyl groups, polymerize readily. Lactones can be opened up by a variety of bases [Na, NaH, K_2CO_3, H_2O, Ti (i-C_3H_7O)$_4$] or sulfonic acids to yield low-melting polymers which tend to revert to monomer.

The following cyclic esters, which have additional strain imposed by a

115

bicyclic system will yield both monomer and polymer under polymerization conditions:[2]

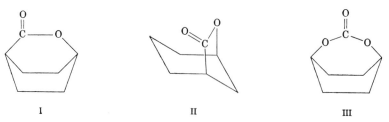

I   II   III

Compound I belongs to the bicyclo [2.2.2] class, II to the bicyclo [3.2.1], while compound III contains the bicyclo [3.2.2] structure. The cyclic carbonate of the bicyclo [3.3.1] class will not polymerize readily.

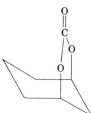

None of the polyesters produced by ring opening has gained any commercial importance. Carothers demonstrated the fact that a six-membered lactone would produce a polyester.[3] The polymerization of propiolactones is quite rapid but the product is low melting.

In addition to the bridged carbonates discussed, several other carbonates, oxalates, and glycolides have been investigated. Trimethylene carbonate is polymerized by base at 130°C. to give a polymer of about 4000 molecular weight.[3]

$$\text{(cyclic carbonate)} \xrightarrow{K_2CO_3} \left[(CH_2)_3-O-\overset{\overset{\displaystyle O}{\|}}{C}-O \right]_n$$

Investigations on the polymerizability and synthesis of various substituted carbonates has shown that when R = methyl and R′ = n-propyl or i-amyl,

$$\left[CH_2-CRR'-CH_2-O-\overset{\overset{\displaystyle O}{\|}}{C}-O \right]$$

$$HOCH_2-CRR'-CH_2OH + (C_2H_5O)_2C{=}O$$

polycarbonates are formed directly from the glycol and diethyl carbonate.[4] When $R = R' =$ ethyl or hydrogen, $R =$ ethyl, $R' =$ phenyl, or the higher glycols 1,3-butanediol and 2,4-pentanediol are the alcohol portions, the cyclic carbonate is formed, and can be converted to polymer. Higher concentrations of the sodium methoxide base, 2.5–5 mole per cent instead of 0.5 mole per cent, produce only the cyclic carbonate.

Ethylene oxalate polymerizes on standing to give a polymer of 3000 molecular weight or higher.[3]

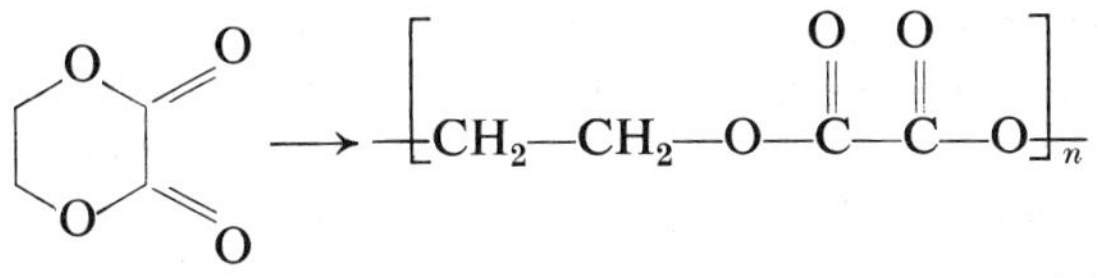

$$\longrightarrow \left[CH_2{-}CH_2{-}O{-}\overset{\overset{O}{\|}}{C}{-}\overset{\overset{O}{\|}}{C}{-}O \right]_n$$

The lactide from hydroxyacetic acid will yield high molecular weight polymer by the action of a Lewis acid catalyst, while attempts to polymerize hydroxyacetic acid itself lead only to the lactide.[5]

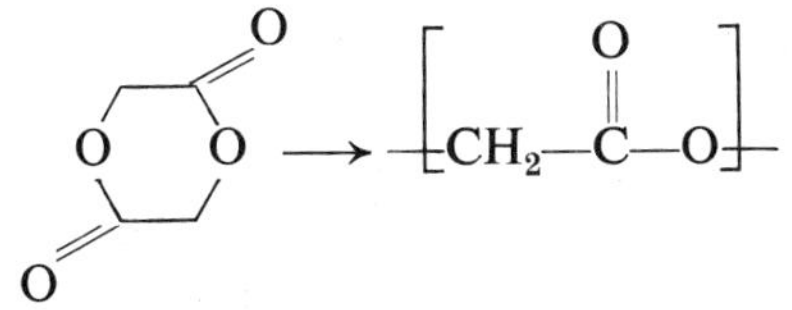

$$\longrightarrow \left[CH_2{-}\overset{\overset{O}{\|}}{C}{-}O \right]$$

A novel synthesis of polyesters involves anhydrosulfites of hydroxy acids which can be polymerized thermally with the loss of sulfur dioxide.[6] Strangely enough the anhydrosulfites of amino acids will not polymerize although the carboanhydrides of α-amino acids do so with the elimination of carbon dioxide.

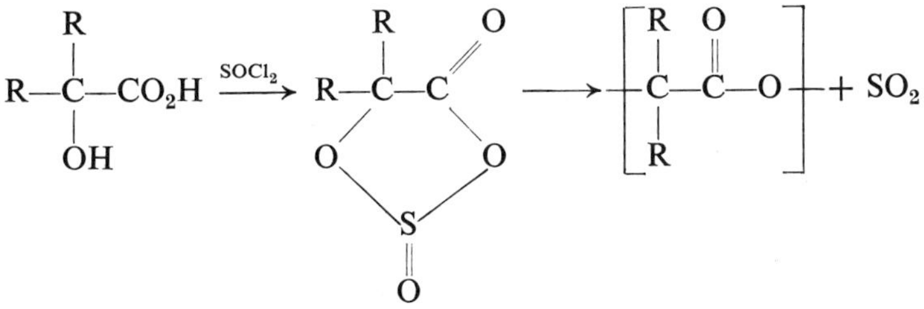

$$R{-}\overset{\overset{\displaystyle R}{|}}{\underset{\underset{\displaystyle OH}{|}}{C}}{-}CO_2H \xrightarrow{SOCl_2} R{-}\overset{\overset{\displaystyle R}{|}}{C}{-}C \longrightarrow \left[\overset{\overset{\displaystyle R}{|}}{\underset{\underset{\displaystyle R}{|}}{C}}{-}\overset{\overset{O}{\|}}{C}{-}O \right]{+} SO_2$$

The monomer 2,2-dimethyl-2-hydroxyacetic acid anhydrosulfite affords a polymer which has a molecular weight of 100,000 and a melting point of 240°C.

7.2   CYCLIC AMIDES

Lactams may be polymerized by water and alkali equally well above 200°C.[7] Alkali metals or their hydrides are effective on the molten monomers while sodium hydride is good even at room temperature. Eight- or nine-membered ring compounds in the lactam series and about half of the seven-membered lactams will polymerize. Five- and six-membered lactams undergo polymerization reactions with difficulty. The five-membered lactone, α-pyrrolidone, may be polymerized at the relatively low temperature of 60–80°C. The polymerization of α-piperidone to low molecular weight polymer is possible only when extremely pure monomer is employed.[8] Apparently the most important factor influencing the equilibrium between polymerization and cyclization is the rate of cyclization, to the lactam which is to some extent determined by the strain in the resulting ring. Alkyl or aryl substituents on the ring tend to decrease the lactam's ability to polymerize and other heteroatoms in the ring system have little effect. Related to the lactams are the imides, ureas, and thioureas. Succinimide will not polymerize but glutarimide will. In general, the cyclic ureas and thioureas will not form polymers.[1]

As in the case of the cyclic esters, certain strained bridged compounds containing nitrogen heteroatoms representing the [2.2.2] octane and [3.2.2] nonane series, especially those in which the cyclohexane ring occurs in the boat form, will yield polymer.[9]

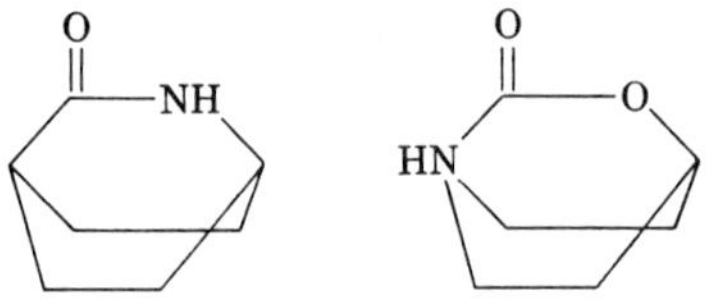

$Tm > 400°C.$

[2.2.2]

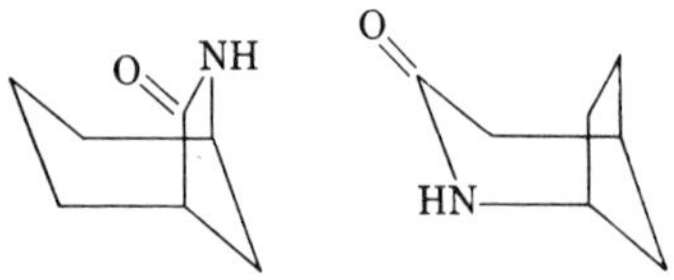

[3.2.1]

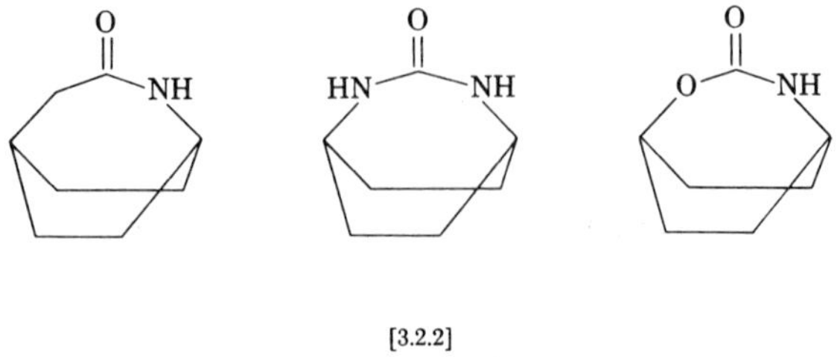

[3.2.2]

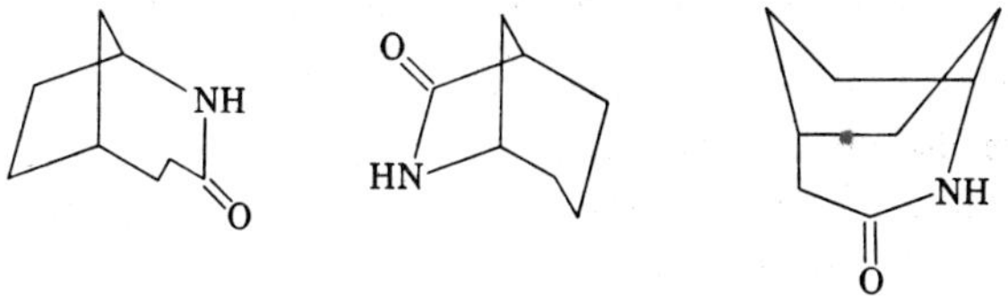

$Tm = 222°$ $Tm > 400°$ $Tm = 212°$

The [3.3.1] compounds, which can possess two stable chair forms, as well as certain other bridged bicyclics, do not polymerize.

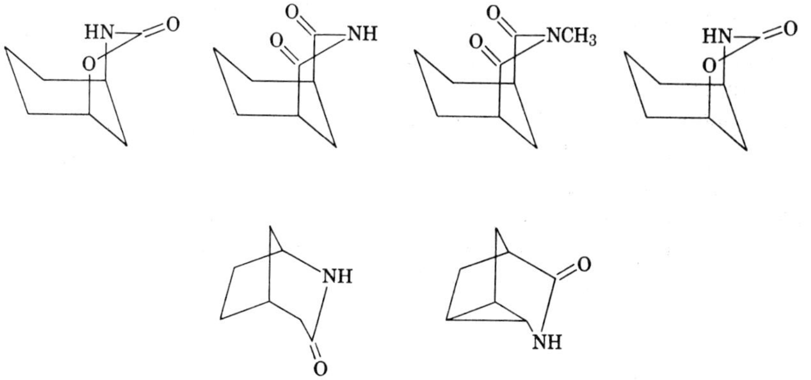

An indication that at least one [3.3.1] monomer will polymerize is evidenced by the fact that attempts to prepare the monomer containing a bridgehead nitrogen led only to polymer.

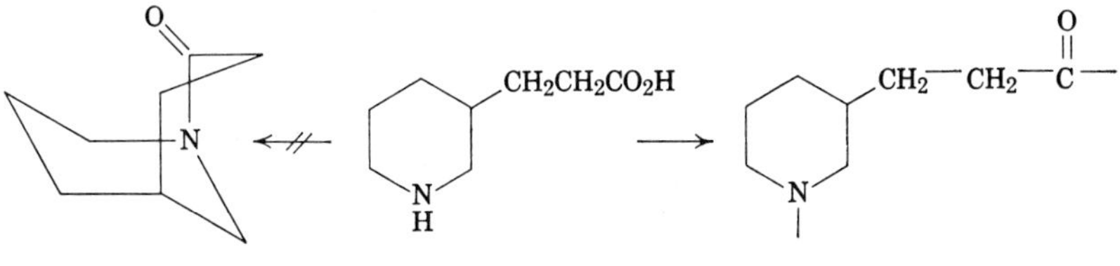

Caprolactam and α-pyrrolidone. Several methods are available for the polymerization of caprolactam.[10] Heating the monomer alone at 220–250°C. for 200 hr. will produce polymer although a trace of water or alcohol speeds up the reaction to 6 hr., and larger amounts of water are also effective. Catalysts such as sodium or potassium hydroxide, and potassium or sodium carbonate,[1,10,11] or the alkali metals and their hydrides, for example sodium, lithium, and sodium hydride,[1,7,10,12] effect a rapid polymerization. Sulfonic acids[1] and dry hydrogen chloride at 245°C.[13] have also been proven to be good catalysts. N-acetylcaprolactam is a promoter in the alkali catalyzed polymerization.[14] This effect becomes clear in a discussion of the mechanisms of polymerization of lactams. In general, higher temperatures and pressures are required (200–280°C.) in aqueous systems than in anhydrous systems with metal or metal hydride catalysts. The N-acetylcaprolactam promoter allows polymerization with an alkali metal catalyst at room temperature.

In the presence of water, there are three possible mechanisms by which caprolactam may polymerize. These involve (1) a ring addition mechanism, (2) hydrolysis and condensation, and (3) insertion of monomer at chain amide links.[15-20] In the presence of acid or base, a chain mechanism seems to be involved.[21]

The polymerization of α-pyrrolidone can be effected by the same catalysts mentioned above.[7] The polymerization with dry potassium hydroxide, however, takes place at a lower temperature[22] (90–100°C.) as does the alkali metal catalyzed polymerization. The N-acetyllactam promoter both in the polymerization of caprolactam and α-pyrrolidone suggests the following mechanism:[7,23]

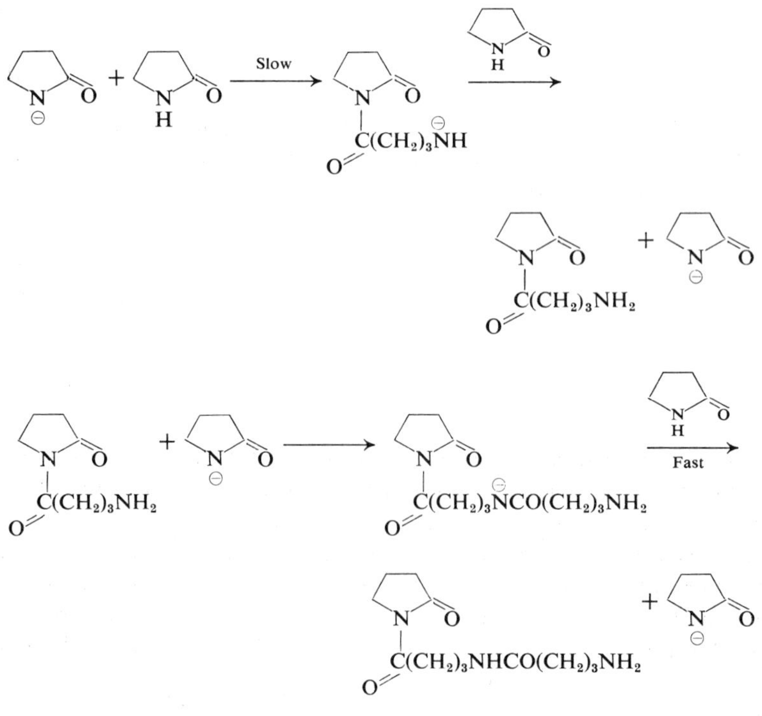

In the commercial production of poly(ε-aminocaproic acid), caprolactam is prepared from cyclohexanone by conversion to the oxime and a subsequent Beckman rearrangement.

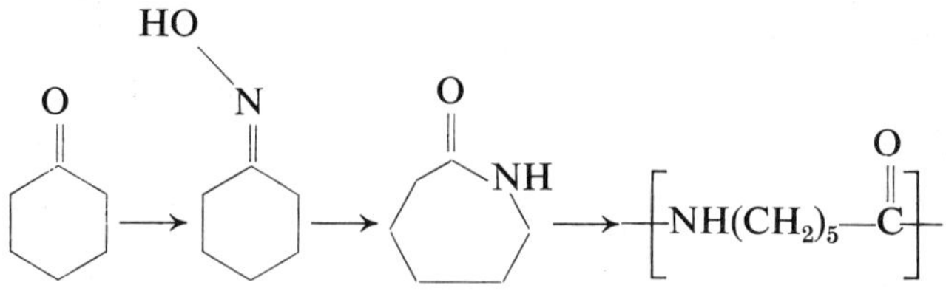

The polymerization can be carried out in either a batch or continuous process. In the batch process, caprolactam and a fourfold amount of water are heated in an autoclave in an oxygen-free atmosphere to 250°C.[10,16,19] The pressure is released and the steam is allowed to escape while maintaining the temperature for several hours. The polymer contains about 10% monomer, which is washed out before spinning.[24] During the melt-spinning process, more monomer is formed and must again be removed. The nylon 6 thus produced is employed mainly as a textile fiber and has a lower crystalline melting point (225°C.) and is more flexible than nylon 66.

7.3   CARBOANHYDRIDES[25]

In 1906, Leuchs[26,27] discovered that carboanhydrides which could be prepared from the reaction of phosgene with amino acids would very readily form poly(amino acids) by the elimination of carbon dioxide.

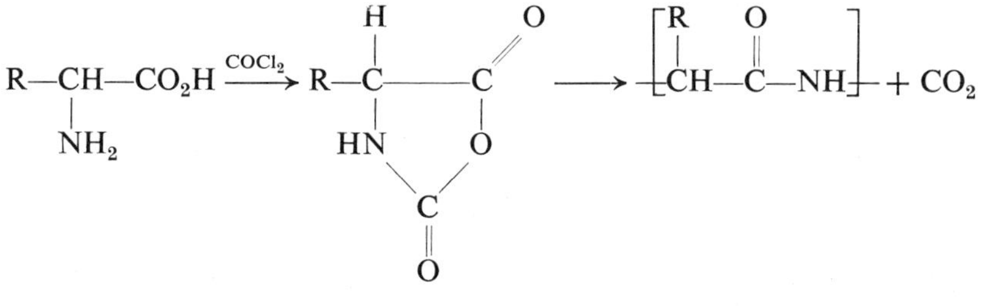

The polymerization reaction can be carried out by heating dry N-carboxyglycine anhydride at 100°C., at which temperature the rapid evolution of carbon dioxide occurs and a high molecular weight polyamide is formed. The monomer, which is stable in water below 15°C. evolves carbon dioxide above this temperature to form glycine. When trace amounts of water, however, are used to initiate the reaction, the product is again polymer.

The carboanhydrides where R = ethyl or benzyl react in the same m anner.[28] Molecular weights of poly(glutamic acid) prepared from the c orresponding anhydride have been reported at 21,000.[29] γ-Benzyl-L-g lutamate is converted to γ-benzyl-N-carboxy-L-glutamate by the reaction o f phosgene.

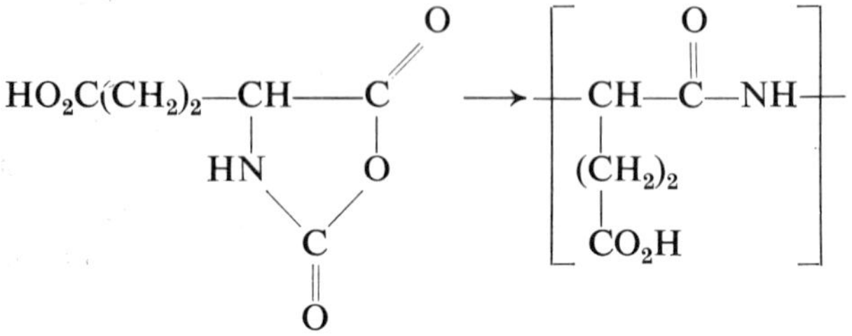

$$
\text{HO}_2\text{C(CH}_2)_2\text{—CH——C} \underset{\underset{\underset{\text{O}}{\|}}{\overset{\overset{\text{HN}\qquad\text{O}}{}}{}}{\overset{\overset{\text{O}}{/\!/}}{}} \longrightarrow \left[\begin{array}{c} \overset{\overset{\text{O}}{\|}}{\text{CH—C—NH}} \\ (\text{CH}_2)_2 \\ \text{CO}_2\text{H} \end{array}\right]
$$

The monomer is polymerized at 25°C. in a 3% solution of the anhydride in dry dioxane or dioxane-tetrahydrofuran mixtures with a sodium hydroxide–methanol initiator. Molecular weights greater than 100,000 are obtained, and in one run a molecular weight of 358,000 ($\eta = 1.87$) was achieved.[30] This high molecular weight is possible only through very pure monomers as it has been shown that acid chlorides inhibit the polymerization.[31] The carboanhydride of N-phenylacetyllysine can be polymerized to the corresponding poly(amino acid) having a degree of polymerization of 32 simply by heating the monomer to 105°C.[32] Random copolymers of any composition can be prepared.

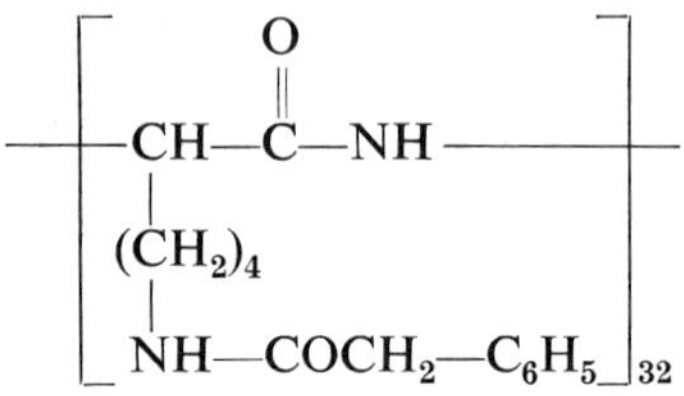

$$
\left[\begin{array}{c} \overset{\overset{\text{O}}{\|}}{\text{CH—C—NH}} \\ (\text{CH}_2)_4 \\ \text{NH—COCH}_2\text{—C}_6\text{H}_5 \end{array}\right]_{32}
$$

Copolymers of L-leucine-glycine,[33] α-aminoisobutyric acid–phenylalanine, and phenylalanine-L-leucine[34,35,36] have been obtained.

The mechanism of polymerization probably involves the hydrolysis of the anhydride to form an unstable N-carboxyl amino acid which loses carbon dioxide to give the amino acid initiator.[37] The amino acid then serves to open anhydride rings successively with the loss of carbon dioxide.

Initiation:

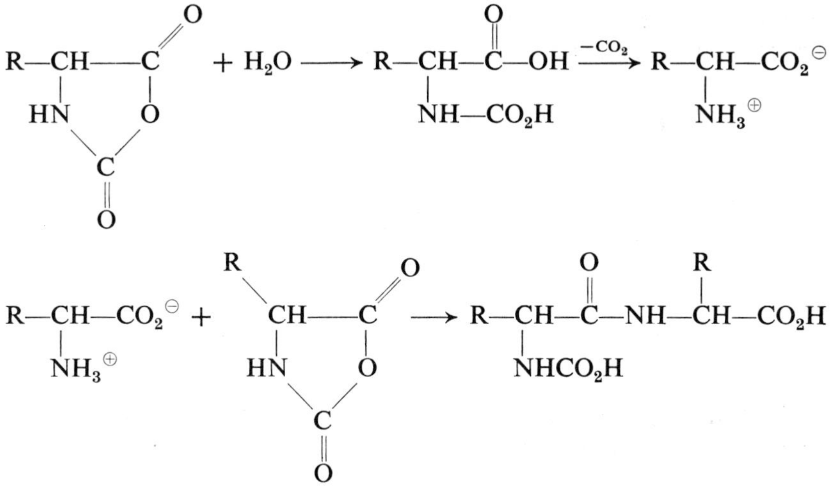

$$R-CH-C(=O)\underset{\underset{C=O}{|}}{\overset{\overset{|}{HN}}{}}O \;+\; H_2O \longrightarrow R-\underset{NH-CO_2H}{CH}-C(=O)-OH \xrightarrow{-CO_2} R-\underset{\overset{\oplus}{NH_3}}{CH}-CO_2^{\ominus}$$

$$R-\underset{\overset{\oplus}{NH_3}}{CH}-CO_2^{\ominus} \;+\; \underset{\underset{C=O}{|}}{\overset{\overset{R}{\diagup}}{\underset{HN}{CH}}}-C(=O)O \longrightarrow R-\underset{NHCO_2H}{CH}-\overset{O}{\overset{\|}{C}}-NH-\overset{R}{\underset{}{CH}}-CO_2H$$

Propagation:

$$R-\underset{\overset{\oplus}{NH_3}}{CH}-\left[\overset{O}{\overset{\|}{C}}-NH-\overset{R}{\underset{}{CH}}\right]_n CO_2^{\ominus} \;+\; \underset{\underset{C=O}{|}}{\overset{\overset{R}{\diagup}}{\underset{HN}{CH}}}-C(=O)O \longrightarrow$$

$$R-\underset{NH-CO_2H}{CH}-\left[\overset{O}{\overset{\|}{C}}-NH-\overset{R}{\underset{}{CH}}\right]_{n+1} CO_2H \quad \xrightarrow[\;]{-CO_2}$$

$$R-\underset{\overset{\oplus}{NH_3}}{CH}-\left[\overset{O}{\overset{\|}{C}}-NH-\overset{R}{\underset{}{CH}}\right]_{n+1} CO_2^{\ominus}$$

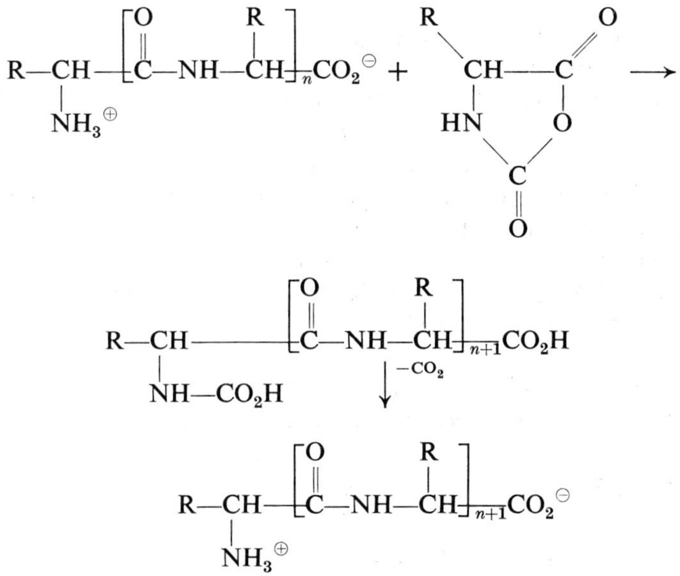

In this study, N-carboxyl-*l*-leucine anhydride and N-carboxyl-*d,l*-phenyl-alanine anhydride were polymerized in refluxing benzene with a trace of water.

The analogous elimination reaction of N-carboxylthioanhydrides also affords high molecular weight polyamides.[38,39] These thio monomers are not as sensitive to water or heat and polymerization takes place at a slightly higher temperature.

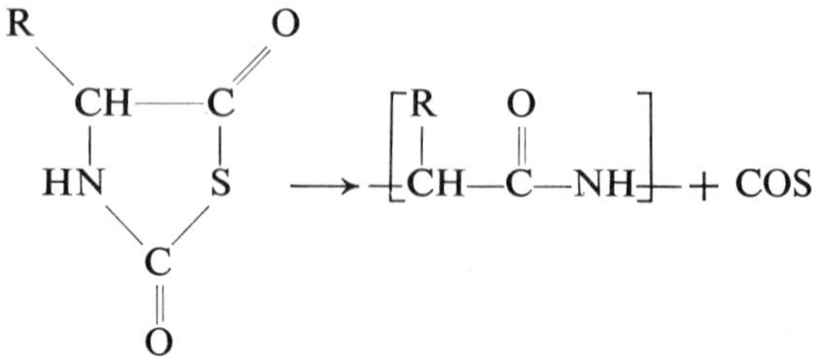

$$\underset{\substack{\text{HN}\text{S}\\\big\backslash\big/\\\text{C}\\\big\|\\\text{O}}}{\overset{\substack{\text{R}\text{O}\\\big\backslash\big\|\\\text{CH}-\text{C}}}{}} \longrightarrow \left[\begin{array}{c}\text{R} \quad \text{O} \\ \big| \quad \big\| \\ \text{CH}-\text{C}-\text{NH}\end{array}\right] + \text{COS}$$

No other high molecular weight polyamide can be prepared by such a mild chemical and physical treatment.

7.4 CYCLIC ETHERS

The only practical way to prepare high molecular weight polyethers, with two exceptions, is through a ring-opening reaction of a cyclic ether. The polymerizability of cyclic ethers can be attributed to ring strain and H—H crowding in certain ring conformations. The cyclic ethers open up under the influence of either anionic or cationic catalysts to give polymers ranging from low molecular weight oils to high molecular weight solid products, depending on the catalyst.

Two general classes of cyclic ethers will be considered: the oxiranes or epoxides, the smallest of the cyclic ethers, and the larger four- (oxetane) and five-membered heterocycles.

Oxiranes. The polymerization of an epoxide to a high molecular weight polyether can be accomplished in a variety of ways. Lewis acid catalysts such as boron fluoride and stannic chloride generally give low molecular weight polymers.

$$\underset{\substack{\big\backslash\big/\\\text{O}}}{\text{CH}_2\text{——}\text{CH}_2} \longrightarrow \text{HO}[\text{CH}_2\text{—}\text{CH}_2\text{—}\text{O}]_n\text{H}$$

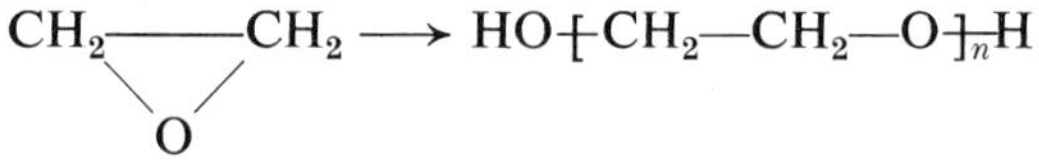

In the boron fluoride catalyzed polymerization of ethylene oxide, a reversible chain transfer occurs in which an equilibrium molecular weight is reached.[40] The equilibrium molecular weight can be approached either from monomer or higher molecular weight polymers. The catalyst is not consumed but the growth stops at a low molecular weight due to dimer formation.

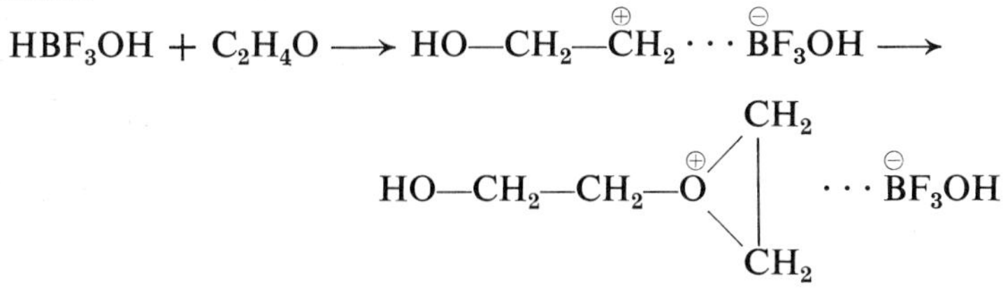

$$HBF_3OH + C_2H_4O \longrightarrow HO-CH_2-\overset{\oplus}{C}H_2 \cdots \overset{\ominus}{B}F_3OH \longrightarrow$$

$$HO-CH_2-CH_2-\overset{\oplus}{O}\underset{\diagdown CH_2}{\overset{\diagup CH_2}{\mid}} \cdots \overset{\ominus}{B}F_3OH$$

Small amounts of water seem to be necessary for this reaction. Each polymer molecule has one hydroxy end group and the dimer formation occurs through a decomposition of the polymer chain.[41]

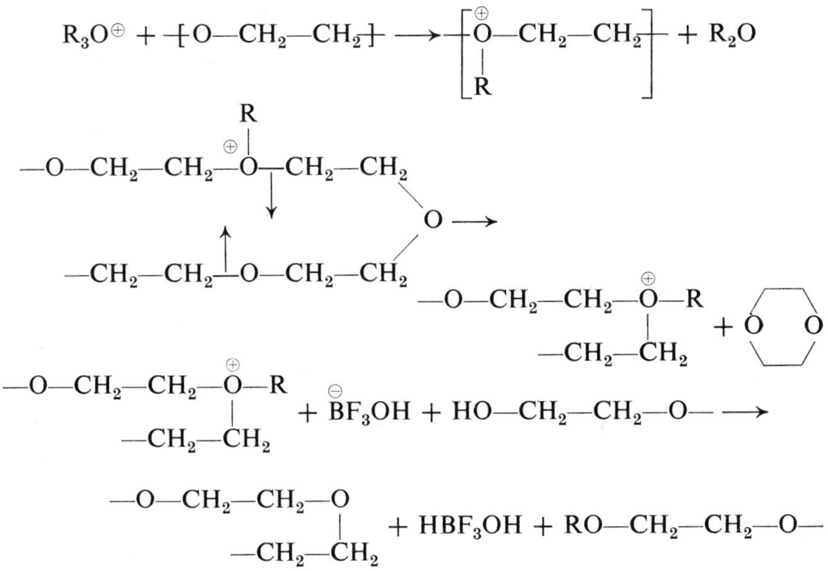

$$R_3O^{\oplus} + \text{-}[O-CH_2-CH_2] \longrightarrow \left[\overset{\oplus}{O}-CH_2-CH_2 \atop \overset{|}{R}\right] + R_2O$$

$$\overset{R}{\underset{\oplus}{-O-CH_2-CH_2-O}}\overset{R}{\underset{|}{-}}O\text{-}CH_2-CH_2$$

$$-CH_2-CH_2\overset{|}{\underset{\uparrow}{-}}O-CH_2-CH_2 \diagup O \longrightarrow$$

$$-O-CH_2-CH_2-\overset{\oplus}{O}-R \atop \underset{-CH_2-CH_2}{|} + O\diagdown\diagup O$$

$$-O-CH_2-CH_2-\overset{\oplus}{O}-R \atop \underset{-CH_2-CH_2}{|} + \overset{\ominus}{B}F_3OH + HO-CH_2-CH_2-O- \longrightarrow$$

$$-O-CH_2-CH_2-O \atop \underset{-CH_2-CH_2}{|} + HBF_3OH + RO-CH_2-CH_2-O-$$

The polymerization of ethylene oxide with stannic chloride differs in that no water is needed, two polymer molecules are formed for each stannic chloride, and chain termination occurs with catalyst destruction and without transfer.[42]

Initiation:

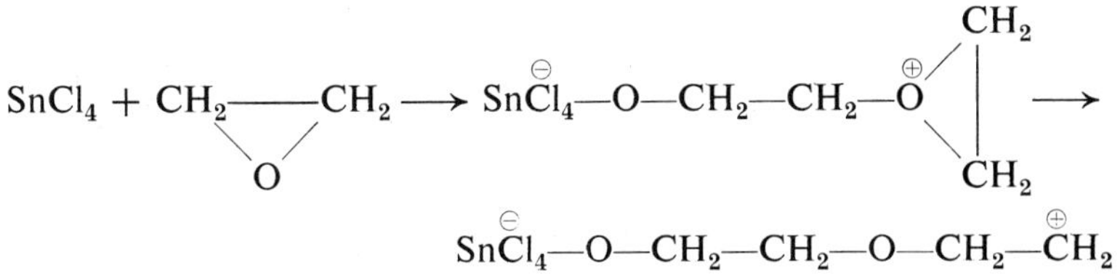

$$SnCl_4 + CH_2\diagdown_{O}\diagup CH_2 \longrightarrow Sn\overset{\ominus}{C}l_4-O-CH_2-CH_2-\overset{\oplus}{O}\underset{\diagdown CH_2}{\overset{\diagup CH_2}{\mid}} \longrightarrow$$

$$Sn\overset{\ominus}{C}l_4-O-CH_2-CH_2-O-CH_2-\overset{\oplus}{C}H_2$$

Propagation:

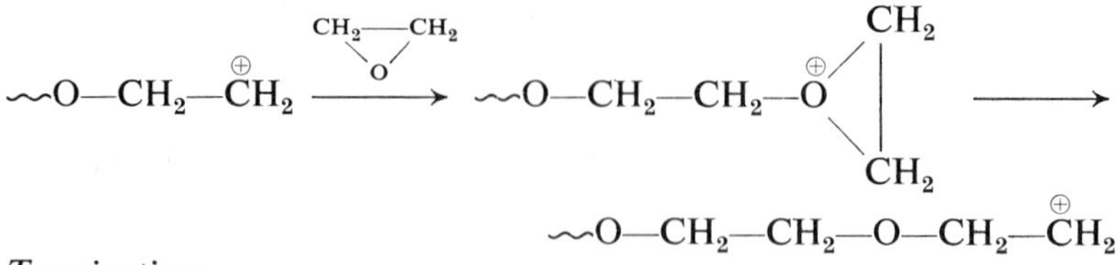

$$CH_2 - CH_2$$
$$O$$
$$\sim\!\!O-CH_2-CH_2 \xrightarrow{\qquad} \sim\!\!O-CH_2-CH_2-\overset{\oplus}{O} \begin{matrix} CH_2 \\ | \\ CH_2 \end{matrix} \xrightarrow{\qquad}$$

$$\sim\!\!O-CH_2-CH_2-O-CH_2-\overset{\oplus}{C}H_2$$

Termination:

$$\overset{\ominus}{Sn}Cl_4O-CH_2-CH_2\!\!\left(O-CH_2-CH_2\right)_{\!\!n}\!OCH_2-\overset{\oplus}{C}H_2 \longrightarrow$$

$$SnCl_3O-CH_2-CH_2\!\!\left(OCH_2CH_2\right)_{\!\!n}\!OCH_2-CH_2Cl$$

Ferric chloride has been shown to react with propylene oxide to give a red catalyst oil which will polymerize propylene oxide to an isotactic polyether.[43-45] The polymerization of *l*-propylene oxide by this catalyst yields an optically active polymer of intermediate molecular weight which has a melting point of 70°C. The polymerization with such Lewis acid catalysts apparently takes place in two stages, the first of which involves the formation of the catalysts in a reaction similar to that postulated with stannic chloride:

Catalyst formation:

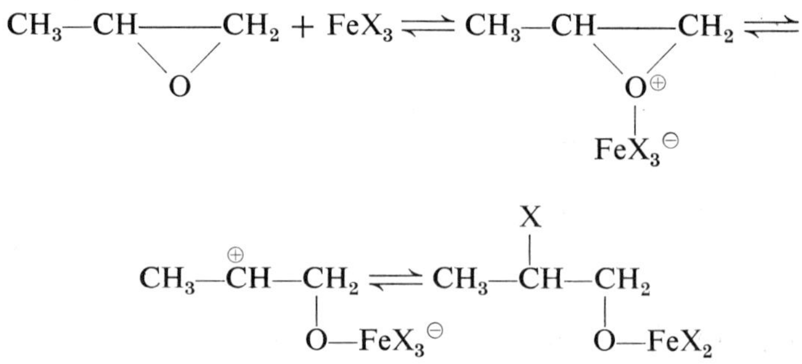

$$CH_3-CH\!\!-\!\!-\!\!CH_2 + FeX_3 \rightleftharpoons CH_3-CH\!\!-\!\!-\!\!CH_2 \rightleftharpoons$$
$$\diagdown\!O\!\diagup \qquad\qquad\qquad \diagdown\!\underset{\displaystyle FeX_3^{\ominus}}{\overset{\displaystyle O^{\oplus}}{|}}\!\diagup$$

$$CH_3-\overset{\oplus}{C}H-CH_2 \rightleftharpoons CH_3-\overset{\displaystyle \overset{X}{|}}{C}H-CH_2$$
$$\underset{O-FeX_3^{\ominus}}{|} \qquad\qquad \underset{O-FeX_2}{|}$$

It has been claimed that this catalyst is not quite as shown, but rather that several consecutive additions of epoxide occur on at least two halogen sites before halogen migration to carbon.[46]

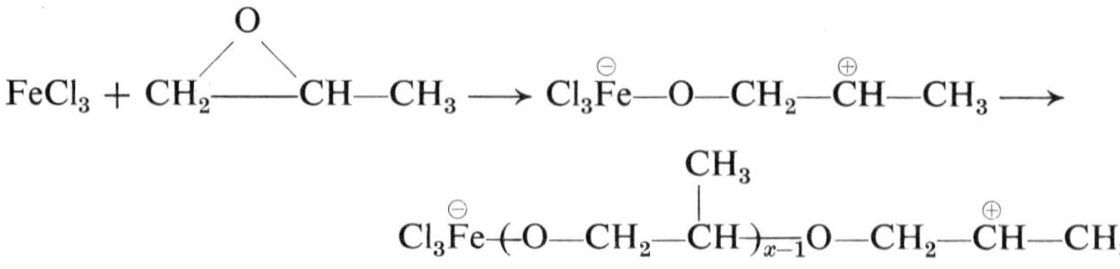

$$O$$
$$FeCl_3 + CH_2\!\!-\!\!-\!\!CH-CH_3 \longrightarrow Cl_3Fe-\overset{\ominus}{O}-CH_2-\overset{\oplus}{C}H-CH_3 \longrightarrow$$

$$Cl_3\overset{\ominus}{Fe}\!\!\left(O-CH_2-\overset{\displaystyle \overset{CH_3}{|}}{C}H\right)_{\!\!x-1}\!\!O-CH_2-\overset{\oplus}{C}H-CH_3$$

$$\text{Cl}_2\text{Fe}\text{+O}-\text{CH}_2-\overset{\overset{\displaystyle \text{CH}_3}{\displaystyle |}}{\text{CH}}\text{+}_x\text{Cl} \longrightarrow \longrightarrow \text{Cl}-\text{Fe}\overset{\displaystyle (\text{OCH}_2-\overset{\overset{\displaystyle \text{CH}_3}{\displaystyle |}}{\text{CH}}\text{+}_x\text{Cl}}{\underset{\displaystyle (\text{O}-\text{CH}_2-\overset{\overset{\displaystyle \text{CH}_3}{\displaystyle |}}{\text{CH}}\text{+}_y\text{Cl}}{}}$$

The catalyst thus formed reacts with epoxide monomer by insertion of monomer between a metal-oxygen bond.[44–48]

$$\text{Cl}-\overset{\displaystyle |}{\text{Fe}}-\text{OR} + \text{CH}_2\underset{\diagdown}{\overset{\text{O}}{\diagup}}\text{CH}-\text{CH}_3 \longrightarrow \text{Cl}-\overset{\displaystyle |}{\text{Fe}}\overset{\displaystyle \text{O}-\text{R}}{\underset{\displaystyle \text{O}}{}} \longrightarrow$$

$$\text{CH}_2\underset{\diagdown}{\overset{\text{O}}{\diagup}}\text{CH}$$
$$\text{CH}_3$$

$$\text{Cl}-\text{Fe}\overset{\displaystyle \text{O}-\text{R}}{\underset{\displaystyle \text{O}-\text{CH}_2-\text{CH}}{}}$$
$$\text{CH}_3$$

Other Lewis acid catalysts which have been investigated probably operate in an analogous manner and ferrous bromide as well as antimony pentachloride yield poly(propylene oxide) and poly(ethylene oxide) in the 10,000–40,000 molecular weight range.[46] Phosphorous pentafluoride polymerizes oxiranes and other higher heterocyclic oxygen compounds to very high molecular weight polymers.[49] Freshly prepared ferric chloride, made by the oxidation of ferrous chloride with chlorine *in situ* is a better catalyst than the preformed catalyst.[50] The proposed metal alkoxide catalyst in the mechanism seems reasonable since aluminum *i*-propoxide zinc chloride mixtures, which presumably form halogen aluminum alkoxides, effect a polymerization to high molecular weight polyethylene oxide ($\eta = 2.0$).[51,52] In addition, aluminum alkyls[51–54] or aluminum alkyls in combination with ferric chloride[54] give polymers of propylene and ethylene oxide where viscosities range from 0.5 to 1.0.

Polymerization of oxiranes will take place with a metal alkyl catalyst such as dibutyl zinc,[55] but the highest molecular weight polyoxiranes are formed with a metal alkyl catalyst such as butyl lithium, diethyl zinc, or diethyl cadmium when used in a binary mixture with alumina, silica, or silica-alumina,[56,57] or equimolar amounts of water.[58] The highest molecular weight poly(ethylene oxide) ($\eta = 9.4$) on this catalyst series is obtained with diethyl zinc on alumina. Poly(propylene oxide) ($\eta = 5.4$) is obtained from the diethyl zinc–water catalyst.

Oxiranes may also be polymerized to low molecular weight polymer by aqueous potassium hydroxide[59] or powdered potassium hydroxide in non-aqueous solvents.[44,60] The highest molecular weight poly(ethylene oxide) has been obtained with an active strontium carbonate catalyst.[61] The freshly precipitated strontium carbonate is activated at 350°C. and must be free from nitrate and chlorate ion impurities. The ethylene oxide is heated under pressure with the heterogeneous catalyst at 70–110°, and polymer with an inherent viscosity as high as 10.0 can be obtained in less than 2 hr. The polymer has 95% crystallinity in which the chains are oriented in parallel helices.[62] The polymer has a melting point of 60°C., and a density of 1.15–1.26.

The solubility properties of poly(ethylene oxide) compared to those of the other polyethers are quite striking.[63,64] Poly(ethylene oxide) is the only polyether which is soluble in water at room temperature while polyformaldehyde [poly(methylene oxide)], poly(propylene oxide), polyacetaldehyde, and polyoxetane are all insoluble.

Epoxy resins.[65,66] One of the biggest uses of an epoxide is in the formation of epoxy resins. Epoxy resins are low molecular weight linear polymers which have been crosslinked with at least a difunctional molecule containing active hydrogens by reaction with an epoxide group present in the low molecular weight polymer.

The most common resin is prepared by the reaction of bisphenol A with epichlorohydrin to give a low molecular weight polymer which has terminal epoxide groups.[67,68]

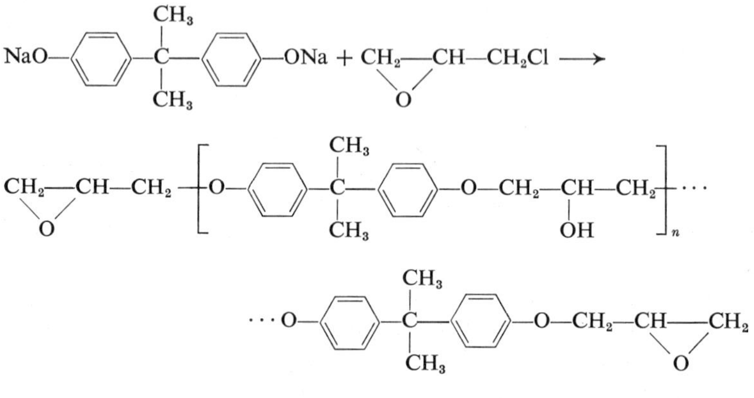

By controlling the excess of epichlorohydrin, epoxide end groups are insured, and the molecular weight can be varied from viscous liquids to high molecular weight solids, depending on the use. The molecular weights for the liquid polymers which are to be used for adhesives range from about 6 to 10 units.

The crosslinking or curing reaction takes place either by the reaction of a polyfunctional amine or alcohol with the terminal epoxide groups or through the reaction of the pendant hydroxyl groups with a polyfunctional acid or acid anhydride in the formation of ester linkages. Diethylenetri-amine will react with the epoxide linkages to form an infusible hard product.

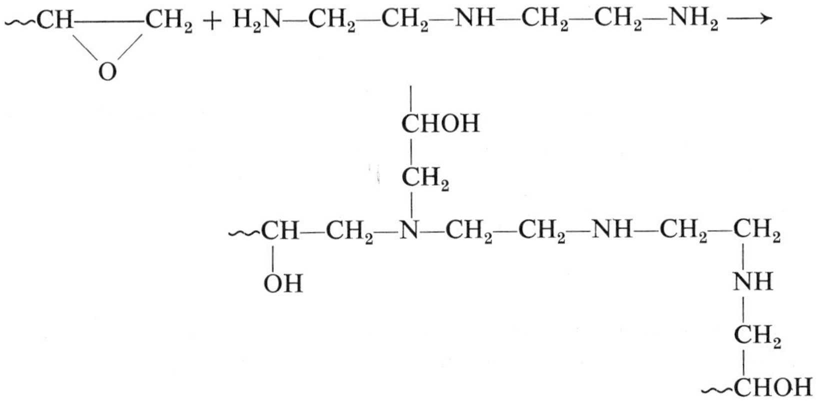

$$\sim CH \overline{\qquad} CH_2 + H_2N-CH_2-CH_2-NH-CH_2-CH_2-NH_2 \longrightarrow$$

$$\overset{\displaystyle |}{CHOH}$$
$$\overset{\displaystyle |}{CH_2}$$
$$\overset{\displaystyle |}{\underset{\underset{OH}{|}}{\sim CH}}-CH_2-\overset{\displaystyle |}{N}-CH_2-CH_2-NH-CH_2-\underset{\underset{\underset{\underset{\sim CHOH}{|}}{CH_2}}{\underset{|}{NH}}}{CH_2}$$

The reaction is complete in 1.5–2 hours at room temperature with 6–14% amine. Crosslinking with maleic anhydride involves both esterification with the pendant hydroxyl groups and the epoxide ends as well as ether formation catalyzed by the added acid.[69]

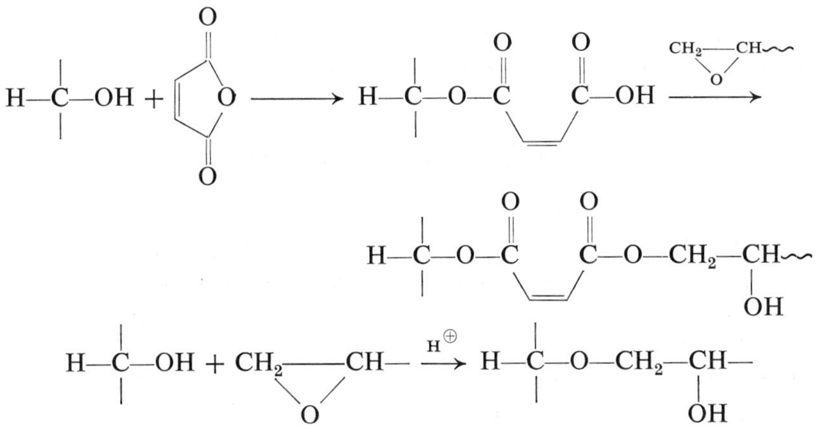

In this reaction, 0.85 mole of anhydride per epoxy equivalent is necessary to obtain the maximum yield point. Addition of tertiary amines to this system increase the rate of cure. Liquid anhydrides are advantageous for obvious reasons when the epoxy is made for the purpose of coating or adhesive, and the following anhydrides are preferred:

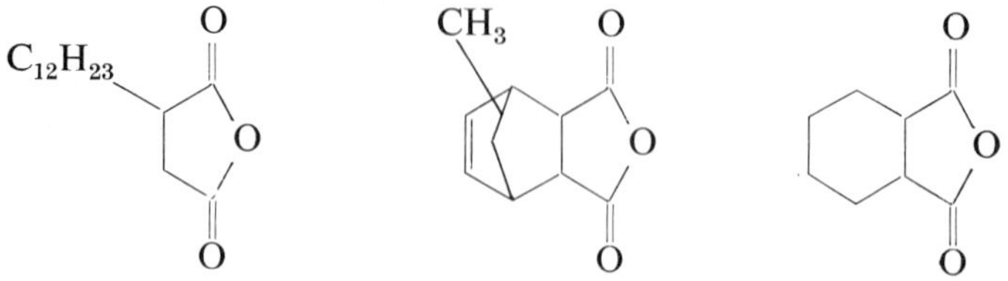

Addition of other resins such as phenolics, ureas, and melamines which contain active hydrogens will also crosslink the linear epoxy polymer.

Resins thus cured are extremely stable to heat and have excellent strength and adhesive properties. They are manufactured mainly for adhesives, surface coatings, or potting resins and will adhere particularly well to metal surfaces.

Oxetanes and furans. The polymerization of various oxetanes has been realized only recently since oxetane is subject to a facile rearrangement reaction.

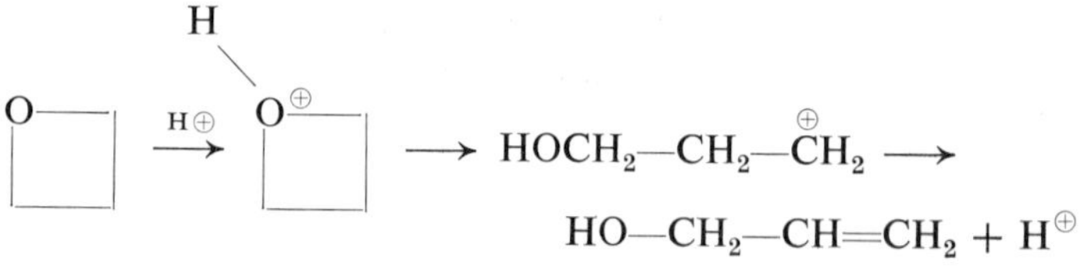

Oxetanes will yield polymers, however, with the nonprotonic acid phosphorous pentafluoride.[70,71] Polyoxetane itself has a melting point of about 180°C.

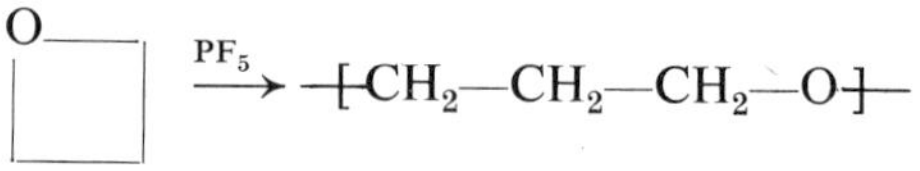

Gem-dialkyl substituted oxetanes have lower melting points while *gem*-dihalomethyl groups lead to polymers with higher melting points.

Tetrahydrofuran[72] can be polymerized by the same catalyst. A solid complex catalyst of tetrahydrofuran and phosphorous pentafluoride can be isolated, which is effective for the polymerization of tetrahydrofuran to a polymer of molecular weight 300,000, $Tm = 55°C$.[49]

Tetrahydropyran has not been polymerized, but various bridged bicyclic ethers are catalyzed by Lewis acids to high molecular weight polyethers because of ring strain and H—H interactions.[49] The bridged bicyclic ethers shown below give polymers with catalyst systems such as phosphorous pentafluoride, ferric chloride–thionyl chloride, antimony trichloride–epichlorohydrine, and antimony pentachloride–propylene oxide, although VII, VIII, and IX do not yield high molecular weight polymers.

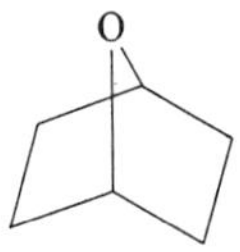

IV 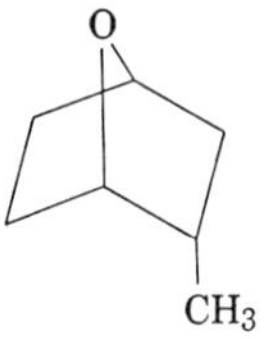   V 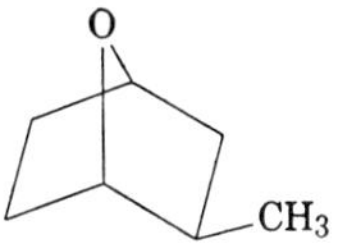   VI

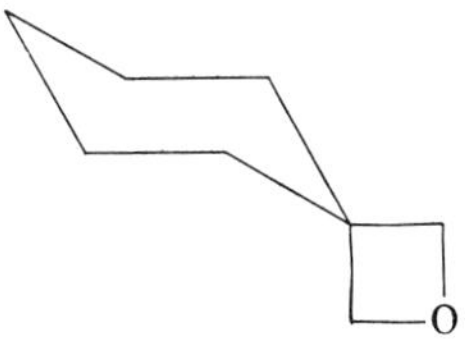

VII 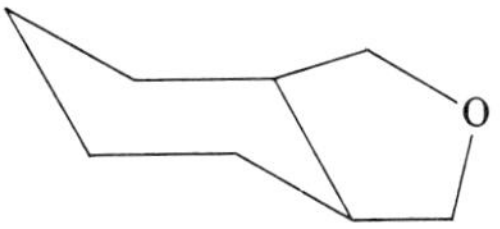   VIII 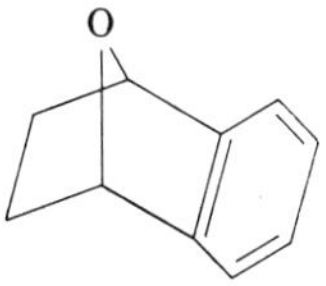   IX

The following cyclic ethers will not polymerize:

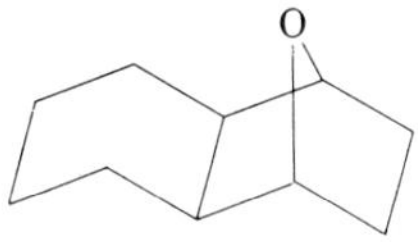

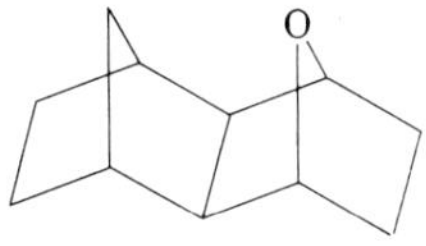

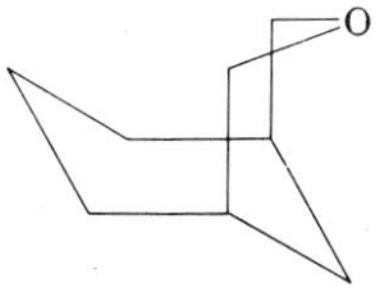

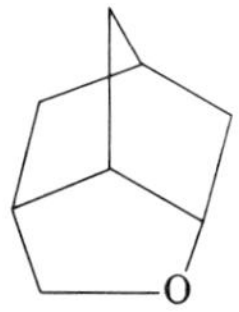

Poly(cyclohexylene ether) from 7-oxabicyclo [2.2.1] heptane (IV) is by far the most interesting polymer in this series. It has a crystalline melting point between 430 and 450°C. and has a molecular weight in the 5,000–10,000 range.

The mechanism of this polymerization can be illustrated as follows:

Initiation:

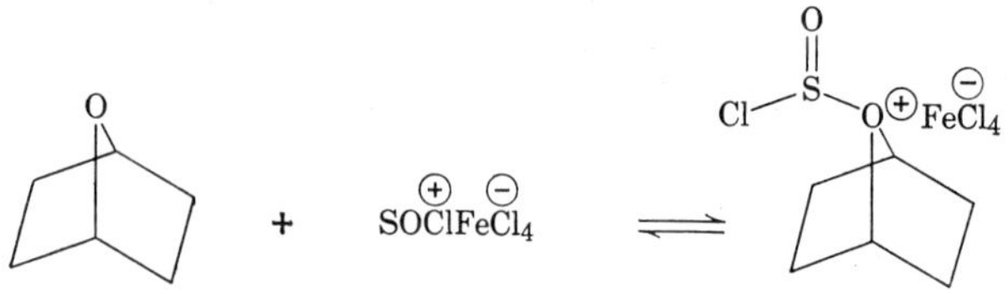

Propagation:

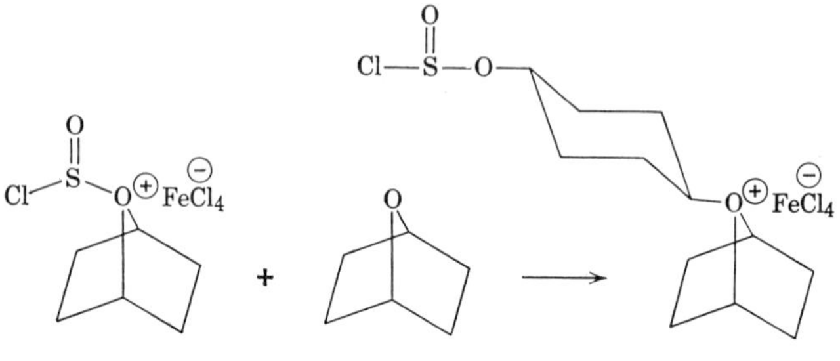

Termination:

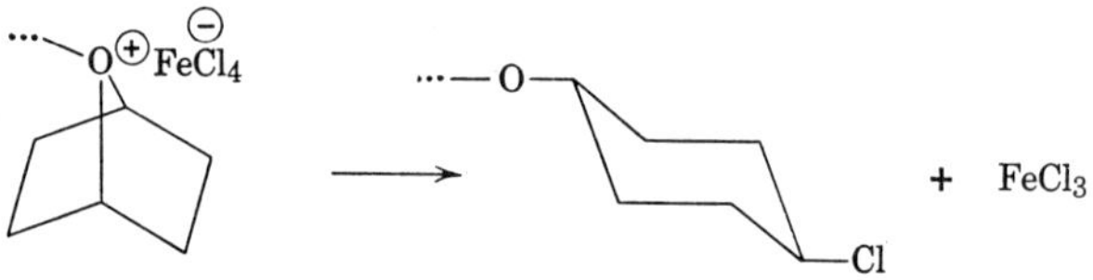

7.5 IMINES

Ethyleneimine undergoes an acid catalyzed polymerization to yield acid soluble polymers.[73] Polyethyleneimine achieves a molecular weight possibly as high as 100 units and the polymerization takes place rapidly at room temperature. At $-78°C.$, little polymerization is effected by such catalysts as boron fluoride-water or hydrochloric acid. The mechanism of the polymerization shown finds support in rate studies and the fact that ethyleneimine and primary amine end groups ($I^+ = H^+$) are found.

Initiation:

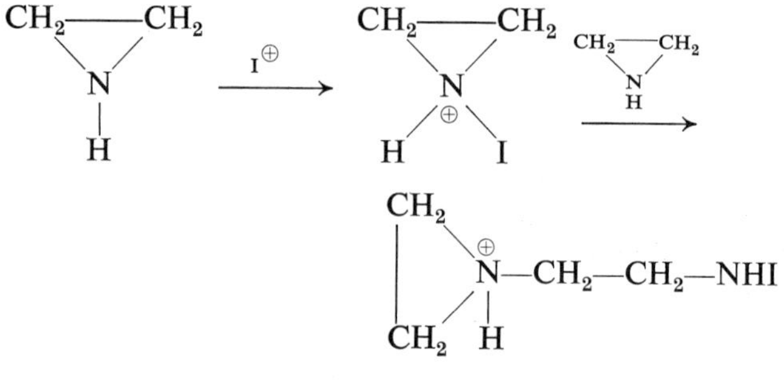

Propagation:

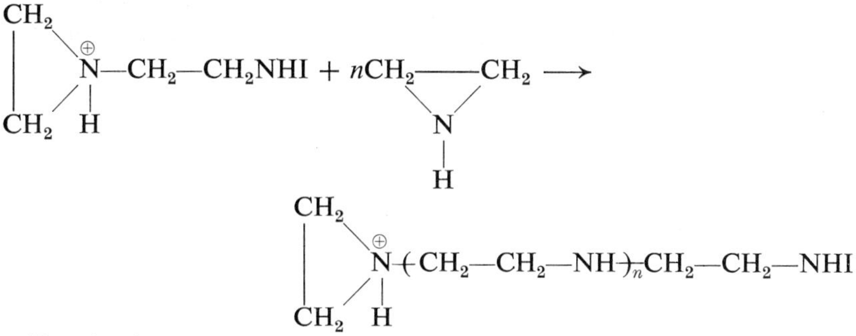

$$\underset{\substack{CH_2 \\ | \\ CH_2}}{}N\overset{\oplus}{\underset{H}{}}-CH_2-CH_2NHI + nCH_2\underset{\substack{N \\ | \\ H}}{\overset{}{\diagdown}}CH_2 \longrightarrow$$

$$\underset{\substack{CH_2 \\ | \\ CH_2}}{}N\overset{\oplus}{\underset{H}{}}-(CH_2-CH_2-NH)_n CH_2-CH_2-NHI$$

Termination:

$$\underset{\substack{CH_2 \\ | \\ CH_2}}{}N\overset{\oplus}{\underset{H}{}}-(CH_2-CH_2-NH)_n CH_2-CH_2NHI \xrightarrow{B\ominus}$$

$$\underset{\substack{CH_2 \\ | \\ CH_2}}{}N-(CH_2-CH_2-NH)_n CH_2-CH_2NHI$$

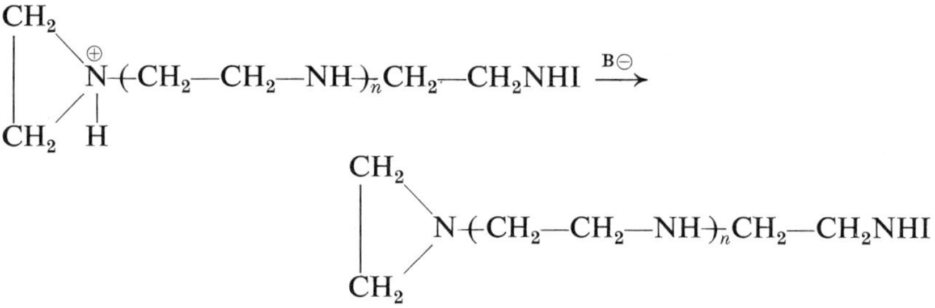

Polymerization of propyleneimine affords only low molecular weight polymers.[74]

One trimethyleneimine, *l*-azabicyclo [4.2.0] octane, has been reported to give high molecular weight polymer at room temperature with a boron fluoride–etherate catalyst.[75,76] Optically active, crystalline isotactic polymers are obtained from optically active monomers.

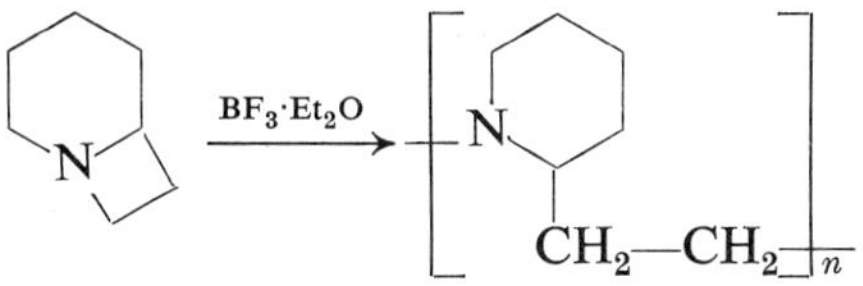

$$\text{(bicyclic structure)} \xrightarrow{BF_3 \cdot Et_2O} \left[N\overset{}{\underset{CH_2-CH_2}{}} \right]_n$$

7.6 SILICONES

Polymerization of cyclic siloxanes, especially tetrasiloxane, by a ring opening reaction affords high molecular weight silicones (Chapter 6). This is possible since tetrasiloxane which results from the hydrolysis of dimethyldichlorosilane may be obtained in a highly purified form by distillation.[77]

Thermally stable silicone oils can be prepared from cyclic siloxanes by the sulfuric acid equilibrium process described in Chapter 6. Hexamethyl-disiloxane added to the reaction mixture in the appropriate amounts will control the molecular weight as well as cap the chain making it thermally stable. The big advantage in these silicone oils over petroleum oils is their insensitivity to change in viscosity over a wide range of temperatures.[78]

$$(CH_3)_2Si \xrightarrow[\text{(CH}_3)_3Si-O-Si(CH_3)_3]{H_2SO_4} (CH_3)_3Si-O\left[\begin{array}{c} CH_3 \\ | \\ Si-O \\ | \\ CH_3 \end{array}\right]_n Si(CH_3)_3$$

The high molecular weight silicones are prepared by opening the siloxane rings with dry potassium hydroxide at elevated temperatures.[79] These silicone elastomers retain their elastic properties over a wide range of temperatures and the high molecular weight elastomers may be crosslinked with metal oxide catalysts by the replacement of methyl groups by oxygen links.

REFERENCES

1. H. K. Hall, Jr., and A. K. Schneider, *J. Am. Chem. Soc.*, **80**, 6409 (1959).
2. H. K. Hall, Jr., *J. Am. Chem. Soc.*, **80**, 6412 (1958).
3. W. H. Carothers, *Chem. Revs.*, **8**, 353 (1931).
4. S. Sarel and L. A. Pohoryles, *J. Am. Chem. Soc.*, **80**, 4596 (1958).
5. C. E. Lowe, U. S. Patent 2,668,162 (Feb. 2, 1954); *C. A.*, **48**, 9111g (1954).
6. C. E. H. Bawn and A. Ledwith, *Chem. and Ind.*, **1957**, 1180.
7. H. K. Hall, Jr., *J. Am. Chem. Soc.*, **80**, 6404 (1958).
8. N. Yoda and A. Miyake, *J. Polymer Sci.*, **43**, 117 (1960).
9. H. K. Hall, Jr., *J. Am. Chem. Soc.*, **82**, 1209 (1960).
10. W. E. Hanford and R. M. Joyce, *J. Polymer Sci.*, **3**, 167 (1948).
11. J. Saunders, *J. Polymer Sci.*, **30**, 479 (1958).
12. D. D. Coffman, N. L. Cox, E. L. Martin, W. E. Mochel, and F. J. van Natta, *J. Polymer Sci.*, **3**, 85 (1948).
13. G. M. van der Want and C. A. Krussink, *J. Polymer Sci.*, **35**, 119 (1959).
14. J. Sebenda and J. Kralicek, *Chem. listy*, **52**, 758 (1958).
15. F. Wiloth, *Makromol. Chem.*, **14**, 156 (1954).
16. P. H. Hermans, *J. Appl. Chem.*, **5**, 493 (1955).
17. F. Wiloth, *Kolloid Zeit.*, **144**, 58 (1955).
18. D. C. A. Kruissink, G. M. van der Want, and A. J. Staverman, *J. Polymer Sci.*, **30**, 67 (1958).
19. P. H. Hermans, D. Heikens, and P. F. van Velden, *J. Polymer Sci.*, **30**, 81 (1958).
20. A. V. Tobolsky and A. Eisenberg, *J. Am. Chem. Soc.*, **81**, 2302 (1959).

21. T. G. Majury, *J. Polymer Sci.*, **31**, 383 (1958).
22. W. O. Ney, Jr., W. R. Nummy, and C. E. Barnes, U.S. Patent 2,638,463, May 12, (1953); *C. A.*, **47**, 96246 (1953).
23. C. E. Barnes, W. O. Ney, and W. R. Nummy, U.S. Patent 2,809,958, Oct. 15 (1957); *C. A.*, **52**, 19252g (1958).
24. J. F. Kohlwey and C. Maters, *Modern Plastics*, **33**, 158 (Sept. 1955).
25. C. H. Bamford, A. E. Elliott, and W. E. Hanby, *Synthetic Polypeptides*, Academic Press, New York, 1956.
26. H. Leuchs, *Ber.*, **39**, 857 (1906).
27. H. Leuchs and W. Geiger, *Ber.*, **41**, 1721 (1908).
28. T. Curtius and W. Sieber, *Ber.*, **55**, 1543 (1922).
29. W. E. Hanby, S. G. Waley, and J. Watson, *Nature*, **161**, 132 (1948).
30. E. R. Blout, R. H. Karlson, P. Doty, and B. Hargitay, *J. Am. Chem. Soc.*, **76**, 4492 (1954).
31. G. E. Moos, H. Budelman, and P. Chen, *J. Polymer Sci.*, **33**, 273 (1958).
32. E. Katchalski, I. Grossfeld, and M. Frankel, *J. Am. Chem. Soc.*, **69**, 2564 (1947).
33. Y. Go and H. Tani, *Bull. Chem. Soc. Japan*, **14**, 510 (1939).
34. D. Coleman, *J. Chem. Soc.*, **1950**, 3222.
35. D. Coleman and A. C. Farthing, *J. Chem. Soc.*, **1950**, 3218.
36. A. C. Farthing, *J. Chem. Soc.*, **1950**, 3213.
37. R. B. Woodward and C. H. Schramm, *J. Am. Chem. Soc.*, **69**, 1552 (1947).
38. J. H. Bradbury and J. D. Leeder, *Textile Research J.*, **30**, 118 (1960).
39. P. Alexander, J. L. Bailey, and D. Carter, *Textile Research J.*, **20**, 385 (1950).
40. D. J. Worsfold and A. M. Eastham, *J. Am. Chem. Soc.*, **79**, 900 (1957).
41. G. A. Latremouille, G. T. Merrall, and A. M. Eastham, *J. Am. Chem. Soc.*, **82**, 120 (1960).
42. D. J. Worsfold and A. M. Eastham, *J. Am. Chem. Soc.*, **79**, 897 (1957).
43. C. C. Price, M. Osgan, R. E. Hughes, and C. Shambelan, *J. Am. Chem. Soc.*, **78**, 690 (1956).
44. C. C. Price and M. Osgan, *J. Am. Chem. Soc.*, **78**, 4787 (1956).
45. F. B. Jones, P. B. Stickney, L. E. Coleman, Jr., D. A. Rausch, and A. M. Lovelace, *J. Polymer Sci.*, **26**, 81 (1957).
46. R. O. Colclough, G. Gee, W. C. E. Higginson, J. B. Jackson, and M. Litt, *J. Polymer Sci.*, **34**, 171 (1959).
47. R. Robinson, *Tetrahedron*, **5**, 96 (1959).
48. F. Eirich and H. Mark, *J. Colloid. Sci.*, **11**, 748 (1956).
49. E. L. Wittbecker, H. K. Hall, Jr., and T. W. Campbell, *J. Am. Chem. Soc.*, **82**, 1218 (1960).
50. M. Osgan and C. C. Price, *J. Polymer Sci.*, **34**, 153 (1959).
51. R. A. Miller and C. C. Price, *J. Polymer Sci.*, **34**, 161 (1959).
52. A. Noshay and C. C. Price, *J. Polymer Sci.*, **34**, 165 (1959).
53. P. E. Ebert and C. C. Price, *J. Polymer Sci.*, **34**, 157 (1959).
54. S. Kambara and M. Hatano, *J. Polymer Sci.*, **27**, 584 (1958).
55. F. E. Bailey, Jr., and H. G. France, *J. Polymer Sci.*, **45**, 243 (1960).
56. J. Furukawa, T. Saegusa, T. Tsuruta, and G. Kakogawa, *Makromol. Chem.*, **36**, 25 (1959).
57. J. Furukawa, T. Tsuruta, T. Saegusa, and G. Kakogawa, *J. Polymer Sci.*, **36**, 541 (1959).
58. R. Sakata, T. Tsuruta, T. Saegusa, and J. Furukawa, *Makromol. Chem.*, **40**, 67 (1960).

59. S. Perry and H. Hibbert, *J. Am. Chem. Soc.*, **62**, 2599 (1940).
60. L. E. St. Pierre and C. C. Price, *J. Am. Chem. Soc.*, **78**, 3432 (1956).
61. F. N. Hill, F. E. Bailey, Jr., and J. T. Fitzpatrick, *Ind. Eng. Chem.*, **50**, 5 (1958).
62. K. L. Smith and R. Van Cleve, *Ind. Eng. Chem.*, **50**, 12 (1958).
63. F. E. Bailey, Jr., G. M. Powell, and K. L. Smith, *Ind. Eng. Chem.*, **50**, 8 (1958).
64. F. E. Bailey, Jr., and R. W. Callard, *J. Appl. Polymer Sci.*, **1**, 56 (1959).
65. H. Lee and K. Neville, *Epoxy Resins*, McGraw-Hill Book Co., New York, 1957.
66. I. Skeist, *Epoxy Resins*, Reinhold Publishing Co., New York, 1958.
67. S. S. Stivala and W. J. Powers, *Ind. Eng. Chem.*, **50**, 935 (1958).
68. S. O. Greenlee, U.S. Patents 2,456,408, Dec. 14 (1948); *C. A.*, **43**, 1996c (1949); 2,493,486, Jan. 3 (1950); *C. A.*, **44**, 2770b (1950).
69. H. K. Weiss, *Ind. Eng. Chem.*, **49**, 1089 (1957).
70. J. B. Rose, *J. Chem. Soc.*, **1956**, 542.
71. J. B. Rose, *J. Chem. Soc.*, **1956**, 546.
72. H. Meerwein, D. Delfs, and H. Morschel, *Angew. Chem.*, **72**, 927 (1960).
73. G. D. Jones, A. Langsjoen, M. M. C. Newmann, and J. Zomlefer, *J. Org. Chem.*, **9**, 125 (1944).
74. Y. Minoura, M. Takebayashi, and C. C. Price, *J. Am. Chem. Soc.*, **81**, 4689 (1959).
75. E. R. Lavagnino, R. L. Chauvette, W. N. Cannon, and E. C. Kornfeld, *J. Am. Chem. Soc.*, **82**, 2609 (1960).
76. M. S. Toy and C. C. Price, *J. Am. Chem. Soc.*, **82**, 2613 (1960).
77. W. Patnode and D. F. Wilcock, *J. Am. Chem. Soc.*, **68**, 358 (1946).
78. C. B. Hurd, *J. Am. Chem. Soc.*, **68**, 364 (1946).
79. E. L. Warrick, U.S. Patent 2,634,252 (1953).

8

SPECIAL
POLYMERIZATION
REACTIONS

There are several polymers and polymerization reactions which do not conveniently fit into the classification of condensation polymers or addition polymers. Such questions as what is the polymer structure, polymerization mechanism, polymer composition compared to monomer composition, and whether or not the same polymer can be made by a different reaction, lead to some unusual answers about the classification of the polymer. They may be initiated by cations, anions, free radicals, or by no apparent initiator. For this reason, these polymers and polymer-forming reactions are discussed separately.

8.1 H-ADDITION POLYMERIZATION

H-addition polymerization involves the addition of a molecule containing an active hydrogen across a double bond which may be either in the same molecule or in another molecule.[1]

$$CH_2{=}CH{-}R{-}X{-}H \longrightarrow {+}CH_2{-}CH_2{-}R{-}X{+}$$

$$CH_2{=}CH{-}R{-}CH{=}CH_2 + H{-}X{-}R'{-}X{-}H \longrightarrow$$

$${+}CH_2{-}CH_2{-}R{-}CH_2{-}CH_2{-}X{-}R'{-}X{+}$$

Acrylamide will undergo such a polymerization reaction to form nylon 3.[2,3] The reaction is catalyzed by bases such as sodium methoxide, sodium *t*-butoxide or sodium metal and the reaction takes place at 80–100°C. in pyridine, acetonitrile, and *t*-butyl alcohol with the alkoxide catalysts or dimethylformamide in the example of the sodium initiated polymerization. The resulting polyamide has a melting point of 325–340°C. and a molecular weight of about 80,000.

Initiation:

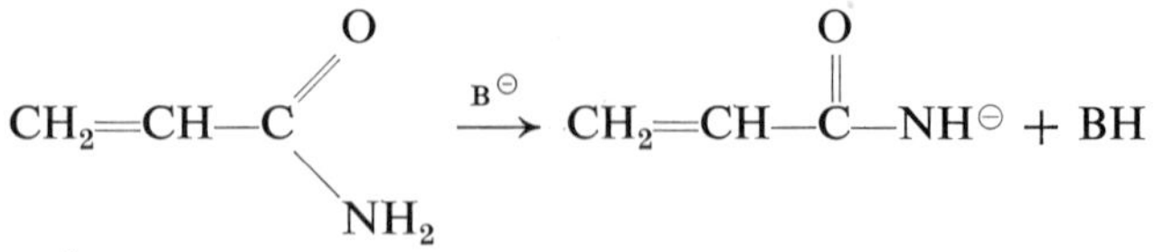

$$CH_2{=}CH{-}C\overset{O}{\underset{NH_2}{\diagup\diagdown}} \xrightarrow{B^{\ominus}} CH_2{=}CH{-}\overset{O}{\overset{\|}{C}}{-}NH^{\ominus} + BH$$

Propagation:

$$CH_2{=}CH{-}CONH^{\ominus} + CH_2{=}CHCONH_2 \longrightarrow$$
$$CH_2{=}CH{-}CONH{-}CH_2{-}\overset{\ominus}{C}H{-}CONH_2$$

$$CH_2{=}CH{-}CONH{-}CH_2{-}\overset{\ominus}{C}H{-}CONH_2 \longrightarrow$$
$$CH_2{=}CH{-}CONH{-}CH_2{-}CH_2{-}CONH^{\ominus}$$

or

$$\xrightarrow{CH_2{=}CH{-}CONH_2} CH_2{=}CH{-}CONH{-}CH_2{-}CH_2{-}CONH_2$$
$$+ CH_2{=}CH{-}CONH^{\ominus}$$

$$CH_2{=}CH{-}CONH{-}CH_2{-}CH_2{-}CONH^{\ominus}$$

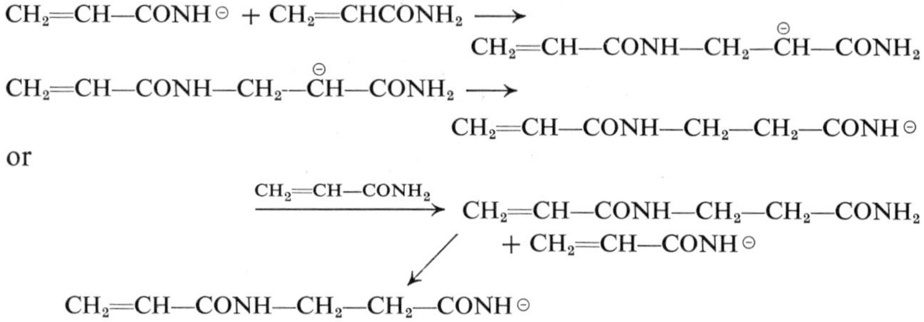

This same reaction type has been demonstrated with diacrylyl methane and ethanol amine.[4,5]

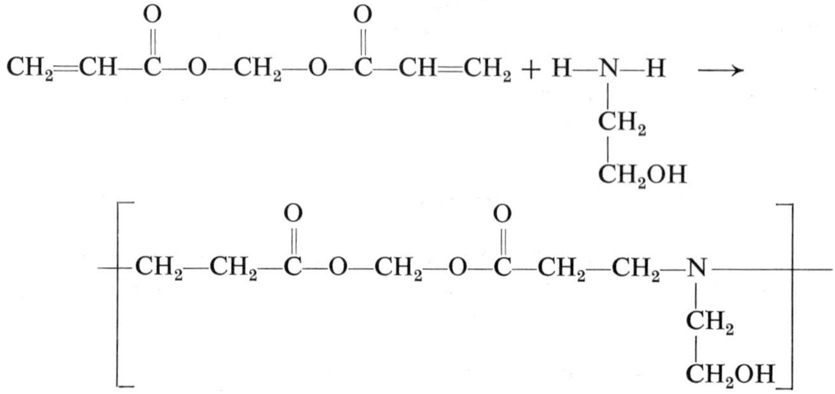

$$CH_2{=}CH{-}\overset{O}{\overset{\|}{C}}{-}O{-}CH_2{-}O{-}\overset{O}{\overset{\|}{C}}{-}CH{=}CH_2 + H{-}\underset{\underset{CH_2OH}{\overset{|}{CH_2}}}{\overset{|}{N}}{-}H \longrightarrow$$

$$\left[{-}CH_2{-}CH_2{-}\overset{O}{\overset{\|}{C}}{-}O{-}CH_2{-}O{-}\overset{O}{\overset{\|}{C}}{-}CH_2{-}CH_2{-}\underset{\underset{CH_2OH}{\overset{|}{CH_2}}}{\overset{|}{N}}{-}\right]$$

Thiols will add across double bonds in the presence of a free radical source, preferably in emulsion to yield polythioethers. The first examples of this polymerization involved a nonconjugated diolefin and a dithiol.[6,7,8]

Initiation:

$$R\cdot + HS{-}R'{-}SH \longrightarrow RH + HS{-}R{-}S\cdot$$

Propagation:

$$HS—R'—S· + CH_2=CH—R''—CH=CH_2 \longrightarrow$$
$$HS—R'—S—CH_2—\overset{·}{C}H—R''—CH=CH_2$$

$$HS—R'—S—CH_2—\overset{·}{C}H—R''—CH=CH_2 \xrightarrow{HS—R'—HS}$$
$$HS—R'—S—CH_2—CH_2—R''—CH=CH_2 + HS—R'—S·$$

or

$$\longrightarrow ·S—R'—S—CH_2—CH_2—R''—CH=CH_2$$

The reaction of biallyl, for example, with hexamethylene dithiol forms a polythioether in which there are six carbons separating sulfur units.

$$HS(CH_2)_6SH + CH_2=CH—CH_2—CH_2—CH=CH_2 \longrightarrow \{(CH_2)_6—S\}$$

The reaction proceeds rapidly initially to give a polymer with the indicated structure, containing mercaptyl end groups. As the reaction proceeds, the end groups are oxidized and the molecular weight of the polymer increases by the formation of disulfide links. The polymer shown has a melting point of 75°C. and an inherent viscosity of about 0.7.

When conjugated diolefins are employed the polymerization reaction will not take place. When the thiol group and the double bond are incorporated in the same molecule, as in allyl mercaptan, the free radical addition reaction will proceed.[2]

$$CH_2=CH—CH_2—SH \longrightarrow \{CH_2—CH_2—CH_2—S\}$$

Alcohols will also add to double bonds if the double bond is activated by other groups. The reaction of pentaerythritol with acrolein provides an acetal which bears two nonconjugated, active double bonds. Diols will now add across the double bonds to form a linear polyether.[9] If pentaerythritol is employed as the alcohol portion, a crosslinked resin is produced. See formula on next page.

The polymer can actually be formed in a one-step reaction if the correct ratio of acrolein and pentaerythritol are properly chosen.

8.2 POLYFORMALDEHYDE AND POLYALDEHYDES

Low molecular weight polymers of formaldehyde have been known for some time,[10] but only recent investigations have enabled the production of high molecular weight polymer. Evaporation of a formaldehyde solution or treatment of the solution with sulfuric acid yields low molecular weight polymer. If the formaldehyde solution is distilled in the presence of 2% sulfuric acid, a large amount of trioxane is passed over in the distillate.

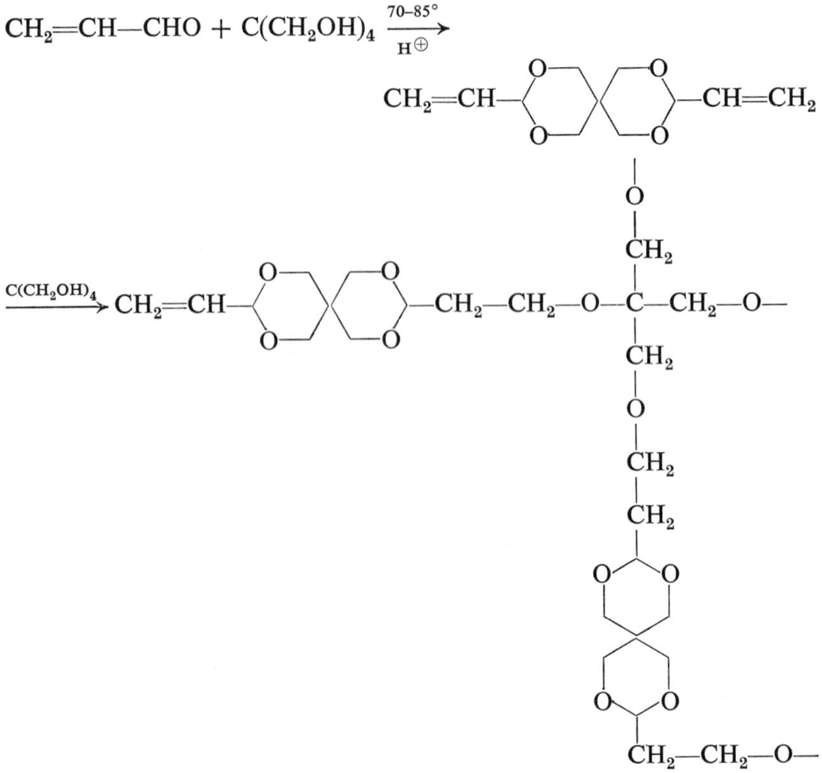

$$\text{CH}_2\text{=CH--CHO} + \text{C(CH}_2\text{OH)}_4 \xrightarrow[\text{H}^\oplus]{70\text{--}85^\circ}$$

The trimer, trioxane, which is a crystalline solid, can be polymerized in a ring-opening reaction by Lewis acid catalysts to a high molecular weight polyoxymethylene.[11] Antimony trifluoride is the most suitable catalyst, and the reaction takes place at 120–130°C. in bulk.

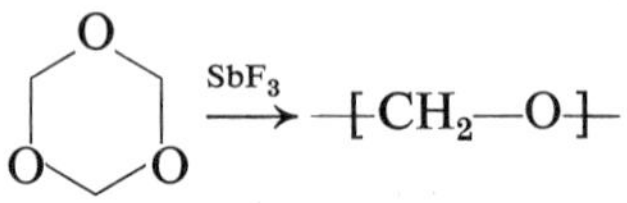

In order to obtain a high molecular weight polyformaldehyde, the monomer must be extremely pure.[12-14] Alkali precipitated formaldehyde (paraformaldehyde) is washed, dried, and pyrolyzed to the gaseous monomer at 150–160°C. The gaseous monomer is passed into a cold trap at −15°C. where some prepolymerization takes place thus further purifying the monomer by removing undesirable impurities. The monomer gas is passed into a reaction vessel containing dry heptane and a triphenyl phosphine catalyst. Tertiary amines will also initiate polymerization and diphenyl amine can be added as a stabilizer.

The polyoxymethylene thus formed is rendered stable by capping the hydroxyl end groups with acid anhydrides. The reaction mixture must maintain a low hydrogen ion concentration since the polymer depolymerizes and a sodium acetate buffer is added to prevent this.

$$\text{+CH}_2\text{—O}\text{+}_m \xrightarrow{160°} \text{CH}_2\text{=O} \xrightarrow{(C_6H_5)_3P} \text{H+CH}_2\text{—O+CH}_2\text{OH}$$

$$\xrightarrow[CH_3CO_2^\ominus]{(CH_3CO)_2O} \text{H+CH}_2\text{—O+CH}_2\text{OCOCH}_3$$

Polyformaldehyde is a tough, heat stable, highly crystalline polymer with an inherent viscosity of 2.0.[15] The polymer is insoluble in most solvents except phenols and can be oriented by cold drawing.

The polymerization of acetaldehyde has been described in which paraldehyde is decomposed by distillation and the monomer is passed onto activated alumina granules at $-70°C$.[16,17]

$$\text{CH}_3\text{CHO} \xrightarrow{Al_2O_3} \left[\begin{array}{c} \text{CH—O} \\ | \\ \text{CH}_3 \end{array}\right]_n$$

The polymer is produced in a 66% conversion and has a molecular weight of 400,000. As in the case of formaldehyde, the high molecular weight polymer is formed only from very pure monomer.

Acetaldehyde and other higher aldehydes are polymerized at low temperatures with organometallic catalysts such as triethyl aluminum, diethyl aluminum chloride, or dibutyl zinc to high molecular weight crystalline polymers.[18-22] In addition, aldehydes higher than acetaldehyde will polymerize under the influence of aluminum bromide, boronfluoride etherate, or ethyl aluminum dichloride.

$$\text{RCHO} \xrightarrow{R'M} \left[\begin{array}{c} \text{CH—O} \\ | \\ \text{R} \end{array}\right]$$

A 1:1 copolymer of acetone and dimethyl ketene can be produced by a butyl lithium catalyst at $-60°C$.[23] The polymerization reaction does not take place by the ring-opening reaction of the four-membered lactone, which is a product of the addition of ketene to acetone, since this lactone will not polymerize under the conditions of the reaction.

$$(CH_3)_2C\text{=}C\text{=}O + (CH_3)_2C\text{=}O \xrightarrow[BuLi]{-60°} \left[\begin{array}{ccc} \text{CH}_3 & \text{O} & \text{CH}_3 \\ | & \| & | \\ \text{C—} & \text{C—O—} & \text{C—} \\ | & & | \\ \text{CH}_3 & & \text{CH}_3 \end{array}\right]$$

The dimethyl ketene dimer itself will polymerize under the influence of an aluminum bromide catalyst to give the two types of polymer chains shown.[24]

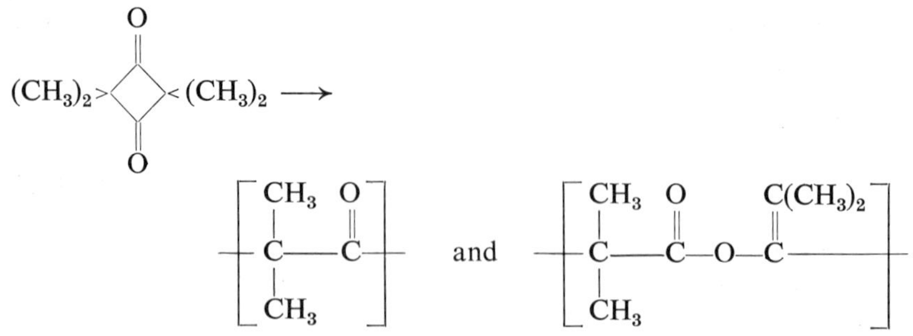

$$(CH_3)_2 >\!\!\!<\!\!\! > < (CH_3)_2 \longrightarrow$$

$$\left[\begin{array}{c} CH_3 \quad O \\ | \quad \quad \| \\ -C\!-\!C- \\ | \\ CH_3 \end{array}\right] \quad \text{and} \quad \left[\begin{array}{c} CH_3 \quad O \quad \quad C(CH_3)_2 \\ | \quad \quad \| \quad \quad | \\ -C\!-\!C\!-\!O\!-\!C- \\ | \\ CH_3 \end{array}\right]$$

Ketene and diketene are also polymerized by boron fluoride,[25] while ketene diacetal may be converted to polymer by cadmium chloride in a hydrocarbon solvent.[26]

Closely related to the polymerization of a ketene or a carbonyl is the polymerization of isocyanates through the nitrogen carbon double bond by sodium cyanide at low temperatures.[27,28] An inherent viscosity of poly-*n*-butylisocyanate as high as 15.7 has been obtained.

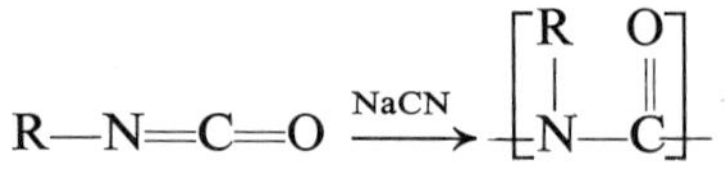

$$R\!-\!N\!=\!C\!=\!O \xrightarrow{\text{NaCN}} \left[\begin{array}{c} R \quad O \\ | \quad \| \\ N\!-\!C \end{array}\right]$$

8.3 DIELS-ALDER POLYMERS[29]

A polymerization reaction which utilizes a Diels-Alder propagation to produce high molecular weight polymer can proceed either by the reaction of a di-dienophile with a di-diene or by the self-reaction of a molecule which contains both a diene portion and a dienophile portion.

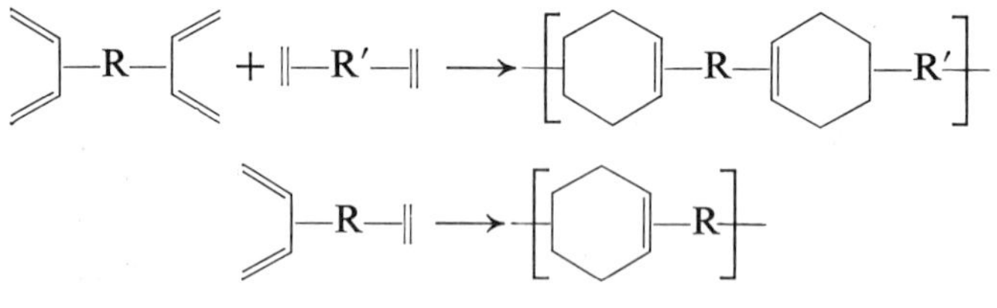

Such a polymerization reaction is catalyzed neither by ion or radical sources, has propagation kinetics and mechanism which are characteristic of condensation polymerization, but has a structure which cannot be considered characteristic of condensation polymers.

The simplest monomer containing both a diene and a dienophilic portion is 2-vinylbutadiene,[30] which polymerizes presumably by a series of Diels-Alder reactions. A series of bis-(cyclopentadienyl)

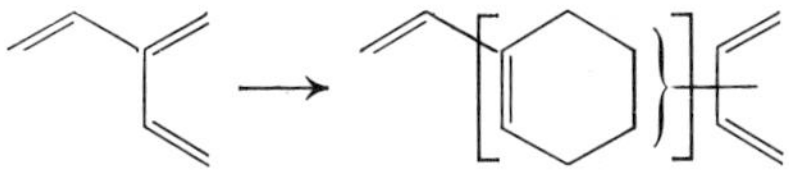

alkanes will give homopolymers since the cyclopentadienyl portion may act either as a diene or a dienophile.[31,32] The polymers are low molecular weight.

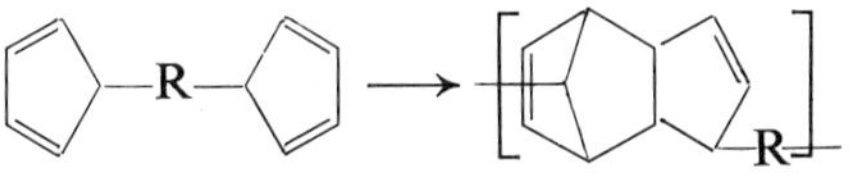

$$R = -(CH_2)_6-, \qquad -(CH_2)_9-, \qquad p-CH_2-C_6H_4-CH_2-$$

A unique method for a Diels-Alder polymerization with a diene-dienophilic monomer involves the formation of the diene end in the polymerization reaction mixture prior to polymerization.[32-34] The reaction makes use of the unstability of certain adducts of bis-maleimides. The reaction of a substituted cyclopentadieneone with a bis-maleimide produces an adduct which loses carbon monoxide at elevated temperatures to yield a diene-dienophilic monomer which is not isolated, but immediately polymerizes to form high molecular weight polymer.[32]

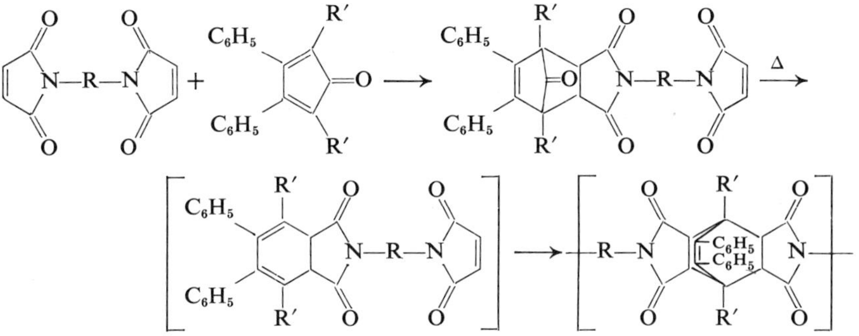

Reduced viscosities as high as 2.0 are obtained. Similar reactions can be carried out with the bis-maleimide and an α-pyrone[33] or a thiophene-1,1-dioxide[34] where carbon dioxide or sulfur dioxide are evolved, respectively, in diene-dienophile formation.

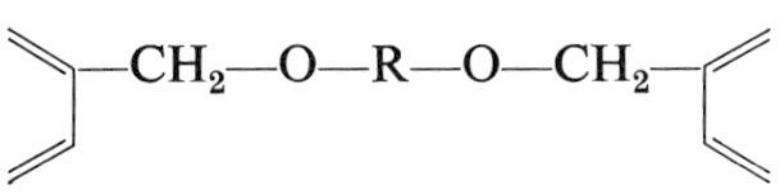

Di-dienes have been utilized in the copolymerization reactions with di-dienophiles. Bis-butadienes of the type shown form 1:1 copolymers with bis-maleimides or quinone.[30] The di-dienes, 1,8-diphenyloctatetraene, 1,5-di(9-anthryl)-1,4-pentadiene-3-one, and anthralazine afford Diels-Alder polymers with bis-maleimides.[35]

The bis-(cyclopentadienyl)alkanes serve as di-dienes in copolymerization reactions with bis-maleimides and quinone.[31,32]

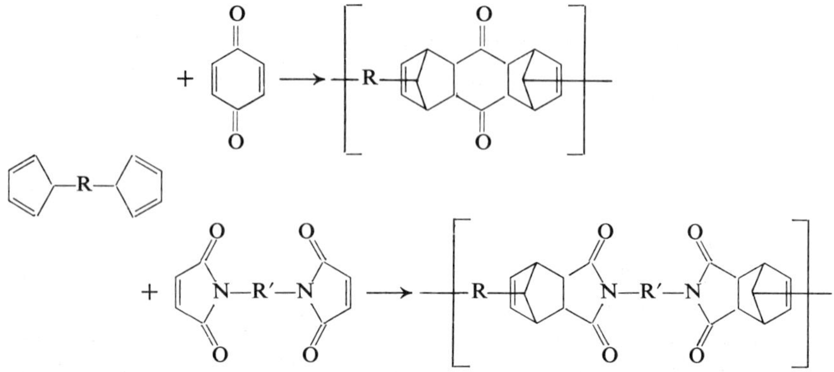

The monomer 2-vinylbutadiene serves as a di-diene since reaction of this monomer with a dienophile generates a new diene portion.[30] Its reaction with a bis-maleimide is illustrated.

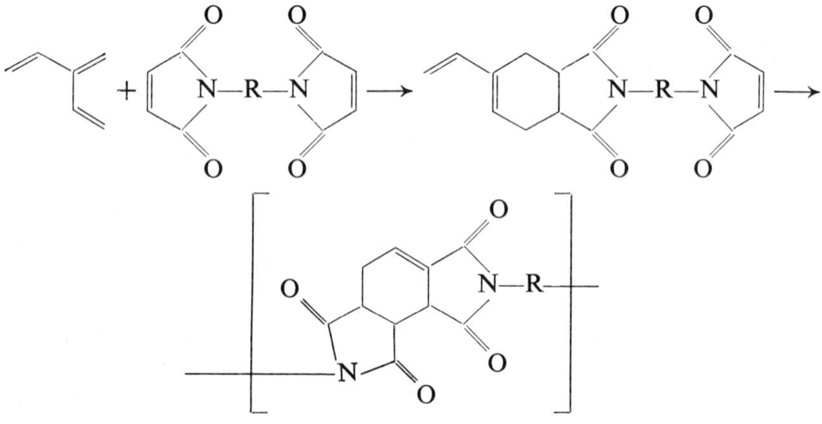

8.4 POLYPHENYLENE ETHERS

The preparation of polyphenylene ethers involves an oxidative free radical reaction, but the product polymer has the appearance of a condensation polymer.

High molecular weight aryl ethers have been prepared by the oxidation of 2,6-dialkyl-4-bromophenols by a ferricyanide oxidation.[36-38]

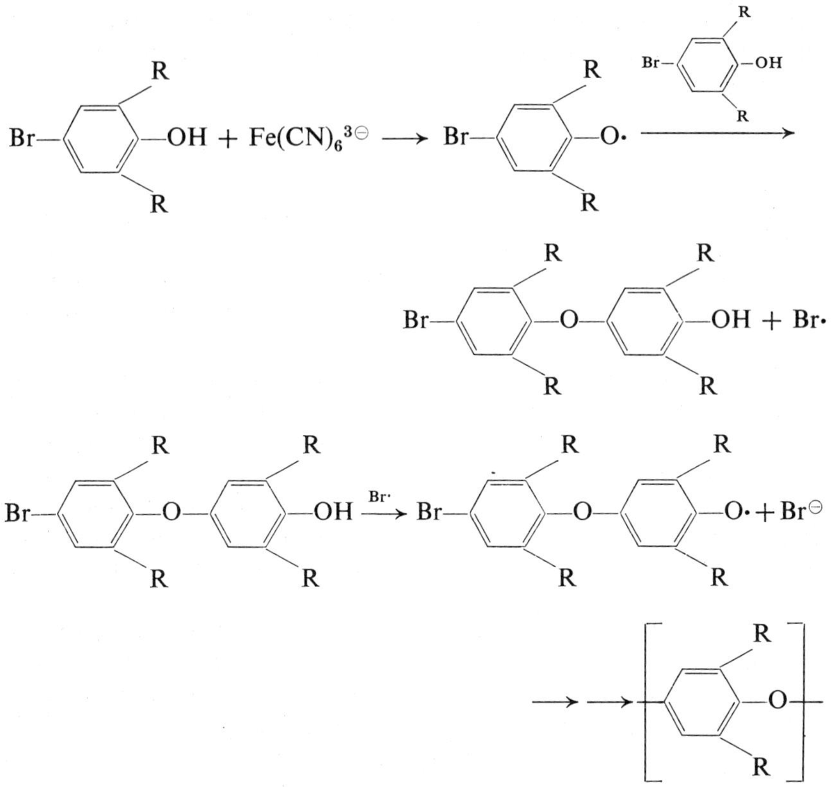

The air oxidation of a 2,6-dialkyl phenol which is unsubstituted in the 4-position will also yield polymer by the same oxidation mechanism.[39] In this reaction, an amine and a copper (I) redox catalyst are added to the reaction mixture. Large alkyl groups seriously hinder the polymer-forming reaction, but where the alkyl groups are methyl, molecular weights of 28,000 are observed.

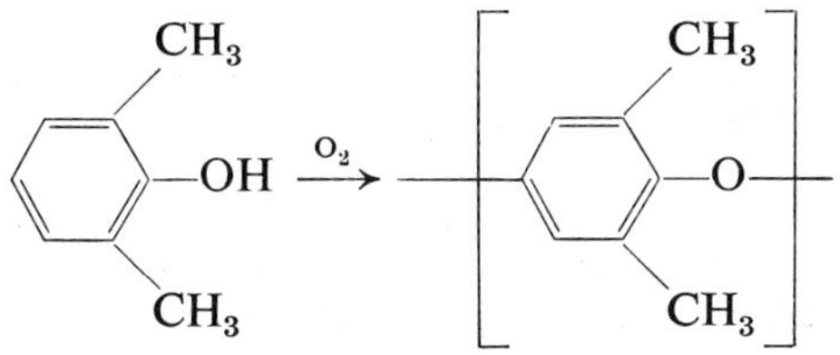

8.5   POLYMERIZATION OF DIAZOALKANES

The preparation of polymethylene by the decomposition of diazomethane was discovered in 1898.[40] The decomposition of lower members of primary diazoalkanes can in fact be utilized in the preparation of polyalkylidenes.

$$RCHN_2 \longrightarrow \left[\begin{matrix} R \\ | \\ CH \end{matrix} \right]_n + N_2$$

A variety of catalysts will effect this conversion to polymer and different mechanisms may be operating with the different catalyst systems.[41] Copper powder or copper salts,[42-45] gold or platinum,[44-46] boron fluoride,[47] and trimethyl borate[48] are a few of the catalysts which operate in solution for the polymerization.

The alkylidene polymers other than polymethylene are not obtained in as high a molecular weight range as polymethylene. Polymethylenes with molecular weights as high as 500,000 have been obtained. The polymer is very nearly linear, has no unsaturation, however, the polymers always contain small amounts of nitrogen. Its orderly structure is responsible for the high degree of crystallinity and a crystalline transition temperature of 132°C. Its physical properties are therefore very nearly the same as those of low pressure polyethylene (Sec. 9.1).

Hard amorphous glasses or crystalline isotactic polyalkylidine polymers can be prepared depending on the catalyst and conditions of the polymerization. Although copper powder seems to provide an amorphous polyethylidine, colloidal gold affords an isotactic polymer, $Tm = 195°C$.

Copolymers may be produced by the simultaneous decomposition of different diazoalkanes. Although the molecular weights of polyalkylidenes other than polymethylene are comparatively low, the molecular weights of alkylidene-methylene copolymers can be very high. This suggests steric interference may play a part in the homopolymerization of the higher diazoalkanes.

REFERENCES

1. C. E. Schildknecht, *Ind. Eng. Chem.*, **50**, 107 (1958).
2. D. S. Breslow, G. E. Hulse, and A. S. Matlack, *J. Am. Chem. Soc.*, **79**, 3760 (1957).
3. A. S. Matlack, U.S. Patent 2,672,480, March 16 (1954); *C. A.*, **47**, 3244e (1955).
4. Hercules Powder Company, British Patent 729,527, May 4 (1955); *Zentr.*, **127**, 5698 (1956).
5. G. E. Hulse, U.S. Patent 2,759,913, Aug. 21 (1956); *C. A.*, **50**, 17533a (1956).
6. C. S. Marvel and P. H. Aldrich, *J. Am. Chem. Soc.*, **72**, 1978 (1950).
7. C. S. Marvel and L. E. Olson, *J. Polymer Sci.*, **26**, 23 (1957).

8. C. S. Marvel, C. W. Hinman, and H. K. Inskip, *J. Am. Chem. Soc.*, **75**, 1997 (1953).
9. H. Schulz and H. Wagner, *Angew. Chem.*, **62**, 105 (1950).
10. W. Kern, H. Chedron, V. Jaacks, H. Diebig, A. Giefer, L. Hohr, and A. Wildenau, *Angew. Chem.*, **73**, 177 (1961).
11. A. K. Schneider, U.S. Patent 2,795,571, June 11, (1957); *C. A.*, **51**, 18699e (1957).
12. C. E. Schweitzer, R. N. McDonald, and J. O. Punderson, *J. Appl. Polymer Sci.*, **1**, 158 (1959).
13. R. N. McDonald, U.S. Patent 2,768,944 (1956); *C. A.*, **51**, 2744h (1957); British Patent 742,135, Dec. 21 (1955); *C. A.*, **50**, 11054a (1956).
14. E. I. du Pont de Nemours and Co., British Patent 766,629, Jan. 23, (1957); *C. A.*, **51**, 10126c (1957).
15. R. G. Alsup, J. O. Punderson, and G. F. Leverett, *J. Appl. Polymer Sci.*, **1**, 185 (1959).
16. J. Furukawa, T. Saegusa, T. Tsuruta, H. Fujii, and T. Tatano, *J. Polymer Sci.*, **36**, 546 (1959).
17. J. Furukawa, T. Saegusa, T. Tsuruta, H. Fujii, A. Kawasaki, and T. Tatano, *Makromol. Chem.*, **33**, 32 (1959).
18. J. Furukawa, T. Saegusa, H. Fujii, A. Kawasaki, H. Imai, and Y. Fujii, *Makromol. Chem.*, **37**, 149 (1960).
19. G. Natta, G. Mazzanti, P. Corradini, and I. W. Bassi, *Makromol. Chem.*, **37**, 156 (1960).
20. H. Fujii, J. Furukawa, T. Saegusa, and A. Kawasaki, *Makromol. Chem.*, **40**, 226 (1960).
21. J. Furukawa, T. Saegusa, and H. Fujii, *Makromol. Chem.*, **44–46**, 398 (1961).
22. O. Vogl, *J. Polymer Sci.*, **46**, 261 (1960).
23. G. Natta, G. Mazzanti, G. Pregaglia, and M. Binaghi, *J. Am. Chem. Soc.*, **82**, 5511 (1960).
24. G. Natta, G. Mazzanti, G. Pregaglia, M. Binaghi, and M. Peraldo, *J. Am. Chem. Soc.*, **82**, 4742 (1960); *Makromol. Chem.*, **44–46**, 537 (1961).
25. R. Oda, S. Munemiya, and M. Okano, *Makromol. Chem.*, **48**, 149 (1961).
26. J. Lal, *J. Polymer Sci.*, **41**, 399 (1959).
27. V. E. Shashoua, *J. Am. Chem. Soc.*, **81**, 3156 (1959).
28. V. E. Shashoua, W. Sweeny, and R. F. Tietz, *J. Am. Chem. Soc.*, **82**, 866 (1956).
29. J. K. Stille, *Fortsch. Hochpolymeren Forsch.*, **3**, 48 (1961).
30. W. J. Bailey, J. Economy, and M. E. Hermes, Preprints of papers presented at the Division of Polymer Chemistry, 138th Meeting of the A. C. S., New York, 1960.
31. J. K. Stille and L. Plummer, Abstracts of Papers Presented at the 136th Meeting of the A. C. S., Atlantic City (1959), p. 3T; J. K. Stille and L. Plummer, *J. Org. Chem.*, **26**, 4026 (1961).
32. E. A. Kraimen, U.S. Patent 2,890,206, June 9 (1959); *C. A.*, **53**, 17572e (1959).
33. E. A. Kraimen, U.S. Patent 2,890,207, June 9 (1959); *C. A.*, **53**, 17572h (1959).
34. S. W. Chow and J. M. Whelan, Jr., U.S. Patent 2,971,944, Feb. 14 (1961).
35. J. S. Meek, P. A. Argabright, and R. D. Stacy, Abstracts of papers presented at the 134th Meeting of the A.C.S., Chicago (1958), p. 23p.
36. G. Staffin and C. C. Price, *Rubber World*, **139**, 408 (1958).
37. G. D. Staffin and C. C. Price, *J. Am. Chem. Soc.*, **82**, 3632 (1960).
38. C. J. Kurian and C. C. Price, *J. Polymer Sci.*, **49**, 267 (1961).
39. A. S. Hay, H. S. Blanchard, G. E. Endres, and J. W. Eustance, *J. Am. Chem. Soc.*, **81**, 6335 (1959).
40. H. von Pechmann, *Ber.*, **31**, 2643 (1898).

41. C. E. H. Bawn, S. Ledwith, and P. Matthies, *J. Polymer Sci.*, **34,** 93 (1959).

42. G. D. Buckley, L. H. Cross, and N. H. Ray, *J. Chem. Soc.*, **1950,** 2714.

43. C. E. H. Bawn and T. B. Rhodes, *Trans. Faraday Soc.*, **50,** 934 (1954).

44. C. E. H. Bawn and A. Ledwith, *Chem. and Ind.*, 1180 (1957).

45. A. C. Nasini, L. Trossavelli, and G. Saini, *Makromol. Chem.*, **44–46,** 550 (1961).

46. A. Ledwith, *Chem. and Ind.*, 1310 (1956).

47. C. E. H. Bawn, S. Ledwith, and P. Matthies, *J. Polymer Sci.*, **33,** 21 (1958).

48. G. D. Buckley and N. H. Ray, *J. Chem. Soc.*, **1952,** 3701.

9

VINYL
ADDITION
POLYMERS

9.1 POLYETHYLENE[1-6]

High pressure process. Solid, high molecular weight polyethylene was first prepared by Fawcett and Gibson in 1933 at the laboratories of Imperial Chemical Industries Ltd. as a result of an experiment designed to obtain styrene from benzene and ethylene at high pressure. This method for polymerization, the high pressure process, expanded rapidly during World War II and several plants for the manufacture of polyethylene by the high pressure method were established in the United States as well. In 1952, several companies in the United States and Karl Ziegler in Germany discovered methods for the polymerization of ethylene which avoided high pressures and temperatures and produced a product of somewhat different physical properties. This low pressure process now afforded a second method for the production of polyethylene.

The free radical polymerization of ethylene was made possible through the development of high pressure equipment. Above 1000 atm., there is no longer a straight line relationship between pressure and density for ethylene. The calculated maximum density of packed ethylene molecules is 0.28 g./cc., and this density is obtained below 300 atm. at 150°C. This proximity of ethylene molecules is necessary for polymerization where the propagation must continue to high molecular weight polymer. There must be a high enough concentration of ethylene around the growing chain for an effective propagation, and this can be obtained by high pressures (Fig. 9.1).

In the high pressure process, small amounts of oxygen (0.01–5%) are compressed with ethylene to at least 500 atm. at a temperature of 200°C.

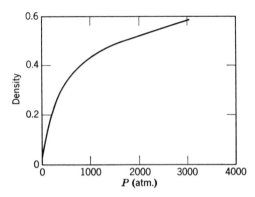

Fig. 9.1. Ethylene density-pressure relationship.[4]

or above. Pressure-temperature curves in ethylene polymerization show an inflection at about 160° and a maximum pressure at 245°C. and 1600 kg./cm.[2] which seems to indicate the beginning of polymerization.

At 2000 atm. at 165°C., the allowable oxygen content is 0.075%. Past this limit an explosive decomposition occurs to yield carbon, methane, and hydrogen. The influence of oxygen per cent on the conversion to polyethylene is marked, and this varies not only with reaction pressure but also temperature. For any given oxygen content, the yield increases and the molecular weight decreases as the temperature rises. Increased reaction pressure at any given oxygen content increases the conversion of ethylene to polymer. At constant temperature and catalyst concentration, the molecular weight increases at increasing pressures.

Ethylene molecules, under such high pressures that have been found necessary for polymerization, is much like a liquid with respect to density but is much above its critical temperature. The oxygen present is probably converted to a peroxide of ethylene which supplies the free radical source. The higher temperatures which are required are apparently necessary in order that the peroxide decompose rapidly enough.

The optimum conditions appear to be 1500 atm., 0.03–0.10% oxygen, and temperatures of 190–210°C.

$$n\mathrm{CH_2{=}CH_2} \xrightarrow[\text{190–210°C.}]{\text{O}_2,\ 1500\ \text{atm.}} \mathrm{{\bf[}CH_2{-}CH_2{\bf]}}_n$$

A typical polymerization process by the high pressure method involves either a tubular reactor or a high pressure tower and the unreacted ethylene is recycled. The high pressures and temperatures made this an extremely dangerous process at least in the early work in this field. The ethylene charged must be a high purity grade, since certain impurities would react with the ethylene under the high temperature and pressure conditions to give polymers with varied properties.

A variety of dilutents and other free radical initiators have been described, but the processes are basically the same. Water is a favorite solvent, and under the high pressure conditions, essentially a solution polymerization can take place in which benzoyl peroxide may be the initiator. The solvents have the advantage that heat is dissipated more rapidly and in general the reaction temperatures and pressures need not be quite so high.

Low pressure process. In the period 1950–1955 there were developed for industrial use a series of catalyst systems which allowed the polymerization of ethylene at low pressure and temperature. These low pressure catalysts (Chapter 5) are complex metal systems of several types. In Germany, Karl Ziegler introduced catalysts composed of a reducing portion, usually an aluminum alkyl such as aluminum triethyl or aluminum triisobutyl and a titanium halide such as titanium tetrachloride. In the U.S. two catalyst systems were simultaneously developed. The Phillips Petroleum Company's chromium oxide on a silica-alumina support requires moderate temperatures and a pressure sufficient to keep the ethylene in a hydrocarbon solvent. The Standard Oil of Indiana process uses reduced molybdenum oxide on a silica-alumina support.

Polymerization with these systems requires a solvent and in practical application enough pressure to ensure the full utilization of the ethylene. Either batch or flow type reactors are employed. The unique feature of these low pressure systems is that the ethylene is absorbed in high concentrations on the surface of the complex metal catalyst, thus allowing an efficient propagation reaction.

A typical Ziegler batch type polymerization would involve an aluminum triisobutyl-titanium tetrachloride catalyst, a hydrocarbon solvent, and 100 p.s.i. of ethylene at 60–70°C. A supported chromia slurry-type continuous operation is run at 400–500 p.s.i. and ethylene is pumped into the stirred catalyst suspension. The catalyst is continually added and the ethylene and solvent flashed off the separated slurry and recycled leaving the solid polyethylene. A typical flow type reactor requires a solvent-ethylene feed under pressure in the range of 1000 p.s.i. at 200°C. At the end of the tube, the solvent and unreacted ethylene are removed and recycled. These operating temperatures keep the polymer in solution until the end of the run.

Structure and properties of polyethylene. The conditions of preparation of polyethylene determine to a large degree the structure and thus the properties of polyethylene. Polyethylene prepared by the high pressure

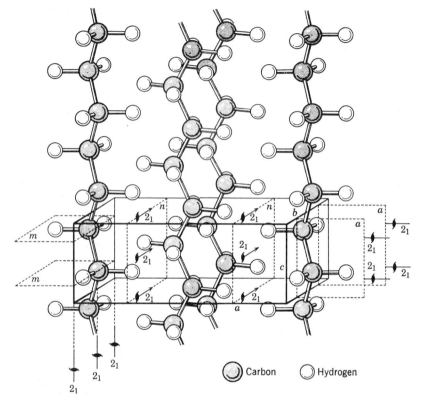

Fig. 9.2. Crystalline polyethylene.[5]

process contains both long and short chain branching (Chapter 4) which can be detected by infrared techniques. Due to this branching, high pressure polyethylene is less crystalline than that produced by the low pressure processes. A simple linear structure is present almost exclusively in the low pressure polyethylene while the high pressure polyethylene has its linear structure interrupted by branching. The regular structure is supported by the fact that even though polyethylene is non-polar, it is a highly crystalline plastic (Fig. 9.2). Indeed low pressure polyethylene has been grown in single crystals, while branching in high pressure polyethylene accounts for interruption in the crystal lattice and the lesser degree of crystallinity. In addition to the small amount of unsaturation which appears in high pressure polyethylene, carbonyl groups can be detected. Polyethylene can be cold-drawn but this does not greatly affect the total amount of crystallinity.

The two types of polyethylene have somewhat different properties because of their differences in structure, the impurities which may remain in* the polymer, and their molecular weights. In general, low pressure polyethylene is more crystalline and thus has a higher melting point, density, stiffness and hardness combined with a lower elongation, impact strength, deformation under load and brittleness temperature than high pressure product (Table 9.1). Most low pressure polyethylene has a broad molecular weight distribution.

TABLE 9.1
Physical properties of polyethylene

Property	High Pressure Polyethylene	Typical Low Pressure Ethylene
Molecular weight	22,000–25,000	as low as 20,000, as high as 3,000,000
Melting point	111°C.	124–134°C.
Per cent crystallinity	60%	100% (usually 90–95%)
Density	0.92	0.95–0.97
Tensile strength at yield (p.s.i.)	1800–2000	3500–4500
Per cent elongation	600	100
Dielectric constant	2.3	2.3
Methyl groups/1000 carbon atoms	21.5	3–1.5

Polyethylene is inert to most solvents below 50°C. but is dissolved by chlorinated hydrocarbons above this temperature. It is inert to most chemicals such as alkali and acid, but oxidizing acids will attack it.

The ease with which polyethylene can be molded, blown and extruded lends itself to a wide variety of uses. During World War II, polyethylene was employed almost exclusively for electrical insulation on cables, wires and other electrical parts. The nonpolar nature of the polymer, its chemical inertness, adhesive property and flexibility are ideally suited for this purpose.

Shortly after World War II, polyethylene found wide use as a packaging material. Today most of the polyethylene produced is sold as a film. The film can be made either by slit extrusion or by blowing an extruded tube above the melting point. Its low density, high tear strength, and high flexibility as well as the low permeability of water vapor (but suitable permeability to other atmospheric gases) are some of the properties which make it an excellent packaging material.

Polyethylene can be molded or extruded into pipe, containers or other objects for which there is a need for flexibility and chemical inertness. Low pressure polyethylene has a high enough melting point so that it may be sterilized without losing its shape.

Polyethylene can be modified with a variety of after treatments. High energy radiation degrades the material somewhat but also serves to cross link it. Material thus treated gains dimensional stability, has decreased solubility in organic solvents, a high melting point and decreased permeability to gases. The properties of irradiated linear polyethylene depend on the physical state during irradiation. Polyethylene irradiated in the melt, for example, retains its amorphous character after crosslinking.[7]

9.2 POLYPROPYLENE AND OTHER 1-OLEFINS[6,8]

Polypropylene has received little attention until recent years when a large supply of high grade propylene became available and low pressure processes were developed for polymerization. Other α-olefins are likewise polymerized but have not received the attention propylene has, partly because of the cost and availability.

The polymer obtained from the polymerization of propylene with various complex metal catalysts may vary in its tactic order and thus its crystallinity. Polypropylene obtained from such catalysts is usually highly crystalline due to its isotactic character. Crystalline isotactic polypropylene has an identity period of 6.5 A., which can be accounted for by a helical configuration for the polymer chain in which each monomer unit is displaced 120° in the helix from the previous one (Fig. 9.3). Other poly(1-olefins) prepared by the stereospecific catalysts likewise are isotactic and have a helical configuration to the chain with an increasing number of monomers per identity period the higher the olefin.

Isotactic polypropylene has a crystalline melting point of 176°C. and a density of 0.92. The densities and melting points of the other straight chain 1-olefins are correspondingly lower (Chapter 3). The mechanical properties of polypropylene depend on the degree of crystallinity, molecular weight and molecular weight distribution. Polypropylene is marketed by several manufacturers as a fiber and it compares favorably with some other fibers in this respect. Polypropylene with a molecular weight 40,000–50,000 corresponds to nylon with a molecular weight of 10,000–20,000 with respect to fiber properties.

Fig. 9.3. Isotactic polypropylene.[9]

9.3   POLYISOBUTYLENE[1]

Isobutylene is polymerized effectively only by cationic catalysts at low temperatures. Some of the aspects of cationic polymerization reactions have been discussed previously (Chapter 5), and the mechanism of isobutylene polymerization is a classic example of cationic polymerization. There are several characteristic features of a cationic isobutylene polymerization which will yield high molecular weight polymers. Low polymerization temperatures and low boiling dilutents are necessary. The reaction is characterized by its highly exothermic character, rapid reaction, and sensitivity not only to catalyst type and concentration but also to various other impurities.

Isobutylene is obtained in a mixture from a cracking process of certain petroleum fractions. Isobutylene is removed from the other olefin cracking products by a sulfuric wash from which it can be regenerated.

Boron fluoride has been extensively employed as a polymerization catalyst for isobutylene. The pure monomer can be polymerized by this catalyst at temperatures of −80°C. or lower, but a low boiling dilutent is usually employed. Pentane, ethylene, propylene, ethylene dichloride, carbon disulfide, ethane, methyl chloride, and ethyl chloride are all suitable solvent dilutents which at the low temperatures help dissipate the heat of reaction. The amount of dilutent is important in the attainment of the highest molecular weight polymer which may be well over a million.

$$CH_2{=}\underset{\underset{CH_3}{|}}{\overset{\overset{CH_3}{|}}{C}} \quad \xrightarrow[\substack{-80°C.\ to\\-100°C.}]{BF_3} \quad {-}\!\left[CH_2{-}\underset{\underset{CH_3}{|}}{\overset{\overset{CH_3}{|}}{C}}\right]\!{-}$$

The industrial polymerization of isobutylene (Vistanex) can be carried out in several ways. Batches can be prepared by the boron fluoride catalyzed polymerization of isobutylene in ethylene at −100°C. with approximately a 1:3 ratio of monomer to dilutent. In a continuous process, an isobutylene-ethylene mixture and an ethylene-boron fluoride mixture are mixed on a steel belt where the polymerization temperature is maintained by the boiling ethylene dilutent.

The polyisobutylene cannot be cured to give a suitable rubber since the polymer has no sites available for crosslinking. For this reason, isobutylene is copolymerized with small amounts of isoprene and most of the isobutylene polymerized is an isobutylene-isoprene copolymer, Butyl rubber. Several other conjugated dienes will enter into the copolymerization reaction and these copolymer products yield nontacky vulcanizates.

Larger amounts of isoprene (5% or greater) inhibit the polymerization of isobutylene so that the amount of isoprene is usually limited to 2% or less. Some dienes such as butadiene more difficultly enter into the copolymerization reaction and higher initial feeds must be employed.

On an industrial scale, continuous processes are employed in the polymerization of isobutylene with isoprene. A typical polymerization requires 1.5% isoprene, 98.5% isobutylene, and a three-fold volume of methyl chloride at −100°C. Aluminum chloride in methyl chloride is added to the mixture at regular intervals, and the polymer formed at each interval is removed before the introduction of fresh catalyst.

Polyisobutylene is amorphous with a coiled or folded chain and shows a crystalline structure only when stretched almost to its break point. The identity period is 18.6 A. which suggests a helical structure in a head-to-tail arrangement with eight monomer units for each 360°. The isobutylene-isoprene copolymer, Butyl rubber, contains the isoprene units along the chain backbone in a 1,4-structure.

Polyisobutylene and its copolymer with isoprene are soluble in aliphatic and aromatic hydrocarbons at room temperature. Vistanex or Oppanol B polyisobutylenes are prepared in varying molecular weight samples from 15,000 where the polymer is a sticky liquid to 50,000 where the polymer is an adhesive semisolid to 200,000 and a rubbery polymer. They have a low dielectric constant and are resistant to most chemicals. The rubbery polymer is flexible even at −50°C. but they are not resistant to cold flow, little improvement in tensile strength is noted with a carbon black reinforcement, and there is little bounce at room temperatures.

Butyl rubber which is manufactured with an isobutylene-isoprene ratio of 98:2 and has a molecular weight in the 40,000–80,000 range also has a low resilience at room temperature but is less tacky than pure polyisobutylene of the same molecular weight.

TABLE 9.2
Butyl rubber

	Unvulcanized	Vulcanized
Density	0.92	0.93
Tg	−67°C. to −73°C.	
% elongation		750–950
Tensile strength, kg./cm.^{2}		180–210
% rebound		8

Vistanex, Oppanol B, and other polyisobutylenes are used primarily as adhesives where their stickiness and softness is actually employed to increase the viscosity of lubricating oils. Other uses include paper coatings and electrical insulations.

Almost all of the tire inner tubes are presently made from Butyl rubber. Vulcanized Butyl rubber is superior to natural rubber in aging with oxygen, in permanent set, and in its impermeability to air. Carbon blacks do not increase greatly the tensile strength of Butyl rubber but the vulcanized Butyl has a greater flex resistance than natural rubber. For these reasons, in addition to the fact that Butyl rubber has good extrusion properties and tear resistance, it makes an excellent inner tube. It has not been widely used for tire tread or carcass stock since it has a high heat build up.

9.4 POLYSTYRENE[1,10,11]

The greatest amount of benzene goes to the manufacture of styrene. In the commercial production of styrene, ethylene is passed into a tower containing benzene and an aluminum chloride catalyst to yield ethyl benzene. The ethyl benzene produced is subjected to a vapor phase dehydrogenation over an alumina catalyst at 600°C.

$$\bigcirc + CH_2{=}CH_2 \xrightarrow[90°]{AlCl_3} \bigcirc{-}CH_2{-}CH_3 \xrightarrow[600°]{Al_2O_3}$$

$$\bigcirc{-}CH{=}CH_2 + H_2$$

Nearly all of the manufactured styrene is converted to polymer although a relatively small proportion is polymerized to the polystyrene homopolymer. The ability of styrene to copolymerize with most other monomers has pushed most of its consumption to the formation of copolymers, especially with butadiene (Chapter 11) where a synthetic elastomer, GRS, results.

$$CH{=}CH_2 \longrightarrow \left[{-}CH{-}CH_2{-} \right]$$

Styrene may be polymerized by free radical initiators in several ways. In bulk polymerizations, heat is all that is usually necessary although the polymerization at 100°C. is slow and free radical initiators speed up the reaction. The polymerization may be finished off at higher temperatures, but initial high temperatures leave bubbles and the reaction may become violent. The heat buildup in large bulk polymerizations becomes a serious problem and the styrene is usually polymerized in layers where large castings are desired.

Solution polymerization solves the heat build up problem, but chain transfer with the solvent may become serious and the last traces of the solvent are difficult to remove from the polymer. Emulsion systems effect a rapid conversion with good dissipation of heat but the optical clarity of the product is poor and the polymer is difficultly precipitated from the emulsion system. Suspension polymerization with a dispersing agent has the advantages of emulsion polymerization but the product again has poor optical properties due to the impurities picked up by the polymer. These last three mentioned methods utilize free radical initiators.

Both cationic catalysts such as boron fluoride, stannic chloride, aluminum chloride and titanium tetrachloride and anionic catalysts will bring about styrene polymerization (Chapter 5). Styrene is readily polymerized by Ziegler-type catalyst and the resulting stereospecific polymer has physical properties which are different than the properties of free radically polymerized styrene.[12]

On a commercial scale, styrene can be polymerized in bulk in a batch process. The initial polymerization stages are carried out at lower temperatures until a critical conversion (30–60%) in which the heat of polymerization is most serious is passed and a conversion of 80–90% is obtained. Heating is continued at elevated temperatures, 150–200°C., until a 95% or better conversion is reached.

In continuous processes, a polymer syrup is formed at low temperatures (80–90°C.) over a long period of time and then passed through a tube or tower with successive heating zones which raise the temperature during a slow pass to 180°C. The polymer at the end of the pass is either extruded and broken into pellets or squirted through a vacuum chamber to remove unreacted monomer before breaking it up. None of these processes use an added free radical initiator since the initiators tend to discolor the polystyrene, increase chain branching, and give a wider molecular weight range. Polymers formed by these methods have molecular weights of nearly 200,000.

Styrene polymerizes to give a head to tail sequence in the polymer chain. Polymer obtained by free radical initiation is atactic in steric order and in general any homogeneous polymerization where the catalyst is soluble in the polymerization medium will not afford a highly stereoregular polymer.

Branching occurs especially when the polymer is prepared at high temperatures and high initiator concentrations. Polystyrene prepared from Ziegler-type catalysts has no branching and is isotactic. The isotactic chain has a helical configuration in which there are three monomer units per identity period[8] (Fig. 9.4). Isotactic polystyrene has about 40% crystallinity in the solid state and is less soluble in most solvents than atactic polystyrene. The glass transition temperature for atactic

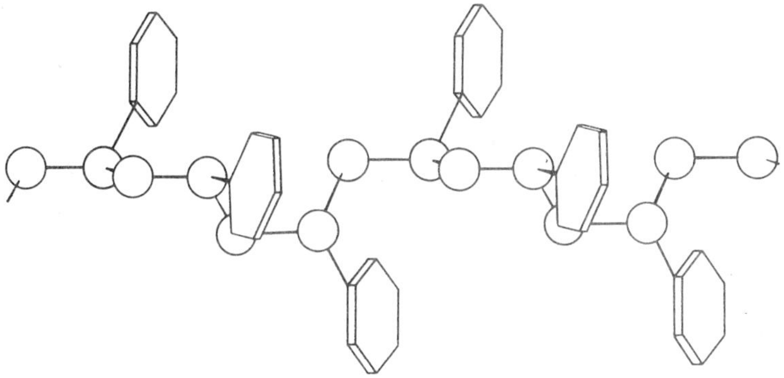

Fig. 9.4. Isotactic polystyrene.[8]

polystyrene is near 85°C. while isotactic polystyrene shows a crystalline melting point at 230°C.

This low glass transition temperature allows polystyrene to be molded quite easily by injection techniques. Most injection moldings are carried out at 190–260°C. Polystyrene has good stability flow characteristics, electrical properties, and excellent clarity. It is rather brittle, however, and has poor impact strength. Internal molding strains make polystyrene craze readily although this can be reduced by annealing.

TABLE 9.3
Physical properties of polystyrene

Specific gravity	1.05–1.07
Index of refraction	1.60
Impact strength, ft.-lb./in.	0.25–0.6
Tensile strength, p.s.i.	5000–8000
Dielectric constant	2.4–2.6

Polystyrene is attacked by reagents which will substitute on an aromatic nucleus by electrophilic substitution. For example, halogens, nitric acid, and sulfuric acid react readily.

Polystyrene finds use as molded objects such as combs, toys, novelties, brush handles, kitchen utensiles, refrigerator parts, and many industrial parts, to mention a few. Polystyrene foam is an effective insulator and is used in novelties especially for advertising. Molded polystyrene's clarity and high refractive index are properties which allow its use as plastic optical pieces. The low dielectric constant and ease of polymerization (mild) make it suited for imbedding electrical parts by polymerization in the mold.

The reaction of polystyrene with chlorosulfonic acid or concentrated sulfuric acid provides the method for sulfonating polystyrene which has been crosslinked in the suspension polymerization process with divinyl benzene. The insoluble polystyrene beads are sulfonated to the extent of 1–1.77 sulfonic acid groups per ring to give cationic exchange resins. Dowex, an exchange resin of this type, is used in water softeners.

Anion exchange resins are prepared from crosslinked polystyrene by chloromethylating the polymer with chloromethyl methyl ether and treating the product with a tertiary amine to obtain the quaternary ammonium salt.

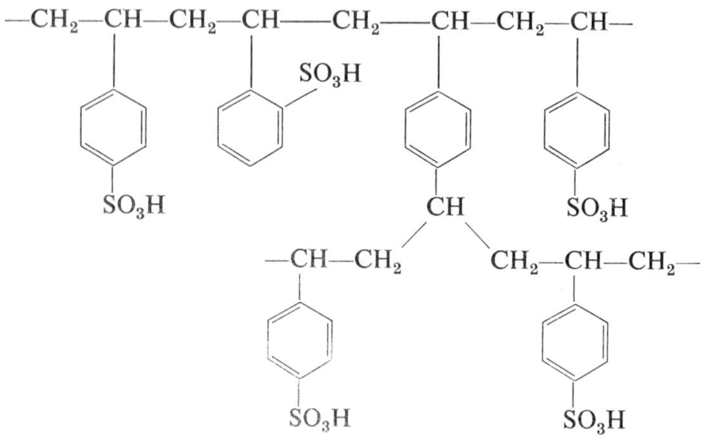

Cation exchange resin

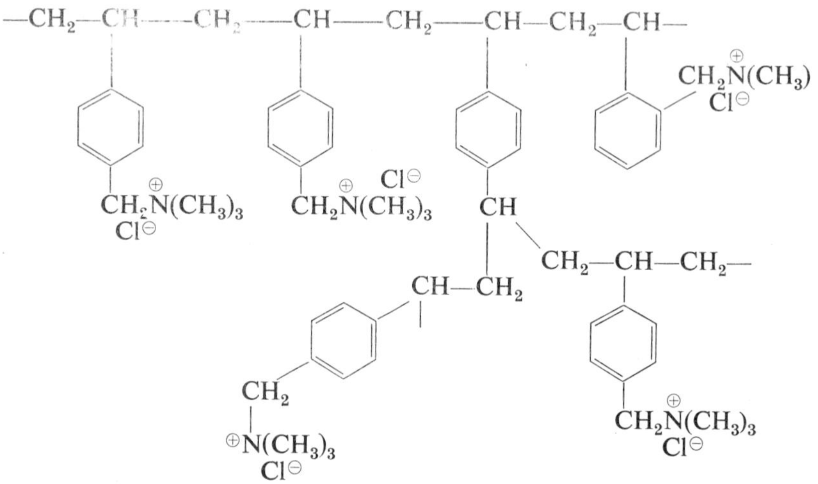

Anion exchange resin

9.5 α-METHYL STYRENE AND OTHER STYRENE DERIVATIVES

The commercial supply of α-methyl styrene is obtained from the reaction of propylene with benzene in a Friedel-Crafts alkylation followed by dehydrogenation under much the same conditions as are employed for the preparation of styrene.

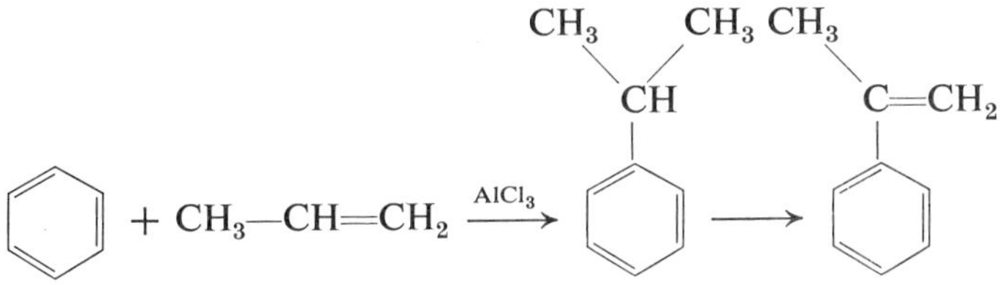

α-Methyl styrene is not readily polymerized by free radical initiators, heat, or ultraviolet light (Chapter 5). Instead, typical cationic systems provide a rapid polymerization to high molecular weight polymer. The best polymerization conditions require low temperatures (-90 to $-130°C.$), a low boiling solvent such as ethyl chloride or carbon disulfide and the Lewis acid catalyst aluminum chloride.[13] Low temperatures ($-130°C.$) and an ethyl chloride solvent provide polymer of molecular weight 60,000 but carbon disulfide appears to be a better solvent since higher molecular weights are obtained at comparable temperatures.

Poly(α-methyl styrene) prepared in this manner has a narrow molecular weight distribution. It is a noncrystalline brittle polymer and is clear like polystyrene.

Many styrene-like monomers have been prepared and successfully polymerized. These may be divided into several classes, and the polymerizability as well as the properties of the polymer can be greatly altered by substituent groups. Ring alkylated styrenes or α-methyl styrenes, halogenated styrenes, and styrenes containing highly polar substituents on the ring have all been studied.

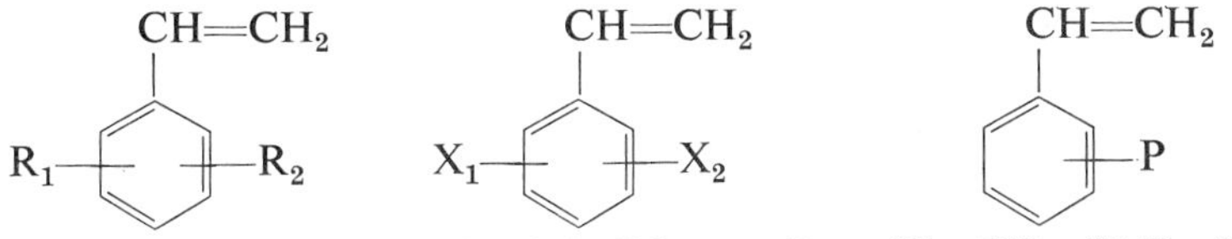

$X_1 = Cl, Br, F, I$
$X_2 = Cl, Br, F, I, H$

$P = -CN, -CHO, -CO_2H, -OCOCH_3$
$-OH, -OCH_3, -NO_2, -NH_2$

The following styrene-like monomers will also undergo addition polymerization:

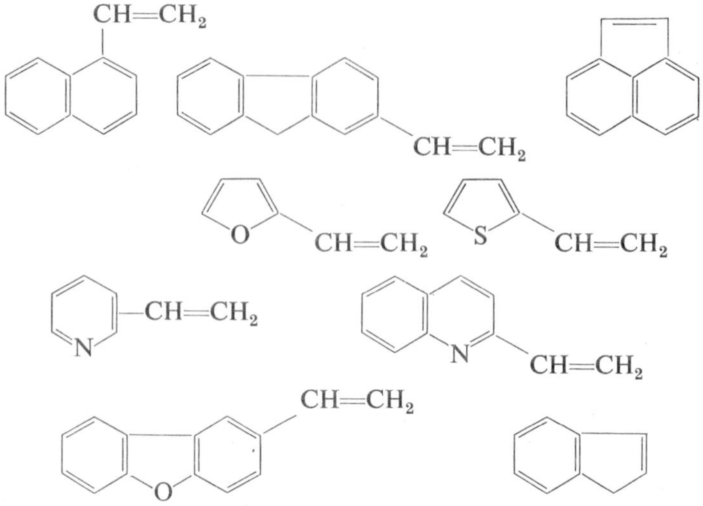

9.6 POLY(VINYL CHLORIDE)[1]

Vinyl chloride is produced commercially by the addition of hydrogen chloride to acetylene. The two gases are passed into a reactor containing a mercuric salt on a silica or other support at 140–280°C.[14]

$$HC\equiv CH + HCl \xrightarrow{H_gCl_2} H_2C\!=\!CHCl$$

Vinyl chloride may be polymerized in bulk, solution, suspension, and emulsion. In practice, the bulk or solution polymerizations cannot be carried out to a conversion greater than 50% since the reaction tends to take off due to local heat build up and poor heat transfer.

Suspension polymerization is carried out with a benzoyl peroxide initiator and a suspending agent. Oxygen has a marked inhibiting effect on vinyl chloride polymerization and must be excluded from all systems. Most of the PVC is produced in emulsion systems with an inorganic initiator and a soap emulsifier.

Poly(vinyl chloride) is susceptible to dehydrochlorination to dark colored polymers, especially in the presence of base, light or strong heat. The structure of poly(vinyl chloride) is such that once one molecule of hydrogen chloride is lost in a polymer chain there is produced a reactive vinylic chloride and the loss of hydrogen chloride continues readily producing unsaturation in the chain. A more stable PVC is obtained with mild polymerization conditions, pure monomers, and added stabilizers. Low molecular weight fractions are more unstable and are removed from a PVC sample. Metal salts and substances which will pick up the evolved hydrogen chloride are good stabilizers. Plasticizers are generally added to poly(vinyl chloride) to give it more elastomeric properties, and are generally high boiling esters or other polymers and copolymers. These will improve the milling properties and low temperature flexibility.

Poly(vinyl chloride) generally falls in the molecular weight range 60,000–150,000. The structure of the polymer has been shown to have the head-to-tail arrangement (Chapter 4) and is only slightly crystalline since the structure is atactic.

$$-CH_2-CH-CH_2-CH-CH_2-CH-$$
$$\underset{Cl}{|}\underset{Cl}{|}\underset{Cl}{|}$$

Although poly(vinyl chloride) contains polar groups in the molecule, it has good electrical properties. This property coupled with its flame resistance make it suitable for an electrical insulator. The brittleness associated with poly(vinyl chloride) and to some extent its electrical properties can be attributed to the bulkyl chlorine groups attached to the backbone which prevent free rotation and mobility in the chains.

TABLE 9.4
Physical properties of poly(vinyl chloride)

	Unplasticized PVC	Plasticized PVC
Density	1.4	1.3
Tensile strength	9000	2600
Flexural strength, p.s.i.	15,000	plastic*
% Elongation	5–25	340
Dielectric constant (60 c.p.s.)	3.2	6.9

* Plasticized PVC has little snap and no definite elastic limit.

As previously indicated, poly(vinyl chloride) has found extensive use as wire and cable coverings. This is accomplished with a minimum amount of plasticizer and a hot extrusion directly around the wire. Clear poly(vinyl chloride) film finds use in rain wear and shower curtains. Cloth or paper can be coated using hot calendering or solution techniques. These coated products are manufactured into upholstery materials and raincoats. The polymer powder may be compression molded at about 150°C. and pipes may be extruded at 200°C. to afford a product resistant to acid and oil.

9.7 POLY(VINYLIDINE CHLORIDE)[1]

Thermal cracking of trichloroethane at 400°C. affords vinylidine chloride. The monomer is also prepared commercially by the chlorination of ethylene chloride under conditions which favor dehydrohalogenation.

$$CH_2Cl—CH_2Cl \xrightarrow{Cl_2} CH_2Cl—CHCl_2 + HCl \longrightarrow CH_2{=}CCl_2$$

Bulk polymerization and solution polymerizations can be accomplished, but in large batches, the heat of polymerization causes difficulties. On an industrial scale, suspensions and emulsion polymerizations with a water soluble free radical initiator are employed.

Poly(vinylidine chloride) is a crystalline head-to-tail polymer which can be oriented on stretching. Since there is no chance for asymmetry along the backbone, an atactic polymer cannot exist and the formation of crystallites is enhanced by some hydrogen bonding between chlorines and methylene hydrogens on adjacent chains. About 20–40% crystallinity ($Tm = 160°C.$) is normally obtained which imparts the translucent character to the polymer.[15] Unoriented polymer has a tensile strength of 8000–10,000 p.s.i. while orientation improves the strength to 30,000–60,000 p.s.i.

The high polymer of molecular weight 100,000 is insoluble in most solvents and dissolves with difficulty in highly chlorinated solvents at elevated temperatures. It softens at 180–200°C. but at elevated temperatures is susceptible to decomposition by the elimination of hydrogen chloride, as is the case with poly(vinyl chloride). Stabilizers such as are added to poly(vinyl chloride) also improve the stability of poly(vinylidine chloride). The poly(vinylidine chloride) homopolymer finds little commercial application and most of the vinylidine chloride is consumed in copolymerization especially with small amounts of vinyl chloride to give the Saran copolymers (Chapter 11).

9.8 POLYCHLOROTRIFLUOROETHYLENE[1,16]

Dechlorination of trichlorotrifluoroethane with zinc yields chlorotrifluoroethane.

$$FCCl_2—CClF \xrightarrow[\text{Ethanol}]{Zn} CClF{=}CF_2$$

The monomer is conveniently converted to polymer with free radical initiators such as *t*-butyl hydroperoxide, AIBN, and ammonium persulfate. The reaction times are long, and conversions are low. Most patented examples describe polymerization in bulk in an autoclave or in a water system under pressure.

The polymer is atactic and has a low degree of crystallinity.[17] Rapidly quenched Kel-F is transparent while slow cooling produces a transluscent polymer due to a more crystalline structure.[18] Kel-F is second only to polytetrafluoroethylene in resistance to chemical attack by such reagents as halogens, strong mineral acids, strong base, fuming mineral acids and oxidizing agents. The polymer is dissolved by high boiling halogenated hydrocarbon solvents such as 1,1,3-trifluoropentachloropropane and usually the polymer is not dissolved below its crystalline melting point, 218°C. The polymer is quite brittle at -100°C., but has useful properties as high as 150°C., depending on the molecular weight.

The resistance of polychlorotrifluoroethylene to chemical attack makes it especially suited for certain industrial manufacturing applications. The low molecular weight polymers (500–5000) are greases and lubricants. The higher molecular weight polymers can be molded or extruded, usually above 200°C. into gaskets, valve seats, tubing and coatings. Although Kel-F is not as chemically resistant as polytetrafluoroethylene, it is easier to fabricate and has a greater transparency.

9.9 POLYTETRAFLUOROETHYLENE[1],[19–22]

The industrial preparation of tetrafluoroethylene involves a pyrrolytic coupling of difluorochloromethane which is obtained from the florination of chloromethane.

$$CH_3Cl + HF \xrightarrow[SbCl_5]{SbF_3} HCF_2Cl$$

$$2HCF_2Cl \xrightarrow{650-800°} F_2C{=}CF_2 + 2HCl$$

The fact that tetrafluoroethylene would polymerize was inadvertently discovered when it was found that a cylinder of the gas had deposited white polymer along the walls. Pure monomer will polymerize explosively. The polymerization by free radical initiators such as persulfates, peroxides, hydrogen peroxide, redox initiators, or oxygen have been reported. Aqueous systems which dissipate the heat of reaction, moderate to high pressures and mild temperatures are general.

$$CF_2{=}CF_2 \longrightarrow {-}[CF_2{-}CF_2]{-}$$

Polytetrafluoroethylene is a linear highly ordered crystalline (93–97%) polymer. The chain segments are apparently very stiff as influenced by restricted rotation and repulsive forces between adjacent fluorine atoms. The carbon fluorine bond distance in *gem* difluorides, 1.35 A. is considerably shorter than the normal C—F bond, 1.42 A., and this accounts in part for the inertness of the polymer. Polytetrafluoroethylene has two crystalline forms, both of which have a helical arrangement. At 19°C. the form which contains 13 CF_2— groups per unit cell changes to a form with 15 CF_2— groups per unit cell. The crystalline melting point is extremely high, 327°C., and there is one other transition temperature besides the 19°C. and 327°C. changes which involves a change in the crystalline phase at 30°C. The glass transition temperature has not been found and is evidently very low since the polymer is still flexible at −100°C. The molecular weight of this polymer is unusually high, perhaps several million.

The physical properties of the polymer depend mainly on molecular weight, crystallinity and void content. The chemical properties can be attributed mainly to the inertness of the C—F bond. It is the most chemically resistant linear organic polymer known and in fact Teflon can be cleaned in a boiling nitric acid-sulfuric acid bath. It is nonflammable and is attacked only by molten alkali metals. It is not soluble in most organic solvents but will dissolve in perfluorinated kerosenes at 300°C.

Polytetrafluoroethylene does not flow well even above its crystalline melting point and this has been attributed to the restricted rotation about the carbon-carbon bonds and the high molecular weight. The liquid will shear under too much force. Molded polytetrafluoroethylene has a high impact strength and poor elastic recovery. The polymer will cold draw at 1500–2000 p.s.i. It has a waxy feeling, a very low coefficient of friction, and is subject to cold flow under force. Its stiffness depends upon the degree of crystallinity as does the flex life.

TABLE 9.5
Physical properties of Teflon

Tm	327°C.
Density	2.2–2.3
Tensile strength, p.s.i.	2500–4500 (unoriented)
	25,000 (oriented)
% Elongation (at break)	300–450%
Dielectric constant	2.0

The high melting point and melt viscosity as well as the poor solubility characteristics of polytetrafluoroethylene make it impossible to fabricate by conventional methods. Fabrication methods resemble powder metallurgy in that the cold powder is pressed into a cake or mold and then sintered at high temperatures. In this manner, gaskets and other simple parts can be fabricated. In wire coating the powder is pressed onto the wire and then sintered.

The chemical inertness, toughness, self-lubricating properties and good electrical resistance make polytetrafluoroethylene an excellent material for electrical insulation, chemically resistant gaskets, valves, diaphragms, and other machine parts.

9.10 OTHER HALOETHYLENES AND THEIR POLYMERS[1]

The polymerizability of haloethylene monomers and polymers formed from many other halogenated ethylene monomers has been studied. Vinyl halides and vinylidine halides in general will polymerize. Substitution on more than one carbon decreases the polymerizability in most cases except where one of the carbons bears a fluorine in a $=CHF$ or $=CF_2$ grouping. The other carbon may contain any of the other halogens where the two are the same or mixed.

Poly(vinyl fluoride) is somewhat like poly(vinyl chloride) with respect to chemical and physical properties, but has a higher degree of crystallinity and thus somewhat better mechanical properties. It is a very tough polymer which can be cold drawn and has better outdoor weathering properties than poly(vinyl chloride). Poly(vinylidine fluoride) is more like polyethylene than poly(vinylidine chloride) in that it is chemically stable and will form a fiber with a tensile strength of 4550 p.s.i.

9.11 POLY(METHYL METHACRYLATE)[1,23-25]

Methyl methacrylate is prepared commercially by the addition of cyanide to acetone with a potassium hydroxide catalyst, followed by a hydrolysis, dehydration, and an esterification step to yield methyl methacrylate.

$$
CH_3COCH_3 \xrightarrow{HCN} CH_3{-}\underset{\underset{CH_3}{|}}{\overset{\overset{OH}{|}}{C}}{-}CN \xrightarrow[CH_3OH]{H_2SO_4} CH_2{=}\underset{}{\overset{\overset{CH_3}{|}}{C}}{-}CO_2CH_3
$$

The intermediates in the reaction need not be isolated. Alternately, the cyanohydrin may be dehydrated and hydrolyzed by sulfuric acid to methacrylamide sulfate which is hydrolyzed and esterified by the addition of methanol and water.

$$
CH_3{-}\underset{\underset{CH_3}{|}}{\overset{\overset{OH}{|}}{C}}{-}CN \xrightarrow[125°]{H_2SO_4} CH_2{=}\underset{}{\overset{\overset{CH_3}{|}}{C}}{-}C\overset{\displaystyle O}{\underset{\displaystyle NH_2 \cdot H_2SO_4}{\big\langle}} \xrightarrow[H_2SO_4,\,90°]{CH_3OH,\,HOH}
$$

$$
CH_2{=}\underset{}{\overset{\overset{CH_3}{|}}{C}}{-}CO_2CH_3 + NH_4HSO_4
$$

The polymerization of methyl methacrylate is severely inhibited by oxygen. Controlling the amount of oxygen has actually been used in controlling the rate of polymerization and the quality of the product. In the presence of free oxygen it is assumed that peroxide formation occurs at a faster rate than polymerization as long as oxygen is present. A growing free radical chain prefers to react with oxygen than monomer thus destroying the active center and only low molecular weight polymers are formed.

It is interesting that gaseous monomer is polymerized by ultraviolet light and deposits on the walls of the container.[26] Growth of the polymer continues on the deposited polymer surface and polymerization continues at the surface even after extinguishing the light. In this "living polymer" system, growth stops when the monomer is used up but will continue 15 hr. later when fresh monomer is readmitted. This long active life has been attributed to the fact that there are no tertiary hydrogen atoms in the polymer molecules to act as chain transfer agents, and this is supported by the fact that methyl acrylate does not produce a living polymer system.

Another interesting point in the polymerization of methyl methacrylate in bulk is that the rate increases as the polymerization reaction proceeds. This has been attributed to an increase in the growing centers and a drop in termination rate. If termination involves the collision of two growing chains, lack of mobility of the chains would drop this rate but the mobility of the adding monomer molecules would remain high.[27] This has been confirmed by adding polymer to a polymerization system thereby increasing the viscosity and the rate.

There are several industrial methods for preparing poly(methyl methacrylate) and the method employed is determined by the desired use as an end product. All of the processes are free radical with benzoyl peroxide, azo initiators, or heat. Bulk polymerization is particularly effective since the gel stage is reached rapidly and the polymer is free from residual monomer. Control can be exercised by polymerization in several stages of increased temperature thereby minimizing convection currents and hot spots.

The monomer may be prepolymerized to a syrup stage, cooled, degassed, and poured into a mold and then finished off. In preparing poly(methyl methacrylate) sheets, either a polymer syrup or the monomer is poured between two plates of heat resistant glass separated by a flexible gasket spacer. The syrup is preferred because less shrinkage occurs during polymerization. The plates are supported vertically and heated at increasing temperatures over a period of time. Generally the heating cycle is started at 40°C. and finished at 100°C. At the end of the polymerization the plates are quickly cooled to free the Plexiglas or Lucite sheet. The sheet is then suspended vertically and heated in an annealing or strain relaxing treatment and finally covered with a paper adhesive to prevent scratching.

Continuous zone polymerization may be applied to the formation of rods. In this process, the syrup with initiator is poured into an aluminum tube and heated from the bottom of the tube upward either by raising the level of the hot water bath (70–80°C.) or lowering the tube slowly into the water. Tubes of poly(methyl methacrylate) may be formed by heating the syrup in a rapidly rotating horizontal tube containing only enough polymer to cover the walls.

Monomer-polymer moldings which are extensively employed in dental castings are prepared from a 50-50 mixture of finely powdered polymer and liquid monomer. Part of the polymer dissolves in the monomer and the slush is finished by heating at 80–150°C. These mixed doughs polymerize with added initiators and pigments without a settling of the polymer particles. Poly(methyl methacrylate) dental fillings are made from the polymer-monomer dough, a benzoyl peroxide initiator, and a tertiary amine activator. This allows polymerization in 5 minutes without heat build up or the external application of heat.

Suspension polymerization techniques are used where the polymer is to be injection molded. Typical recipes include monomer, water, benzoyl peroxide, and suspending agent. This polymer has a more uniform molecular weight and the molecular weight is in the desired range for molding or extrusion.

Solution polymerization has little commercial use. Emulsion systems with redox initiators are employed in the preparation of polymer lattices for leather and textile finishes.[28]

Poly(methyl methacrylate) prepared by the methods described is high molecular weight (as high as 10^6), atactic, and amorphous. Methyl methacrylate polymers can be obtained in an isotactic, syndiotactic, or isotactic-syndiotactic stereoblock order depending on the method of polymerization with the metal alkyl catalyst, 9-fluorenyl lithium[29] (Table 9.6).

Syndiotactic poly(methyl methacrylate) has a five-unit two-turn helix. Two 300° turns with five monomer units in each 360° turn are necessary because of the odd number of monomer units per repeat distance. If the first unit in the turn were of the *d* configuration, the sixth unit, which lies over the first, would be *l*, thus making necessary another revolution and a repeat distance of 10.55 A.[30]

Commercial poly(methyl methacrylate) has better resistance to alkali than poly(methyl acrylate), probably by virtue of the shielding presented by the α-methyl group. The polymer is outstanding in stability and optical properties, particularly in clarity and light transmission. Plexiglas will withstand 5000 p.s.i. for years with no more than 10% cold flow. The polymers do have poor abrasion resistance, however, and scratch quite easily. They also are susceptible to crazing especially when the sample has not been given a heat annealing treatment. It has a tensile strength of 8000–10,000 p.s.i. and a shear strength of 7500–11,000 p.s.i.

TABLE 9.6

Properties of poly(methyl methacrylate)

	Polymerization Conditions				
	Solvent	Temperature	Tg, °C.	Tm, °C.	Density
I. Isotactic	Dimethoxyethane	−60°	115	200	1.19
II. Syndiotactic	Toluene	−60°	45	160	1.22
III. I–II block	Toluene and dioxane	−70°	60–95	170	1.20–1.22
Atactic	Conventional free radical		104	—	1.188

Poly(methyl methacrylate), because of its excellent optical properties, has been used for piping light for advertising and medical devices. Internal reflection allows rods bent in curves to transmit light around the curve along the rod. Other products which take advantage of the optical properties are contact lenses, camera lenses, watch crystals and aircraft glass. Plexiglas sheets can be shaped to bubble type canopies at 130–150°C. and double Plexiglas sheets laminated with poly(vinyl butyral) are used for aircraft glass in pressurized cabins.

In most cases the polymer will not cause allergies so that dentures, fillings, artificial eyes and braces are manufactured. The fact that the monomer may be polymerized under mild conditions and that the polymer can be colored in the polymerization process add to its attractiveness in many applications. Various other novelties and parts such as handles, jewelry, and knobs are fabricated from the polymer.

9.12   OTHER POLYACRYLATES[1,23]

Poly(methacrylic esters). Many other methacrylate esters have been prepared and polymerized. Most of these esters have been made from methyl methacrylate by an alcohol interchange reaction.[31] Cyclohexyl methacrylate polymers were developed for military optical instruments. Methacrylate polymers with higher alcohol portions show marked difference in physical properties depending on the size, nature, degree, and position of branching in the alcohol portion. Hardness and softening point are increased by branching, especially at the β-carbon. Long

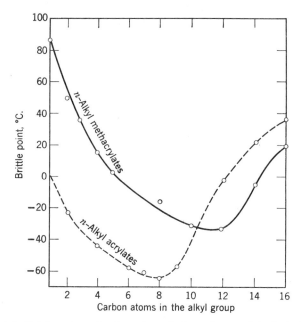

Fig. 9.5. Brittle points of polymeric *n*-alkyl acrylates and methacrylates.[23]

straight chain alkyl groups have a plasticizing effect making the polymer more elastomeric. The glass transition temperatures of the polymers decrease as the alcohol portion becomes longer up to the octyl and decyl methacrylates ($Tg = -70°$) and then increases with higher members of the series. The same is true with the acrylate esters. This variation in glass transition temperature is reflected in the brittle points of the polymers (Fig. 9.5).

Poly(methyl α-chloroacrylate). Poly(methyl α-chloroacrylate) has been investigated extensively since it is a clear plastic and has improved hardness, less cold flow, a higher softening point and better craze-resistance than poly(methyl methacrylate). It is, however, an expensive polymer and is difficult to prepare without a yellow cast. The monomer polymerizes more readily than methyl methacrylate but cannot be molded without discoloration. A number of different esters of α-chloroacrylic acid have also been prepared and polymerized.[32]

Poly(methyl acrylate).[1,23,33] Methyl acrylate is commercially produced by the addition of hydrogen cyanide to ethylene oxide. The resulting cyanohydrin is hydrolyzed, esterified and dehydrated in a one step process with sulfuric acid and methanol.[34] Higher acrylate esters may be prepared in this manner or by the ester interchange reaction with methyl acrylate.

$$CH_2\!\!-\!\!CH_2 + HCN \longrightarrow$$
$$\underset{\diagdown O \diagup}{}$$

$$\underset{\overset{|}{OH}}{CH_2\!-\!CH_2\!-\!CN} \xrightarrow[\text{H}_2\text{SO}_4]{\text{CH}_3\text{OH}} CH_2\!\!=\!\!CH\!-\!CO_2CH_3$$

Methyl acrylate is polymerized commercially by emulsion polymerization since the resulting polymer is tough and adhesive and cannot be easily removed from molds. A standard persulfate emulsion recipe gives rapid polymerization at low temperatures. The polymers are slightly tacky at room temperatures but are tough and flexible.

The *t*-butyl ester of acrylic acid may be polymerized by a lithium dispersion either in bulk or heptane solution to give a crystalline polymer with molecular weights in the 160,000–2,000,000 range.[35] They have a higher softening point than the amorphous polymer (72°C. vs. 32°C.) and a higher density (1.05 vs. 0.99). No other ester (methyl, *n*-butyl, *s*-butyl, or *i*-butyl) of acrylic or methacrylic acid with the exception of *t*-butyl methacrylate will give a crystalline polymer with this catalyst.

The acrylates find application primarily in textile and paper finishes.

Poly(acrylic acid). Acrylic acid is made industrially from ethylene cyanohydrin[36] or by the addition of carbon monoxide and water to acetylene with a nickel carbonyl catalyst. Acrylic acid is polymerized in a basic aqueous solution by a persulfate initiator. Since the polymer is soluble in water and brittle when dry, it has application mainly as a thickening agent and an adhesive.

9.13   POLYACRYLONITRILE[1]

Polyacrylonitrile was considered useless for a time as a fiber forming or plastic material since there seemed to be no solvent for the polymer and the material decomposed at its softening temperature. Fabrication of the polymer became possible upon the discovery of several suitable solvents.

Acrylonitrile monomer is prepared on an industrial scale by two methods. Ethylenecyanohydrin dehydration proceeds rapidly with suitable catalysts either in the liquid or vapor phase.[37]

$$CH_2\!\!-\!\!CH_2 \xrightarrow{\text{HCN}} \underset{\overset{|}{OH}}{CH_2\!-\!CH_2CN} \xrightarrow{200\text{–}350°} CH_2\!\!=\!\!CH\!-\!CN + H_2O$$
$$\underset{\diagdown O \diagup}{}$$

This process is more expensive than the addition of hydrogen cyanide to acetylene but a relatively pure product is obtained initially. In the acetylene hydrogen cyanide process, pure reactants must be employed. Mixtures of hydrogen cyanide with an excess of acetylene are passed through an aqueous solution at a pH of 1–3 containing a cuprous chloride catalyst. Another series of patents describe the addition of hydrogen cyanide in the vapor phase over a sodium cyanide impregnated charcoal catalyst or other suitable catalysts at temperatures ranging from 200 to 600°C.

$$HC\equiv CH + HCN \xrightarrow[H_2O]{Cu_2Cl_2} H_2C=CH-CN$$

Bulk and emulsion polymerization of acrylonitrile have not been generally practiced. In emulsion, the latex often precipitates during polymerization since a large portion of the polymer forming reaction occurs in the aqueous phase. Polyacrylonitrile also separates from the monomer phase in bulk polymerizations as a precipitate and the reactions are difficult to control. Oxygen is a serious inhibitor to polymerization and long induction periods are noted if oxygen is not removed.

Aqueous solution polymerizations of acrylonitrile with persulfate or a ferrous sulfate-hydrogen peroxide redox initiator occur rapidly and are suitable for the industrial preparation.

Polyacrylonitrile is hydrolyzed by hot concentrated base to the sodium salt of polyacrylic acid. On heating polyacrylonitrile at temperatures above 200°C., the product becomes red and finally quite dark at 350°C. The dark product will withstand high temperatures with little decomposition but is a brittle polymer. It has been suggested[19] that the following transformation takes place and a polynuclear aromatic ring system exists at least for short segments in the chain:

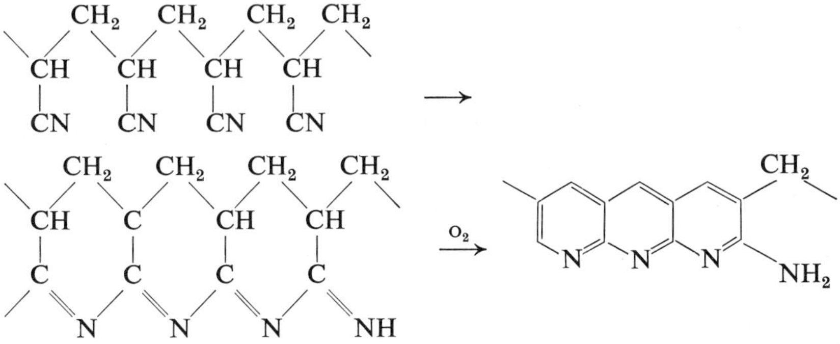

Polymethacrylonitrile which must lose methyl groups to become aromatic also colors on heating so that the original colored products from these polymers probably result from an addition polymerization across the —C≡N groups at least for short segments along the chain.

The structure of the polyacrylonitrile molecule is such that hydrogen bonding occurs readily and this is reflected in the high strength, insolubility and high softening point. Because of the insolubility of polyacrylonitrile in most solvents, it was believed earlier that the polymer was

$$
\begin{array}{ccc}
& H & H & H \\
CH_2 & | & CH_2 & | & CH_2 & | \\
& C & & C & & C \\
& | & & | & & | \\
& C & & C & & C \\
& ||| & & ||| & & ||| \\
& N & & N & & N \\
& \vdots & & \vdots & & \vdots \\
& H & & H & & H \\
CH_2 & | & CH_2 & | & CH_2 & | \\
& C & & C & & C \\
& | & & | & & | \\
& C & & C & & C \\
& ||| & & ||| & & ||| \\
& N & & N & & N
\end{array}
$$

crosslinked.   There are several suitable solvents for polyacrylonitrile, among them dimethyl formamide from which the polymer is spun.[38]

Solutions of polyacrylonitrile are spun into fibers by either dry or wet spinning techniques.   Dry spinning is accomplished from solutions of polymer of about 100,000 molecular weight by squirting downward through a spinnerette into a heated air space where the solvent rapidly evaporates.   In this process, the fiber is drawn during winding.   The dimethyl formamide solutions are also wet spun into an aqueous salt bath, a glycerin bath or other higher boiling solvent bath where temperatures of 100–200°C. can be maintained.   The fibers are also drawn during winding in the wet spinning process.

These fibers which are sold under the trade names Orlon and Acrilan have the best weathering properties of all organic fibers.   They have good strength and somewhat the lustre and hand of silk.   Orlon and Acrilan fabrics or knitted goods consume most of the polyacrylonitrile.   The fabric launders well without shrinkage, stains are readily removed, and it is insect resistant.

The major difficulty with polyacrylonitrile fabrics are their limited dyeability.   In addition to clothing, fabrics which must stand rough outdoor wear are manufactured from the fiber.   Orlon-wool blends or all Orlon sweaters have a large market.

9.14 RELATED ACRYLIC POLYMERS

Methacrylonitrile may be prepared by the dehydration of acetone cyanohydrin. It is polymerized by essentially the same methods as acrylonitrile but in addition, polymerization can be effected in an emulsion. Various anionic catalysts produce high molecular weight polymethacrylonitrile.[39] Sodium in liquid ammonia, Grignard reagents or triphenylmethyl sodium are good catalysts at low temperatures.

Polymers prepared by free radical methods are clear but anionic polymerizations give colored polymers. In addition, the polymer discolors readily on heating, much like acrylonitrile, and takes on a bright red color. The color has been attributed to the presence in the polymer of the structure shown.[40–42]

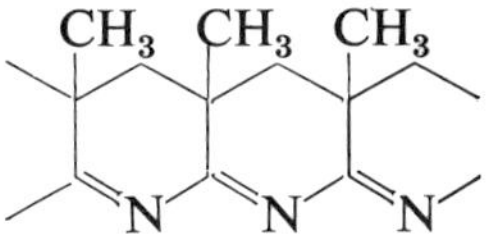

Many substituted acrylonitriles have been prepared, but none have gained any commercial importance. An interesting acrylonitrile type monomer is methylene malonitrile. It polymerized as soon as it is formed, especially if water is present. This monomer is extremely sensitive to anionic catalysts since weak bases such as alcohol, water, amines, and amides effect its polymerization.

Acrylamide is polymerized readily by heat or free radical initiators, but with strong base a polymer of a different structure is formed via an H-addition polymerization (Chapter 8).

9.15 POLY(VINYL ACETATE), POLY(VINYL ALCOHOL), AND RELATED POLYMERS

Poly(vinyl acetate).[1] Vinyl acetate is prepared by the addition of acetic acid to acetylene either in the liquid or vapor phase.[43] Acetylene is passed through glacial acetic acid containing complex mercury salts and sulfuric acid at temperatures ranging from 30°C. to 90°C. In the vapor phase, acetylene is blown through acetic acid at 120°C. to give a vapor mixture of acetylene and acetic acid in the molar ratio 5:1. The mixture is then passed over catalysts such as zinc acetate on a charcoal support at 180°C.

$$CH_3CO_2H + HC\equiv CH \longrightarrow CH_3CO_2CH=CH_2$$

The vinyl acetate monomer is very unreactive but the vinyl acetate radical is one of the most reactive. For this reason, vinyl acetate will not readily react with itself to form a homopolymer if there is another monomer present (Chapter 5). The reactive vinyl acetate radical reacts with other components of a reaction mixture, including the polymer chains. This accounts for the large amount of chain transfer and branching in the structure of the polymer. The monomer must be exceptionally pure in order to obtain high molecular weight polymer in good conversion because of the reactivity of the radical.

Industrial bulk polymerizations are usually not carried to 100% conversion due to chain branching and eventual crosslinking. A semi-continuous process has been effected with a benzoyl peroxide initiator and a propionaldehyde regulator at 85°C. where monomer was added stepwise to control the heat build up. Solution polymerizations have also been carried out. Free radical suspension polymerizations give hard beads of poly(vinyl acetate). The suspending agent is usually another polymer such as poly(vinyl alcohol) or a styrene-maleic anhydride copolymer.

During polymerization, chain transfer takes place which leads to a highly branched structure when the polymerization is carried to high conversion. The chains are almost all head to tail as shown by chemical studies on the polymer (Chapter 4). Branching can occur both at the α-carbon on the acetate group or on the tertiary carbons along the polymer backbone (α-vinyl carbon) by the abstraction of hydrogen by a vinyl acetate radical. Branching which occurs from an acetate carbon is lost from the chain on hydrolysis to give a chain of fewer branches.

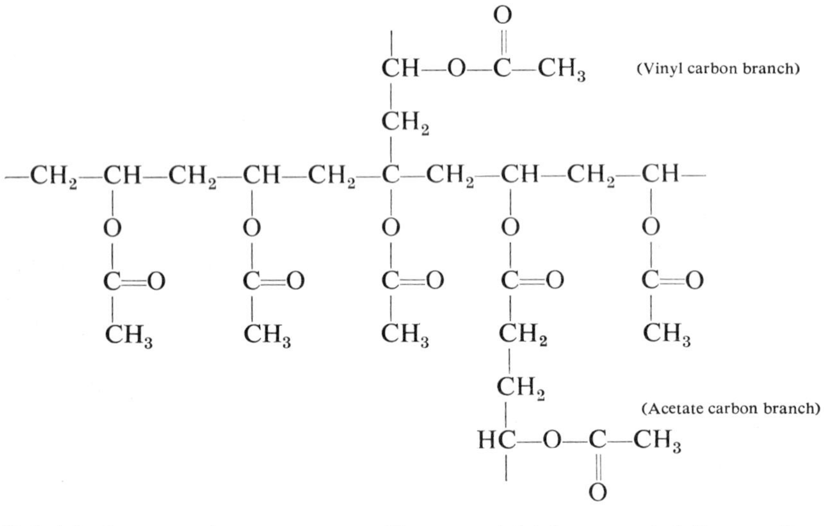

$$
\begin{array}{c}
\text{CH—O—C—CH}_3 \quad \text{(Vinyl carbon branch)}\\
|\\
\text{CH}_2
\end{array}
$$

—CH$_2$—CH—CH$_2$—CH—CH$_2$—C—CH$_2$—CH—CH$_2$—CH—

with pendant groups: O, O, O, O, O → C=O, C=O, C=O, C=O, C=O → CH$_3$, CH$_3$, CH$_3$, CH$_2$, CH$_3$

CH$_2$

(Acetate carbon branch)

HC—O—C—CH$_3$

O

Poly(vinyl acetates) are not crystalline as might be expected from a free radical polymerization which would give an atactic and highly branched polymer.

Poly(vinyl acetates) are too soft and have too low an unmolding temperature to serve as molded plastics. The low polymers are soft gummy resins. At higher temperatures, high molecular weight poly(vinyl acetates) are not rubbery but are subject to cold flow and have no snap. Typical polymers have densities of about 1.2, tensile strengths in the 1500–5000 p.s.i. range and softening temperatures from 40–90°C. The glass transition temperature is 40°C.

In contrast, poly(vinyl trifluoroacetate) ($[\eta] = 1.1$–1.3) is hard and fibrous with a softening temperature at 172°C. ($Tg = 46°C.$).[44] The stretched fiber shows a crystalline x-ray pattern. This may be attributed in part to the fact that no branching can take place through the acetate groups and consequently the polymer is more nearly linear.

Poly(vinyl acetate) is a good adhesive, binder and coating material. In cloth, paper, leather and cork where quick drying, high strength, and water resistance are not important, the polymer is a cheap binder. The low polymers are put in chewing gum as an extender for chicle.

Poly(vinyl alcohol). Poly(vinyl alcohol) is prepared by the alcoholysis of poly(vinyl acetate). Ethanol or methanol solutions of poly(vinyl acetate) or alcoholic-acetate ester solutions with either acid or base catalysts effect the conversion by a transesterification. The poly(vinyl alcohol) precipitates from the solution. Acid catalyzed reactions are slower and produce some ether links in the poly(vinyl alcohol).

$$\left[CH_2-CH \atop OAc \right] \xrightarrow{CH_3OH} \left[CH_2-CH \atop OH \right] + CH_3CO_2CH_3$$

Poly(vinyl alcohol) is primarily a head-to-tail polymer (Chapter 4). Although it is atactic, it is highly crystalline and has nearly the same crystal lattice as polyethylene, with a repeat distance of 2.57 A.[45,46] The presence of crystallites in this atactic molecule is probably due to the small size of the hydroxyl groups which can fit into the lattice and the high degree of hydrogen bonding between adjacent chains.

The polymer loses water above 100°C. to form double bonds which impart a color to it. Poly(vinyl alcohol) is soluble in water and the polymer or its aqueous solutions are unstable to acid or base. Acid promotes the formation of ether crosslinks which gel the polymer. Unplasticized molded PVA may have tensile strengths up to 22,000 p.s.i., and a density of 1.3. The polymer does not melt but softens at 200°C. with decomposition. The polymers are good binders in pigmented coatings for paper, ceramics, and leathers. One of the largest applications is a warp size for yarn. Molded or extruded plasticized poly(vinyl alcohol) tubes and sheets have good oil resistance and can be used in contact with organic solvents where there is little likelihood of water contact.

Poly(vinyl acetals). Poly(vinyl butyral) is made by the acid catalyzed condensation reaction of PVA with butyraldehyde. The poly(vinyl butyrals) must be stabilized with base to prevent viscosity changes, discoloration and brittleness on aging.

$$
\begin{array}{c}
\text{CH}_2 \quad \text{CH}_2 \quad \text{CH}_2 \quad \text{CH}_2 \quad \text{CH}_2 \\
\text{CH} \quad \text{CH} \quad \text{CH} \quad \text{CH} \quad \text{CH} \\
\text{OH} \quad \text{OH} \quad \text{OH} \quad \text{OH} \quad \text{OH}
\end{array}
\xrightarrow[\text{H}^\oplus]{\text{C}_3\text{H}_7\text{CHO}}
$$

$$
\begin{array}{c}
\text{CH}_2 \qquad \text{CH}_2 \qquad \text{CH}_2 \\
\text{CH} \\
\text{O}\quad\text{O} \qquad\qquad \text{OH} \qquad \text{O}\quad\text{O} \\
\text{C}_3\text{H}_7 \qquad\qquad\qquad\qquad \text{C}_3\text{H}_7
\end{array}
$$

Complete acetal formation does not take place since hydroxyl groups become isolated and have no opportunity to form a cyclic acetal. Calculations show that 13.5% of the hydroxyl groups should remain unreacted.[47] Poly(vinyl formal) fibers have been prepared by extruding an aqueous solution of poly(vinyl alcohol) into an ammonium sulfate-sulfuric acid solution, followed by a treatment with formalin.

The properties of commercial poly(vinyl butyrals) depends on the proportion of unreacted hydroxyl groups and the amount of plasticizer. Tensile strengths range from 1000 to 3500 p.s.i. and per cent elongation at the break are 400 and 200 respectively. Plasticized poly(vinyl butyral) is used in safety glass laminates because of its better stability, adhesion, and cold break as compared to cellulose esters. The poly(vinyl butyral) which has about 25% of the hydroxyl groups remaining is plasticized with about 30 parts ester and an alcohol solvent. The mass is extruded through a slit into a brine solution which leaches out the alcohol. The sheets are dusted with talc to prevent sticking during storage. Before lamination, the sheet is washed, dried and placed between two plates of glass. The lamination is accomplished by heat and pressure. The higher than theoretical amount of hydroxyl groups is required for good bonding. Poly(vinyl butyral) also serves as a thermoplastic adhesive and waterproof fabric coating.

Poly(vinyl formal) has excellent toughness, abrasion resistance and a higher softening point than poly(vinyl butyral). A commercial poly(vinyl formal), Formvar, has a density of 1.23 and a tensile strength of 10,000 p.s.i. Poly(vinyl formals) are not soluble in ketones, chlorinated hydrocarbons, and dioxane. Formvar coatings on the inner walls of aircraft fuel tanks give self sealing tanks. It is applied to wire from a solution along with some phenol as a crosslinking agent to give an electrical wire covering enamel. The textile fibers from poly(vinyl formal) have the appearance of cotton and a hand which may be made to resemble wool or linen. The fiber has a water absorption higher than any fiber other than the cellulosics.

9.16 OTHER VINYL POLYMERS

Poly(vinyl ethers).[1] Vinyl alkyl ethers are made by the addition of alcohols to acetylene. Either the vinyl ether is obtained directly from the reaction in a 1:1 ratio or the acetal may be formed first and is cracked to the vinyl ether with the loss of alcohol.[48]

$$CH{\equiv}CH + ROH \xrightarrow[130-180°]{KOR} CH_2{=}CHOR$$

$$\downarrow \begin{array}{l} H^{\oplus} \\ H_g^{+2} \end{array}$$

$$CH_3{-}CH(OR)_2 \xrightarrow[\text{Catalyst}]{200-300°} CH_2{=}CHOR + ROH$$

$$CH_2{=}CH{-}OR \longrightarrow \left[\begin{array}{c} CH_2{-}CH \\ | \\ OR \end{array} \right]$$

The ethers are not polymerized by free radical initiators but are converted to polymers under the catalytic influence of Lewis acids at low temperatures. Methyl vinyl ether yields balsams or viscous liquids when polymerized near 0°C. with boron fluoride hydrate in dioxane. An elastomer of poor strength is obtained by the irridation of vinyl methyl ether with $Co^{60}\gamma$.[49] Poly(vinyl ethyl ethers), which are also prepared by cationic catalysts have been used as plasticizers and tackifiers.

Vinyl isobutyl ethers as well as other vinyl ethers give crystalline isotactic or amorphous atactic polymers depending on the mode of polymerization. A solution of vinyl isobutyl ether in liquid propane at −60 to −70°C. is treated with boron fluoride in a "flash" polymerization to give a rubber like pressure sensitive adhesive. When the polymerization is carried out at low temperatures by the dropwise addition of a boron fluoride-etherate complex catalyst and the reaction is maintained at −80 to −60°C., a partially crystalline nonadhesive polymer is obtained. The catalyst in this reaction is heterogeneous. The crystalline plastics are harder and can be cold drawn. The polymer may be either entirely isotactic having a helical chain or a stereoblock polymer composed of long segments of d and l asymmetric carbons.[6,50]

Various other ethers have been polymerized where substituent groups appear on the alcohol portion or the α-carbon of the vinyl portion. The poly(vinyl aryl ethers) have different properties and are subject to the Claisen type rearrangement during polymerization. Poly(vinyl phenyl ether) prepared at $-10°C$. with boron fluoride or aluminum chloride is hard and glassy.

The polymerization of phenyl allyl ether with an aluminum i-propoxide–zinc chloride catalyst or an aluminum triethyl catalyst yields both a crystalline benzene insoluble polymer (Tm 185–210°C.) and an amorphous lower melting fraction soluble in benzene.[51]

Poly(vinyl ketones).[1] Methyl vinyl ketone is prepared either by the hydration of vinyl acetylene or by the condensation of formaldehyde with acetone.

$$2HC{\equiv}CH \xrightarrow[\text{HCl,NH}_4\text{Cl}]{\text{Cu}_2\text{Cl}_2} CH_2{=}CH{-}C{\equiv}CH \xrightarrow[\substack{\text{H}_2\text{SO}_4 \\ \text{H}_2\text{O}}]{\text{H}_2\text{SO}_4}$$

$$CH_2{=}CH{-}\overset{\overset{\text{O}}{\|}}{C}{-}CH_2 \longleftarrow CH_3{-}\overset{\overset{\text{O}}{\|}}{C}{-}CH_3 + CH_2O$$

It is an extremely reactive monomer and when pure will polymerize within a few hours to a solid mass either by light or peroxide initiation. The polymer has predominately a head to tail structure (Chapter 4). It has a low softening point and is unstable in that it very readily undergoes internal aldol-type condensation reactions.

Isopropenyl methyl ketone polymerizes rapidly at room temperature and this polymer also has the head-to-tail structure.

Nitrogen vinyl polymers.[1] Vinyl aryl amines are polymerized by light, peroxide initiators, Lewis acids or heat alone. The polymer obtained from N-vinyl carbizole is a white solid melting at 65°C. Bulk polymerizations are carried out by heating at 85–120°C. to yield a clear, colorless glass.

Peroxide initiated polymerizations in emulsion, suspension and boron fluoride catalyzed solution polymerizations at $-15°C$. are effective. The polymers have good electrical properties but their softening temperatures are too high for molding or melt casting. Some electrical insulation applications have been realized by polymerization *in situ*.

N-vinyl pyrrolidone polymerizes to a hard clear glass on exposure to light or with peroxide initiators. Water solutions of the monomer are polymerized by hydrogen peroxide and an ammonia activator.[52]

The polymer is used in the preparation of a synthetic blood plasma. A 20% aqueous solution of polymer with a number average molecular weight of 25,000 is mixed with various inorganic salts, water, and buffers.

REFERENCES

1. C. E. Schildknecht, *Vinyl and Related Polymers*, John Wiley and Sons, New York, 1952.
2. R. A. V. Raff and J. B. Allison, *Polyethylene*, Interscience Publishers, New York, 1956.
3. A. Renfrew and P. Morgan (eds.), *Polyethylene*, 2nd Edition, Interscience Publishers, New York, 1957.
4. T. O. J. Kresser, *Polyethylene*, Reinhold Publishing Corp., New York, 1957.
5. S. L. Aggarwal and O. J. Sweeting, *Chem. Revs.*, **57**, 665 (1957).
6. N. G. Gaylord and H. F. Mark, *Linear and Stereoregular Addition Polymers*, Interscience Publishers, New York, 1959.
7. L. Mandelkern, D. E. Roberts, J. C. Halpin, and F. P. Price, *J. Am. Chem. Soc.*, **82**, 46 (1960).
8. J. K. Stille, *Chem. Revs.*, **58**, 541 (1958).
9. G. Natta, *Scientific American*, **197**, No. 3, 102 (1957).
10. R. H. Boundy, R. F. Boyer, and S. M. Stoassar, *Styrene, Its Polymers, Co-polymers, and Derivatives*, Reinhold Publishing Corp., New York, 1952.
11. W. C. Teach and G. C. Kiessling, *Polystyrene*, Reinhold Publishing Corp., New York, 1960.
12. C. G. Overberger, F. Ang, and H. Mark, *J. Polymer Sci.*, **35**, 381 (1959).
13. A. B. Hersberger, J. C. Reid, and R. G. Heiligmann, *Ind. Eng. Chem.*, **37**, 1073 (1945).
14. H. Schalit, "Vinyl Chloride" (in *Monomers*, E. R. Blout and H. Mark, (eds.), Interscience Publishers, New York, 1949.
15. C. S. Fuller, *Chem. Revs.*, **26**, 143 (1940).
16. G. D. Jones, J. Zomleffer, and K. Hawkins, *J. Org. Chem.*, **9**, 500 (1944).
17. H. Lee, *Product Eng.*, **25**, 168 (1954).
18. F. P. Price, *J. Am. Chem. Soc.*, **74**, 311 (1952).
19. F. W. Billmeyer, Jr., *Textbook of Polymer Chemistry*, Interscience Publishers, New York, 1957.
20. *Teflon, Tetrafluoroethylene Resin Bulletin*, E. I. du Pont and Co., Inc., Wilmington, Delaware (1955).
21. M. M. Renfrew and E. E. Lewis, *Ind. Eng. Chem.*, **38**, 870 (1946).
22. W. E. Hanford and R. M. Joyce, *J. Am. Chem. Soc.*, **68**, 2082 (1946).
23. E. H. Riddle, *Monomeric Acrylic Esters*, Reinhold Publishing Corp., New York, 1954.

24. R. S. Corley, "Methyl Methacrylate" (in *Monomers*, E. R. Blout and H. Mark, eds.), Interscience Publishers, New York, 1949.
25. M. B. Horn, *Acrylic Resins*, Reinhold Publishing Corp., New York, 1960.
26. M. H. MacKay and H. W. Melville, *Trans. Faraday Soc.*, **46**, 63 (1950).
27. R. G. W. Norrish and R. R. Smith, *Nature*, **150**, 336 (1942).
28. Rohm and Haas Company, *Emulsion Polymerization of Acrylic Esters*, (1959).
29. T. G. Fox, B. S. Garrett, W. E. Goode, S. Gratch, J. F. Kincaid, A. Spell, and J. D. Stroupe, *J. Am. Chem. Soc.*, **80**, 1768 (1958).
30. J. D. Stroupe and R. E. Hughes, *J. Am. Chem. Soc.*, **80**, 2341 (1958).
31. R. S. Corley, "Esters of Methacrylic Acid other than Methylmethacrylate" (in *Monomers*, E. R. Blout and H. Mark, eds.), Interscience Publishers, New York, 1949.
32. C. S. Marvel, J. Dec, H. G. Cooke, Jr., and J. C. Cowan, *J. Am. Chem. Soc.*, **62**, 3495 (1940).
33. W. C. Mast and C. H. Fisher, *Ind. Eng. Chem.*, **41**, 790 (1949).
34. J. T. Clark, "Esters of Acrylic Acid" (in *Monomers*, E. R. Blout and H. Mark, eds.), Interscience Publishers, New York, 1949.
35. M. L. Miller and C. E. Rauhut, *J. Am. Chem. Soc.*, **80**, 4115 (1958).
36. J. T. Clarke, "Acrylic Acid (in *Monomers*, E. R. Blout and H. Mark, eds.), Interscience Publishers, New York, 1949.
37. American Cyanamide Co., *The Chemistry of Acrylonitrile*, Beacon Press, New York, 1951.
38. R. C. Houtz, *Textile Research J.*, **20**, 786 (1950).
39. R. G. Beaman, *J. Am. Chem. Soc.*, **70**, 3115 (1948).
40. N. Grassie and I. C. McNeill, *J. Polymer Sci.*, **27**, 207 (1958).
41. N. Grassie, J. N. Hay, and I. C. McNeill, *J. Polymer Sci.*, **31**, 205 (1958).
42. N. Grassie and I. C. McNeill, *J. Polymer Sci.*, **39**, 211 (1959).
43. P. Fram, "Vinyl Acetate" (in *Monomers*, E. R. Blout and H. Mark, eds.), Interscience Publishers, New York, 1949.
44. H. C. Haas, E. S. Emerson, and N. W. Schuler, *J. Polymer Sci.*, **22**, 291 (1956).
45. C. W. Bunn and E. V. Garner, *Proc. Roy. Soc. (London)*, **A189**, 39 (1947).
46. C. W. Bunn, *Nature*, **161**, 929 (1948).
47. P. J. Flory, *J. Am. Chem. Soc.*, **72**, 5052 (1950).
48. C. E. Schildknecht, "Vinyl Ethers" (in *Monomers*, E. R. Blout and H. Mark, eds.), Interscience Publishers, New York, 1949.
49. D. Duffey, *Ind. Eng. Chem.*, **50**, 1267 (1958).
50. C. E. Schildknecht, S. T. Gross, H. R. Davidson, J. M. Lambert, and A. O. Zoss, *Ind. Eng. Chem.*, **40**, 2104 (1948).
51. A. Noshay and C. C. Price, *J. Polymer Sci.*, **34**, 165 (1959).
52. H. Fikentscher and K. Kerrle, *Modern Plastics*, **23**, No. 3, 157 (1945).

10

POLYMERS
FROM CONJUGATED
DIENES[1-4]

There are a number of methods for the polymerization of conjugated dienes or the butadienes such as butadiene itself, isoprene, chloroprene, and various other substituted butadienes. Polymers with different structures and properties are obtained depending on the method and conditions. For example, in the simple case of polybutadiene, the polymer may have a 1,4-*cis* or *trans* structure, or a 1,2-structure which may be isotactic, atactic or syndiotactic or a mixture of all of these.

10.1 POLYBUTADIENE

Butadiene is now obtained from petroleum products by fractionation of cracking products and separating 1-butene. 1-Butene is catalytically dehydrogenated to 1,3-butadiene.

One of the first studied homopolymerizations of butadiene was the sodium initiated[5] reaction practiced in Germany which produced Buna Rubber. About the same time or earlier the polymerization in emulsion systems was discovered. The initiator in these reactions, unknown to the discoverers, was a peroxide of butadiene which is formed by oxygen. Neither of these methods for the formation of butadiene homopolymers is too important now.

Butadiene can be polymerized to a polymer having any desired structure utilizing the proper Ziegler-type catalysts[6,8] (Chapter 5). Predominately *trans*-1,4-structures are obtained from aluminum triethyl and titanium or vanadium trichlorides or vanadium oxyhalides. The structure of the

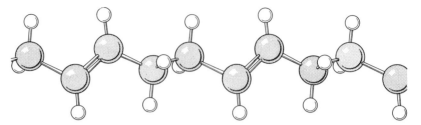

Fig. 10.1. *Trans*-1,4-polybutadiene.[8]

product polymer is also dependent on the ratio of the aluminum alkyl to titanium tetrachloride. A ratio near 1:1 produces both *cis* and *trans*-1,4 while lower ratios yield only the *trans*-product. Aluminum alkyls and titanium tetraiodide are specific for the polymerization to a *cis*-1,4 polymer. An alkali metal aluminum hydride, titanium tetrachloride and a trace of aluminum chloride afford the 1,2-polymer. Many other Ziegler-type catalyst systems with slight modifications which will affect the course of polymerization have been described.

Extraordinarily high molecular weight polybutadiene ($M_w = 7,000,000$) which has predominately a *trans*-1,4 structure is produced by the Alfin catalyst[6] (Chapter 5). A fine dispersion of lithium metal in petroleum jelly or another inert petroleum hydrocarbon will polymerize butadiene either in bulk or solution to afford a polymer whose structure depends somewhat on the reaction temperature, but is predominately *cis*-1,4.

Lithium alkyls alone polymerize butadiene with difficulty to a low molecular weight polymer in poor yields. The polymer structure is random in contrast to the affect of lithium alkyl catalysts on isoprene. All these polymerizations involving metal or organometallic catalysts take place at ordinary temperatures and pressure. Butadiene polymerization from a commercial standpoint is not nearly as important as isoprene polymerization.

Emulsion polybutadiene may be stretched to give an x-ray pattern which shows an identity period along the fiber axis of 5.0 A., indicating the *trans*-1,4 structure for the main portion of the crystalline region. The *trans*-1,4-polymer prepared by Ziegler catalysts exists in two crystalline modifications. Below 60°C. the hexagonal cell contains a zig-zag chain structure (identity period = 4.9 A., Fig. 10.1). Above 60°C., the chains are helical.

The *cis*-1,4-polybutadiene shows a crystalline x-ray pattern below 30°C. in which the monoclinic lattices show four monomer units per identity period (8.60 A.) and the cell contains two chains of two monomer units each (Fig. 10.2).

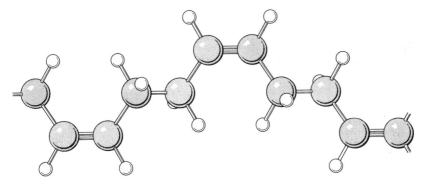

Fig. 10.2. *Cis*-1,4-polybutadiene.[8]

Two different crystalline 1,2-polybutadienes are obtained with Ziegler-type catalysts. Isotactic 1,2-polybutadiene has a rhombohedral cell in which the polymer chains show three monomer units per helical turn (6.5 A.) (Fig. 10.3). A syndiotactic arrangement in a polymer was first shown with 1,2-polybutadiene prepared by Ziegler catalysts. The polymer has a rigid linear zig-zag chain with carbon bond angles of 113° and an identity period of 5.14 A. (Fig. 10.4).

The Alfin polybutadiene has a greater proportion of *trans*-1,4-structure than polybutadiene prepared by conventional free radical emulsion systems. The ratio of *trans*-1,4- to 1,2- may be varied however from 0.66 to 3.7. Lithium polybutadiene has a mixed structure of 35% *cis*-1,4-, 52%

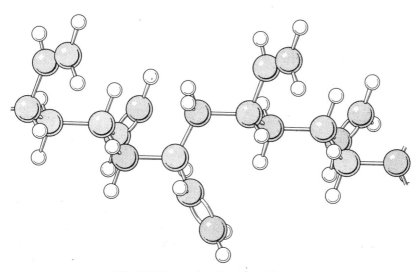

Fig. 10.3. Isotactic 1,2-polybutadiene.[8]

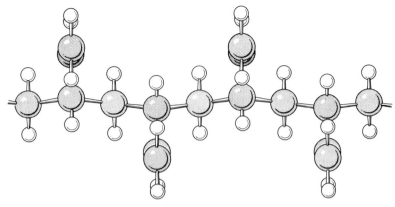

Fig. 10.4. Syndiotactic 1,2-polybutadiene.[8]

trans-1,4- and 13% 1,2-. The structure may be altered from 12% 1,2- to 78% 1,2- by the addition of ether to the system.

Table 10.1 shows the effect of structure on the properties of polybutadiene. Butadiene is widely employed in copolymerization reactions with other monomers in the formation of synthetic elastomers, but there has been little application, with the exception of Buna rubbers, for

TABLE 10.1

Physical properties of polybutadiene

Polymer Structure	Density	Tm, °C.	% Rebound at	
			20°C.	90°C.
trans-1,4- <60°C. (zig-zag)	0.96–1.02	135–148	75–80	90–93
60°C. (helical)		130		
cis-1,4	1.01	dependent on degree of crystallinity	88–90	92–95
1,2-isotactic	0.96	120–125	45–55	90–92
1,2-syndiotactic	0.96	154–155		

butadiene homopolymers. The butadiene rubbers are inferior in many respects even to other synthetic rubbers and were synthesized in lieu of a supply of natural rubber. Amorphous polybutadienes with the 1,4-linkage have a low ratio of hysteresis to elastic deformation; lower than the 1,2-polymers.

10.2 POLYISOPRENE

The polymerization of isoprene has become increasingly important with the discovery of various catalyst systems which will polymerize the monomer to any desired structure. Thus a synthetic natural rubber can now be prepared whose structure and properties are identical to natural rubber. In 1954, Goodrich Gulf announced the synthesis of an all *cis*-1,4-polyisoprene, Ameripol SN which was prepared from a Ziegler type catalyst. Shortly thereafter Firestone announced a synthetic natural rubber, Coral Rubber obtained by lithium metal. Butyl lithium is another catalyst which will produce a synthetic rubber identical in all respects to *Hevea* rubber.

Isoprene is obtained from the cracking products of the refineries and is recovered from C_5 cut by fractional distillation and extraction. The particular type of Ziegler catalysts which are effective for the polymerization of butadiene also serve for isoprene polymerization. The 1,4-structure is obtained with aluminum alkyls and titanium or vanadium salts. The 1,2- and 3,4- structures are obtained with the aluminum alkyls and oxygen containing compounds of the group IV–VI metals. The polymer is an all *cis*-1,4-polyisoprene,[9] (Ameripol SN) when the aluminum to titanium ratio is 1:1 or greater, with more *trans*-1,4-structure below that ratio. Aluminum alkyls in conjunction with titanium alkoxides or acetylacetonates give predominately the 3,4-polyisoprene. In the polymerization of isoprene with a lithium aluminum hydride-titanium tetraiodide, the *trans*-1,4-polymer is obtained.

The polymerization of isoprene with a lithium dispersion is carried out in the following way:[10] The dispersion is prepared in petroleum jelly or a high boiling hydrocarbon solvent at 200°C. with a high speed stirrer. This dispersion can be added to the pure monomer or a solution of the monomer in an inert solvent in an inert atmosphere. About 0.1 g. of lithium is needed for 100 g. of monomer. The molecular weight of the polymer as well as the reaction rate are dependent on the amount of catalyst. The lower the amount of lithium, the higher the molecular weight and the slower the reaction. The polymerization is carried out at ordinary temperatures and the resulting polyisoprene, Coral Rubber, is almost entirely *cis*-1,4. Other alkali metals produce polyisoprenes of mixed *cis*- and *trans*-1,4-, 1,2- and 3,4-structures.

Alkyl lithium polymerizations of isoprene may also be carried out in bulk or solution at room temperature. Again the polymer structure is *cis*-1,4. In this polymerization the molecular weight is proportional to the conversion.

Polyisoprene can exist in nine different forms: *cis*-1,4, *trans*-1,4, the

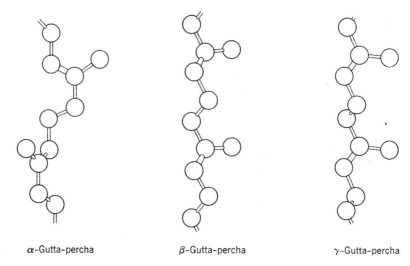

α-Gutta-percha   β-Gutta-percha   γ-Gutta-percha

Fig. 10.5. Gutta-percha.

atactic, isotactic and syndiotactic structures of 1,2- or 3,4- addition and a random species which can have all of these structural features associated with it. In addition, there are different crystalline modifications of some of these forms.

Gutta-percha and balata are impure natural *trans*-1,4- polyisoprenes which are obtained from rubber trees found in Malaya and Central America, respectively, and have molecular weights of about 100,000. There are three crystalline modifications of *trans*-1,4- polyisoprene; the α, β, and γ forms which have identity periods of 8.75, 4.77, and 9.21 A. respectively (Fig. 10.5). The *trans*-1,4-polyisoprenes prepared by Ziegler-type catalysts show x-ray diagrams which can be interpreted to explain the β and γ forms. In addition, these forms may have both left and right handed helices.

Natural *Hevea* rubber is an all *cis*-1,4-polyisoprene which has a number average molecular weight of 350,000 and an identity period of 8.1 A. Firestone's Coral Rubber (lithium metal), Goodrich-Gulf's Ameripol SN (Ziegler type) and polyisoprene prepared from butyl lithium in hydrocarbon solvents are nearly identical to *Hevea* in structure and properties. Coral rubber is 93.8 % *cis*-1,4- while *Hevea* is 97.8 % *cis*-1,4. The remainder of the structure in these rubbers is 3,4- (Fig. 10.6).

Isotactic and syndiotactic 1,2-polyisoprenes, which have been prepared by Ziegler-type catalysts have not as yet had their crystalline structures elucidated.

Table 10.2 lists some of the physical properties of the polyisoprenes. The all *cis*-1,4-polyisoprenes are employed mainly for carcass stock in tires. The raw *Hevea* rubber and synthetic natural rubber are treated in essentially the same way. Crepe rubber results when sodium bisulfite is

TABLE 10.2

Physical properties of the polyisoprenes

Structure	Identity Period, A.	Mol. Wt.	Density	Tm, °C.
trans-1,4	8.75			50
	4.77	30,000–100,000	1.04	
	9.21			
Ziegler (*trans*-1,4)		300,000–500,000		70–75
cis-1,4-*Hevea*	8.1	350,000	0.965	
Coral	8.1	as high as 700,000	0.96	22 ($Tg = 65$)
Ameripol SN	8.1	230,000–as high as 800,000	0.96	22 ($Tg = 70$)

added to bleach the rubber. The crepe can be rolled into sheets and air dried. Smoked sheets are obtained by treating rolled sheets at 50°C. in a smoke house.

This rubber is masticated in a Banbury mixer in the absence of oxygen in order to decrease the molecular weight and obtain a gummy mass suitable for vulcanization or curing.

There are several types of curing that can be carried out. Sulfur, sulfur chloride or other sulfur compounds crosslink the rubber with sulfur atoms in the linkage. Oxidizing agents, usually metals or metal oxides and peroxides which generate free radicals are two other types of curing agents. Vulcanization crosslinks the polymer with the expected effects on its physical properties. It gives the polymer greater tensile strength and modulus, decreases the flow but at the same time preserves its elasticity.

The vulcanization of rubber by sulfur and heat can be speeded up by

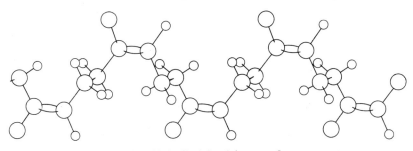

Fig. 10.6. *Cis*-1,4-polyisoprene.[7]

the addition of certain organic or inorganic accelerators. These accelerators in general are either some thioureas, mercaptans, thiophenols, thio acids, or metal salts of these compounds. Some of these accelerators require the presence of activators or promoters which are usually metal oxides such as zinc oxide.

The sulfur vulcanization reaction is quite complex and not all of the sulfur which reacts forms crosslinks. The greater portion of the sulfide links are formed by removing hydrogens which are most susceptible to free radical attack and leave behind stable free radicals. Thus the disulfide links appear allylic to the double bonds along the chain backbone.

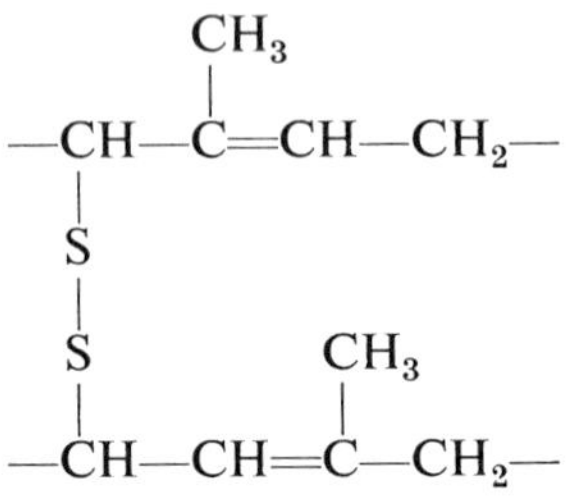

$$
\begin{array}{c}
CH_3 \\
| \\
-CH-C{=}CH-CH_2- \\
| \\
S \\
| \\
S \qquad CH_3 \\
| \qquad | \\
-CH-CH{=}C-CH_2-
\end{array}
$$

Some of the double bonds add hydrogen sulfide in a reaction which produces no crosslinks. The allylic free radicals formed may add across a double bond in another chain to form crosslinks.

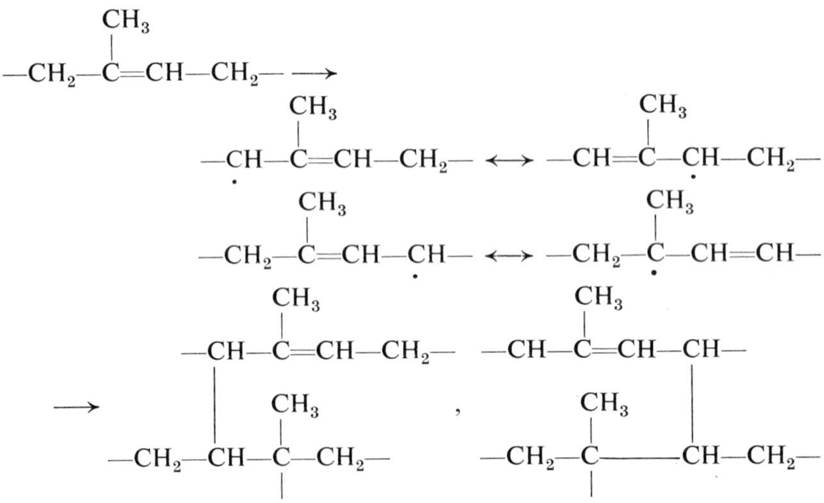

$$
\begin{array}{c}
CH_3 \\
| \\
-CH_2-C{=}CH-CH_2- \longrightarrow
\end{array}
$$

$$
\begin{array}{ccc}
CH_3 & & CH_3 \\
| & & | \\
-CH-C{=}CH-CH_2- & \longleftrightarrow & -CH{=}C-CH-CH_2- \\
\cdot & & \cdot \\
CH_3 & & CH_3 \\
| & & | \\
-CH_2-C{=}CH-CH- & \longleftrightarrow & -CH_2-C-CH{=}CH- \\
\cdot & & \cdot \\
CH_3 & & CH_3 \\
| & & | \\
-CH-C{=}CH-CH_2- & & -CH-C{=}CH-CH- \\
& & | \\
\longrightarrow \qquad | \quad CH_3 & , & CH_3 \quad | \\
| & & | \\
-CH_2-CH-C-CH_2- & & -CH_2-C{-}{-}{-}{-}{-}CH-CH_2- \\
| & & |
\end{array}
$$

In a vulcanization process with an oxidizing agent or peroxides, a free radical attack on the allylic carbon occurs as shown. Once one of the four free radical species shown above has been formed, this radical may add to double bonds in a propagation step which forms crosslinks.

The vulcanizates may be made hard or soft depending on the degree of crosslinking. A product which has been cured for a long period of time and has picked up 30 parts of sulfur to 100 of rubber is a hard rubber or ebonite. A maximum tensile strength (optimum cure) in rubber is obtained with 5–10 parts sulfur.

A typical vulcanization recipe (Table 10.3) combines accelerators and

TABLE 10.3
Vulcanization recipe

Rubber	100
Sulfur	0.25–1.5
Accelerator	0.25–1.5
Activator (zinc oxide)	1–10
Soap (stearic acid)	1–5
Antioxidant	0–1.5

activators in the sulfur rubber mixture. This recipe is a pure-gum vulcanizate which is soft and pliable and serves for the manufacture of rubber tubing, bands, gloves, and sheets but is unsuitable for tires.

When certain reinforcing fillers are added to the pure-gum vulcanizate the product is a loaded stock which has improved tensile strength, stiffness, tear resistance, and abrasion resistance. Carbon blacks are the best and most inexpensive reinforcing fillers although talc, zinc oxide, and others are serviceable. The amount of reinforcement obtained by a rubber depends also on the amount of filler, particle size, and type of elastomer.

10.3   POLYCHLOROPRENE,[1,4,11]

Neoprene was the first synthetic rubber to be developed in the United States, largely through the efforts of W. H. Carothers. In an investigation of the reactions of vinyl acetylene, it was found that the addition of hydrogen chloride gave 2-chloro-1,3-butadiene (chloroprene). The reaction was carried out with concentrated hydrochloric acid and a cuprous chloride-ammonium chloride catalyst.

$$HC{\equiv}C-CH{=}CH_2 \xrightarrow{HCl} CH_2{=}\underset{\underset{Cl}{|}}{C}-CH{=}CH_2$$

The pure monomer polymerized over a period of time at room temperature to yield a polymer which Carothers called μ-polychloroprene. Initiation was apparently obtained from a peroxide formed from oxygen present in the system. Chloroprene is polymerized on an industrial scale by emulsion techniques where free radical initiators are engaged. Sulfur

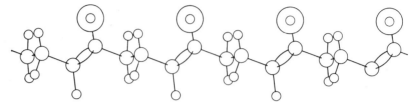

Fig. 10.7. Polychloroprene.

may be introduced into the emulsion system to produce some crosslinks and thus obtain a latex with elastomeric properties.

The x-ray pattern of neoprene has a striking similarity to the pattern of β-gutta-percha. The identity period of 4.89 A. which indicates that the structure is *trans*-1,4 with the chlorine atoms (which are nearly the same size as methyl groups) occupying the positions of the methyl groups in β-gutta-percha (Fig. 10.7).

Neoprene prepared in emulsion has a molecular weight of 100,000–300,000 and swells but does not dissolve in benzene or hydrocarbon solvents. It is elastic like rubber but has a higher modulus of elasticity. The polymer is particularly resistant to oils; more so than rubber. The rubber has a density of 1.23, a tensile strength of about 2000 p.s.i., and 800% elongation at the break.

Neoprene can be vulcanized by heat alone or in the presence of metal oxides such as zinc or magnesium oxide. Sulfur alone or sulfur with the conventional accelerators cures neoprene only very slowly. At room temperature, neoprene is tougher than unvulcanized rubber but becomes soft above 70°C. It has a high tensile strength 3000–4000 p.s.i., in the absence of a filler and the compounding with a carbon black does not appreciably reinforce vulcanized neoprene.

The neoprene vulcanizates have excellent resistance to weathering and oil. Outstanding but expensive tires can be made from the polymer. Its chief application is in the fabrication of tubes, washers, electrical coatings, etc. where an oil resistant elastomer is needed.

10.4 POLY(DIMETHYLBUTADIENE)

The substituted butadiene, 2,3-dimethylbutadiene, can be prepared from the bimolecular reduction of acetone to pinacol and the subsequent dehydration over an alumina catalyst.

$$2CH_3-COCH_3 \longrightarrow (CH_3)_2C-C(CH_3)_2 \longrightarrow CH_2{=}\overset{\overset{\displaystyle CH_3}{|}}{C}-\overset{\overset{\displaystyle CH_3}{|}}{C}{=}CH_2$$
$$\underset{OH\ OH}{}$$

Dimethylbutadiene polymerizes rapidly under the influence of sodium or free radical initiators to "methyl rubber." During World War I, a variety of methyl rubbers were manufactured in Germany. Methyl rubber H (hard) was prepared by the spontaneous polymerization of the monomer in bulk at 30°C. over a period of three months. Methyl rubber W (soft) was prepared under pressure at 70°C. in a 6-month polymerization. H-rubber was suitable for hard rubber applications such as battery cases.

Recently 2,3-dimethylbutadiene has been polymerized with Ziegler-type catalysts,[12] and the structure of the polymer is probably all *cis*-1,4 with less than 2% 1,2-.[13]

10.5 POLYMERIZATION OF OTHER CONJUGATED OLEFINS

Many other conjugated dienes or polyenes will undergo polymerization reactions. The phenyl substituted butadienes such as 2-phenyl-butadiene polymerizes under the influence of cationic[14] and Ziegler-type catalysts.[15] Cyclopentadiene gives low molecular weight polymers by a Diels-Alder reaction (Chapter 8) but will polymerize with free radical initiators or Ziegler-type catalysts.

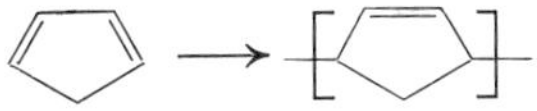

The next higher member in this cyclic series, 1,3-cyclohexadiene, has been converted to a low molecular weight polymer with Ziegler-type catalysts. The resulting polymer can be dehydrogenated to poly(*p*-phenylene).[16]

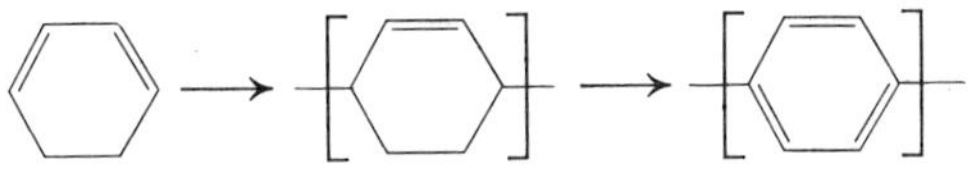

Several 1,2-dimethylene cycloalkanes have been polymerized to crystalline polymers. The monomer 1,2-dimethylenecyclohexane gives a crystalline necessarily all *cis* polymer with a melting point of 165°C. Hydrogenation of this polymer affords a polymer which has the *cis* stereochemistry on the cyclohexane ring.[17]

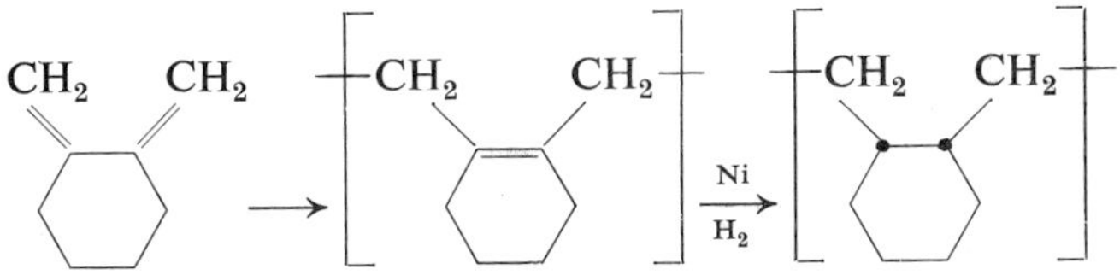

This monomer has also been polymerized by Ziegler-type catalysts and in general is much more readily polymerized than its lower ring analogs, 1,2-dimethylene cyclopentane and cyclobutane.[18]

$$CH_2 \qquad CH_2 \qquad\qquad CH_2 \qquad CH_2$$

The polymerization of some conjugated triolefins has also been reported. Alloöcimene is polymerized by Ziegler catalysis to form a polymer by 1,2- and 1,4-addition, ignoring a vinylidine double bond which is conjugated with the other two double bonds.

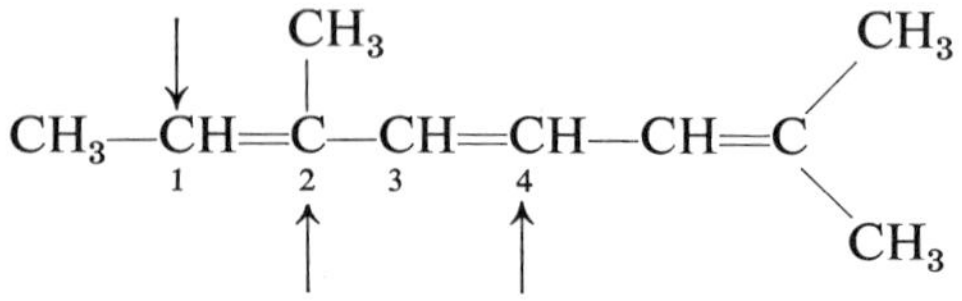

$$CH_3 \qquad\qquad CH_3$$
$$CH_3-CH=C-CH=CH-CH=C$$
$$\underset{1}{} \quad \underset{2}{} \quad \underset{3}{} \quad \underset{4}{} \qquad\qquad CH_3$$

Carothers first reported that the reaction of α,α'-dibromo-p-xylene gave a low molecular weight polymer on treatment with magnesium.[19] The poly(p-xylylene) formed probably proceeds through the reactive quinone-dimethide. Similar results have been obtained with α,α'-dichloro-o-xylene.[20]

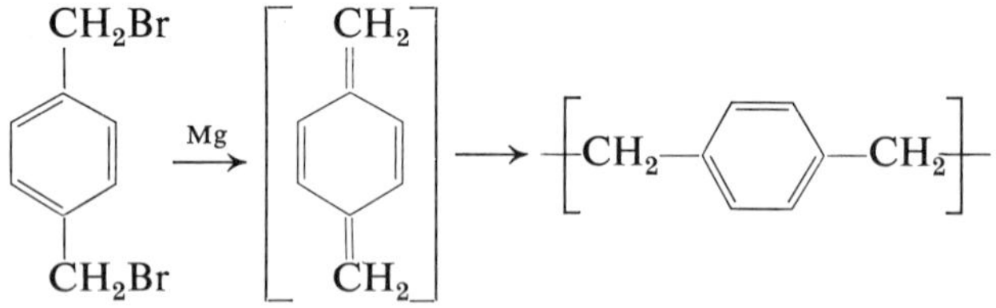

$$CH_2Br \qquad\qquad CH_2$$

$$\xrightarrow{Mg}$$

$$CH_2Br \qquad\qquad CH_2$$

A high molecular weight poly(p-xylylene) is obtained by the pyrolytic dehydrogenation of p-xylene at 900–1000°C. and 1–5 mm. pressure.[21–25] The quinonedimethide vapor polymerizes on cooling to room temperature. High molecular weight polymer is also obtained by the action of alkali on trimethyl(p-methylbenzyl) ammonium bromide.[26,27]

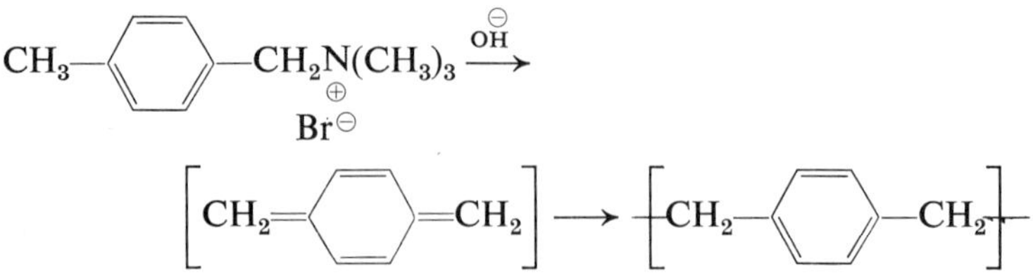

$$CH_3-\langle\rangle-CH_2N(CH_3)_3 \xrightarrow{\overset{\ominus}{OH}}$$
$$Br^{\ominus}$$

This polymer is more linear and less crosslinked than that prepared by dehydrogenation. It is interesting that [2.2] paracyclophane a by-product of the polymerization,[28] will undergo a thermal ring opening reaction to yield the same polymer.

Poly(p-xylylene) is stable at temperatures above 300°C. This crystalline polymer will form tough clear films directly when the polymerization of the vapor is carried out on a surface but the polymer is otherwise difficult to fabricate. Fabricated films are highly crystalline and brittle.

REFERENCES

1. G. S. Whitby, C. C. Davis, and R. F. Dunbrook, eds., *Synthetic Rubber*, John Wiley and Sons, New York, 1954.
2. C. E. Schildknecht, ed., *Polymer Processes*, Interscience Publishers, New York, 1956.
3. F. A. Bovey, *Emulsion Polymerization*, Interscience Publishers, New York, 1955.
4. M. Morton, ed., *Rubber Technology*, Reinhold Publishing Corp., New York, 1959.
5. C. S. Marvel, W. J. Bailey, and G. E. Inskeep, *J. Polymer Sci.*, **1**, 275 (1946).
6. N. G. Gaylord and H. F. Mark, *Linear and Stereoregular Addition Polymers*, Interscience Publishers, New York, 1959.
7. J. K. Stille, *Chem. Revs.*, **58**, 541 (1958).
8. G. Natta, *Scientific American*, **197**, 98 (1957).
9. S. E. Horne, Jr., and coworkers, *Ind. Eng. Chem.*, **48**, 784 (1956).
10. F. W. Stavely and coworkers, *Ind. Eng. Chem.*, **48**, 778 (1956).
11. W. H. Carothers, in *Collected Papers by W. H. Carothers on High Polymeric Substances*, H. Mark and G. S. Whitby, eds., Interscience Publishers, New York, 1940.
12. O. Solomon and C. A. Stonicesseu, *Revista de Chemie (Romania)*, **9**, 507 (1958).
13. T. F. Yen, *J. Polymer Sci.*, **35**, 533 (1959).
14. P. de Radzitzski, M. C. de Wilde, and G. Smets, *J. Polymer Sci.*, **13**, 477 (1954).
15. J. K. Stille and E. D. Vessel, *J. Polymer Sci.*, **49**, 419 (1961).
16. C. S. Marvel and G. E. Hartzell, *J. Am. Chem. Soc.*, **81**, 448 (1959).
17. W. J. Bailey and H. R. Golden, *J. Am. Chem. Soc.*, **76**, 5418 (1954).
18. A. T. Blomquist and D. T. Longone, *J. Am. Chem. Soc.*, **79**, 3916 (1957).
19. W. H. Carothers, *Chem. Revs.*, **8**, 353 (1931).
20. F. G. Mann and F. H. C. Stewart, *J. Chem. Soc.*, **1954**, 2826.
21. M. Szwarc, *J. Chem. Phys.*, **16**, 128 (1948); *J. Polymer Sci.*, **6**, 319 (1951).
22. L. A. Auspos, L. A. R. Hall, J. K. Hubbard, W. Kirk, Jr., J. R. Schaefgen, and S. B. Speck, *J. Polymer Sci.*, **15**, 9 (1955); **15**, 19 (1955).
23. J. R. Schaefgen, *J. Polymer Sci.*, **15**, 203 (1955).

24. L. A. Errede and M. Szwarc, *Quart. Rev.*, **12**, 301 (1958).
25. L. A. Errede and B. F. Landrum, *J. Am. Chem. Soc.*, **79**, 4952 (1957).
26. E. I. du Pont and Co., Inc., British Patent 807,196, Jan. 7 (1959); C. A., **53**, 8711h (1959).
27. H. E. Winberg, F. S. Fawcett, W. E. Mochel, and C. W. Theobald, *J. Am. Chem. Soc.*, **82**, 1428 (1960).
28. J. E. Dunabin, H. Mason, A. P. Seyfang, and F. J. Woodman, *Nature*, **164**, 915 (1949).

11

COPOLYMERS[1-2]

The term *copolymer* as used here refers to a polymer having two different monomers incorporated into the same polymer chain. In most cases, these are random copolymers in which the units of one monomer and the units of the other have no definite order or arrangement along any given chain, and generally one chain may have a slightly different composition or ratio of one monomer to the other. *Block copolymers* on the other hand have a long segment or block, one monomer followed by a block of a second monomer. The effect is that of joining end-to-end some chains of two different homopolymers.

Stereoblock polymers are those which have blocks of the same monomer with different stereochemical configurations. The term *graft copolymer* refers to a type of block copolymer in which one monomer has been grafted onto the main chain of the other.

Copolymers are important industrial products since the properties of a copolymer are those unobtainable by a homopolymer of either of the monomers making up the copolymer.

11.1 RANDOM COPOLYMERS

Ethylene copolymers.[3-6] Copolymers of ethylene have been prepared by radical initiation in emulsion systems with relatively low ethylene pressures. The monomers diethylfumarate, vinyl chloride, ethyl acrylate, and maleic anhydride will copolymerize with ethylene. The maleic anhydride co-polymer is nearly a 1:1 copolymer. Until recently, copolymers of vinyl acetate and ethylene prepared by peroxide initiators in emulsion had received the most attention since these monomers are both unreactive towards homopolymerization but form a copolymer very readily. The amount of vinyl acetate may be varied widely from ethylene-vinylacetate ratios of 400:1 to 1:28. The copolymers may be hydrolyzed to obtain ethylene-vinyl alcohol copolymers.

Most of the recent interest in ethylene copolymers has centered around the ethylene-propylene copolymers prepared by Ziegler-type catalysts. A highly dispersed catalyst obtained from a combination of vanadium oxytrichloride and aluminum trihexyl undergoes no additional breakdown during aging or polymerization so that the rate of polymerization and the reactivity ratios of the monomers remain constant. In contrast, the conventional Ziegler-type catalysts produce only small amounts of a true copolymer. Copolymers in the range of 30–80% ethylene with high intrinsic viscosities can be obtained in good yields. In order to incorporate, for example, 40 mole per cent propylene, a 2:1 ratio of propylene to ethylene feed is required. The reactivity ratios of ethylene and propylene are 17.95 and 0.065 respectively, for this catalyst. Even though the high reactivity of ethylene presents some difficulties in copolymerization, polymers of any average composition can be obtained by operating the feed charge continuously. The catalyst system vanadium tetrachloride-aluminum trihexyl presents more favorable conditions for copolymerization in that the reactivity ratios are 7.08 and 0.088 for ethylene and propylene respectively.

Ethylene-propylene copolymers have lower transition temperatures than either of the homopolymers. The high resilience in the copolymers

TABLE 1[7]

Copolymer	% Rebound at	
	20°C.	90°C.
Ethylene-propylene (35–65% C_2H_4)	55–65	65–80
Ethylene-propylene-isoprene (10% C_5H_8)	50–65	65–80
Propylene-isoprene (10% C_5H_8)	18–20	55–65
Butyl rubber	16–20	55–60

has been attributed to the increase in chain flexibility brought about by reduced steric hindrance compared to that of the propylene homopolymer, the low second-order transition temperature, and the noncrystalline character of the ethylene segments because of the propylene units in the chain. The best values for elastic properties are obtained from copolymers with just enough propylene (40%) to prevent the formation of crystallites of polyethylene.

The copolymers, which tend to crystallize on stretching, have low initial elastic modulus, high tensile strength, and low hysteresis loss.

Copolymerization of the monoolefins with butadiene yields butadiene

1,2- and 1,4-units in the copolymer. Copolymers of isoprene contain mostly 3,4-segments.

Vinyl chloride copolymers. The copolymerization of vinylidine chloride with lesser amounts of vinyl chloride in bulk with free radical initiators and the shaping of these polymers by a quenching process has been known for thirty-five years.[3] Mixtures of vinylidine chloride and vinyl chloride copolymerize only about one-tenth as fast as either monomer separately and vinyl chloride enters into the polymer chain much more reluctantly than vinylidine chloride.

Copolymers may also be prepared in emulsion systems with persulfate initiators and a reductive activator. Saran plastics are usually prepared by an aqueous suspension polymerization system with peroxide initiators. A typical Saran copolymer which contains 10–15% vinyl chloride and 85–90% vinylidine chloride may be prepared by constantly regulating the feed charge. In this way the higher reactivity of vinylidine chloride can be compensated and a more uniform copolymer is obtained.

When the copolymers are heated up and rapidly quenched an amorphous polymer is obtained which only slowly forms crystallites on standing. However, if the copolymer is stretched while cool its tensile strength may be improved from 8000–10,000 p.s.i. to 30,000–60,000 p.s.i. by the formation of oriented crystallites.

The Saran copolymer is plasticized only difficultly as most plasticizers exude from the finished product. The physical properties of the Saran plastic can be varied according to the copolymer composition and the plasticizer. Saran has a softening point of 115–138°C. and tubes and pipes are extruded at 120–190°C.

The Sarans have good resistance to outdoor weathering as well as resistance to water, organic solvents, and mineral acids. Fibers, filaments, and rigid tubing where a high tensile strength in one direction is needed can be fabricated from Saran. A large portion of the Saran which is manufactured in the form of monofilament fibers is woven into automobile seat covers and other fabrics where a durable but easy to clean material is desirable. Saran pipes and pipe fittings are resistant to aqueous acids and alkalies and may be joined by welding at 300°C.

Another big use of Saran is the plastic film. These films have low moisture transmission, good toughness and tear strength and the ability to cling or adhere to other materials. For these reasons, it makes an excellent packaging material. Saran moldings have the disadvantage that the plastic discolors on heating.

Polymerization of a mixture of vinyl chloride and vinyl acetate is accomplished in a solution polymerization with special solvents and free radical initiators. The solvents engaged are those from which the co-polymer will separate when the desired molecular weight is reached. For example, a hexane solvent and a benzoyl peroxide initiator at 40°C. is effective. Copolymers of a narrow molecular weight range which are colorless and clear are essential to the manufacture of good vinylites. These properties may be obtained by operating at low temperatures (30°C.) with an active acetyl benzoyl peroxide initiator in a butane solvent. Tensile strengths of 9000 p.s.i. may be obtained from polymers of molecular weight values of 11,000.

An improvement in durability and adherence of vinylite lacquer resins is obtained by adding small amounts of maleic anhydride to the copolymer recipe. An 86:13:1 terpolymer of vinyl chloride: vinylacetate: maleic anhydride is hydrolyzed to produce a few free carboxylic acid groups along the chain. A coating of the resulting polymer can be applied with a ketone solvent and baked to give a partially insoluble resin.

Vinyl chloride–acrylonitrile copolymers are obtained by free radical initiation in bulk or solution. The reactivity ratio of acrylonitrile exceeds that of vinyl chloride to the extent that an 83.5–98 % vinyl chloride feed is used in order to obtain a 45–80 % vinyl chloride copolymer. The addition of portions of acrylonitrile during the polymerization give a more constant monomer ratio in the product.

The copolymer manufactured by Carbide and Carbon is sold under the trade names of Vinyon N and Dynel.[8] The Dynel fibers which are spun from an acetone solution are woven into various fabrics. The fabrics are shrink resistant, water resistant and are not flammable.

Butadiene-styrene copolymers (GR-S).[3,9,10] Extensive work on butadiene-styrene copolymers as a synthetic rubber was accomplished by the German industries before the First World War. Even at this time, the polymerizations were carried out in emulsion systems. The German Buna-S rubbers were 75–25 copolymers of butadiene-styrene prepared in emulsion with a persulfate initiator and a mercaptan regulator or chain transfer agent. Much of the technical information gained by the German plants was enlarged and expanded during the Second World War when the United States was forced to the production of synthetic rubber.

The copolymer manufactured in this country, GR-S, had a lower viscosity than the standard Buna-S so that the polymer could be worked at ordinary temperatures in the existing natural rubber machinery. The mutual recipe for the process is shown in Table 11.2. The polymerization was carried to 78 % conversion at 50° for 14 hr. The intrinsic viscosity of the resulting polymer is about 2 or 2.5. The chain transfer agent, dodecyl-mercaptan, also acts as a reducing agent in the redox initiation system.

The selection of a mercaptan chain transfer agent was therefore a fortunate one. If the soap is an unsaturated acid salt, it will use up the generated free radicals so that pure saturated soaps are required for consistent results. The reactivity ratio of styrene compared to butadiene in this emulsion system is such that with a 25:75 initial feed of styrene to butadiene, the copolymer first formed contains a lower portion of styrene (17%). At 80% conversion, the incorporation rises to 21% due to the increased proportion of styrene in the mixture.

TABLE 11.2
Mutual GR-S recipe

Charge	Parts
Butadiene	75
Styrene	25
Dodecyl mercaptan	0.5
Water	180
Potassium persulfate	0.3
Soap	5.0

The initial commercial production of GR-S was carried out in large batch type reactors which would operate under pressure. At the end of the polymerization reaction, hydroquinone was added to stop the polymerization reaction. The volatile, unreacted butadiene was removed, an antioxidant was added and the copolymer latex was coagulated by an acid-salt solution. The resulting coagulated polymer was washed and dried. Continuous reactors were later employed and increased production rates were obtained.

A "cold rubber" can be prepared in emulsion systems at temperatures as low as $-10°C$. by engaging an initiation system which is active at low temperatures and an antifreeze such as methanol. These initiation systems were the redox pair composed of organic hydroperoxides such as p-menthane hydroperoxide and ferrous sulfate. These "cold rubbers" had a better quality than the 50°C. GR-S.

GR-S shows little tendency to crystallize on stretching and can be considered to be a random polymer with several irregularities in its structure. The butadiene segments in the chain are about 80% 1,4-structure, most of which are *trans*. The remainder of the units are 1,2-. There are some clusters of styrene units along the chain and some branching takes place, probably from the pendant vinyl units. "Cold rubber" has a higher degree of chain order and less branching. The molecular weight may range from 25,000 to 500,000 in certain samples and the copolymer is soluble in benzene and other aromatic hydrocarbons.

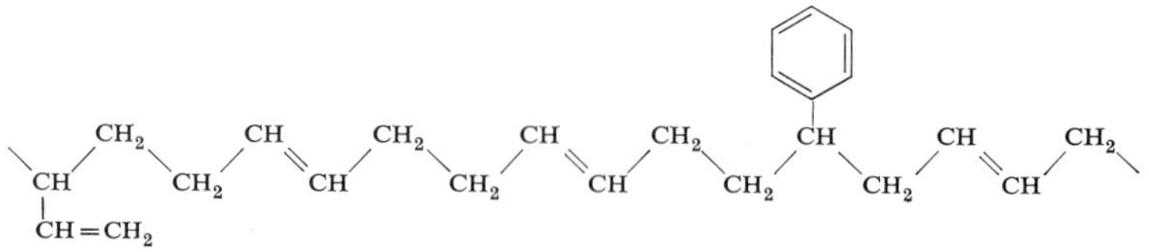

GR-S requires some mastication, but the process is not as extensive as that for natural rubber since the molecular weight and molecular weight range are fairly well controlled by the modifiers. Vulcanization is carried out with sulfur but less sulfur is required for an optimum GR-S cure than with a natural rubber cure. Even with sulfide accelerators and activators the cure is slower than a *Hevea* cure (Table 11.3). Good tensile strength

TABLE 11.3
Vulcanization recipe for GR-S

Component	Amount (parts)
GRS	100
Carbon black	50
Petroleum softener	5.0
Zinc oxide	5.0
Stearic acid	1.5
Captax accelerator	1.2
Sulfur	2.0

and other desirable physical properties are obtained only with a carbon black reinforcing filler. Unfilled GR-S (vulcanized) has a tensile strength of only 400 p.s.i. which is raised to 3000 p.s.i. with reinforcing whereas vulcanized *Hevea* has a tensile strength of 3000 p.s.i. before filling.

The carbon filler can be added as a slurry before coagulation of the latex and the carbon coprecipitates in the coagulation masterbatch process. GR-S rubber can be extended by mixing an oil with a high viscosity GR-S in order to reduce the viscosity and make the rubber easier to work. The oil can also be added to the latex as an emulsion before coagulation. A comparison of some of the physical properties of GR-S and *Hevea* are given in Table 11.4.

The use of GR-S in tread and carcass stocks of tires arose out of necessity. The properties of GR-S which are important to a good tire are inferior to natural rubber. The GR-S vulcanizates do not have the good snap, liveliness, and resilience of natural rubber. The GR-S rubbers have

TABLE 11.4
Physical properties of GR-S and Hevea

	Hevea		GR-S	
	Vulcanizate	Vulcanizate with 33% Carbon Black	Vulcanizate	Vulcanizate with 33% Carbon Black
% elongation	750–850	550–650	400–600	400–600
tensile strength, p.s.i.	2500–3500	3500–5000	200–400	2500–4000
% rebound	75	45–55	65	40–50

a high heat buildup which make them unsatisfactory for the tire carcass of large tires. The GR-S tire treads have, however, given good road wear, even though the tensile strengths are somewhat lower than natural rubber. Cold rubber tensile strengths are comparable to *Hevea* but at elevated temperatures this strength is lost. Ozone resistance of GR-S is superior to that of natural rubber.

Butadiene-acrylonitrile copolymers (GR-N).[3,9] The butadiene-acrylonitrile copolymers were first developed in Germany to supplement the butadiene-styrene copolymers in that the Buna-N rubbers were oil resistant. A typical emulsion recipe requires a 75–25 charge of butadiene to acrylonitrile. At low conversion, the amount of incorporated acrylonitrile is high and this incorporation decreases in the chains formed near the end of the polymerization. An ammonium persulfate initiator, a bicarbonate buffer and a mercaptan regulator are other components of the system. A typical recipe for the polymerization at 30°C. to 75% conversion is given in Table 11.5. The polymerization to this conversion took about 24 hr. and contained 25% incorporated acrylonitrile. In some improved

TABLE 11.5
Emulsion recipe for Buna-N or Perbuna

Component	Amount (parts)
Butadiene	75
Acrylonitrile	25
Water	150
Potassium persulfate	0.2
Diproxid (regulator)	0.3
Nekal BX	3.6
Sodium pyrophosphate	0.3
Sodium hydroxide	0.1

processes, the monomer feed is constantly adjusted in order to make a more uniform polymer of a constant composition. The butadiene-acrylonitrile copolymers produced in the United States (GR-N) were made with a similar recipe.

At the end of the polymerization, the residual monomer is removed by steam and the polymer coagulated by the addition of salt. The product is washed and dried. Vulcanization and compounding are preceded by mastication. A sulfur formula with activators, accelerators, and a carbon black reinforcing filler are used in the compounding and vulcanization process.

The GR-N rubbers have limited flexibility at low temperatures. Copolymers which have a low content of acrylonitrile (25%) and a reasonable oil resistance have a brittle point of $-45°C$. The GR-N's which have a higher acrylonitrile content and thus better oil resistance have higher brittle points.

These nitrile rubbers, GR-N, Buna-N or Perbuna are used where there is a need for a rubber with a good oil resistance. They are less resilient than *Hevea* rubber but have been extensively used for gasoline and oil hoses, fuel tanks and the like.

Olefin–sulfur dioxide copolymers. The olefin–sulfur dioxide copolymers are included here not because they have any commercial importance, but because they are formed from an interesting and unusual type of copolymerization reaction. The polymerization reaction, first investigated extensively by Staudinger[11] and Marvel[12–18] is one which affords a 1:1 copolymer of an olefin and sulfur dioxide. The polymerization is carried out in bulk, usually at room temperature by combining equal volumes of the monomers and a free radical initiator.

$$RCR'=CH_2 + SO_2 \longrightarrow \left[\begin{matrix} R \\ | \\ CR'-CH_2-SO_2 \end{matrix} \right]_n$$

$$R=R'=H$$

$$R'=H; \quad R=CH_3-, \; CH_3(CH_2)_n-, \; C_6H_5-, \; HO_2C(CH_2)_8-$$

$$n = 1\text{–}10$$

$$R=R'=CH_3$$

for

$$R-CH=CH-R' + SO_2 \longrightarrow \left[\begin{matrix} R & R' \\ | & | \\ CH-CH-SO_2 \end{matrix} \right]$$

$$R=R'=CH_3- \; (cis \text{ and } trans)$$

$$R=CH_3-, \; R'=CH_3-CH_2-$$

and

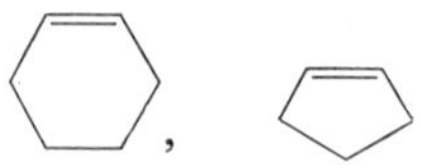

It was originally believed that these copolymers had a head-to-head–tail-to-tail structure but a rigorous chemical proof of the head-to-tail structure of the propylene-sulfur dioxide copolymer has been given.[19] Inherent viscosities as high as 3.5 have been obtained with this copolymer but copolymers of this type will decompose into the monomer fragments at temperatures near 300°C.

The ceiling temperatures for polymerization vary with the structure of the olefin.[20-24] Isobutylene-sulfur dioxide mixtures, for example, yield copolymer at 0°C., but not at room temperature. In general, branching on the double bond lowers the ceiling temperature, Tc, as evidenced by the series ethylene 135°, propylene 90°, butene-1 60°, butene-2 34°, pentene-2 8°, and heptene-2 −38°C. Cyclic olefins have a higher Tc than 2-olefins. Cyclopentene and cyclohexene have ceiling temperatures of 120° and 24°C. respectively.

The mechanism of copolymerization involves addition of monomer to a free radical chain end.[25-28] The copolymerization of *cis*- and *trans*-2-butene with sulfur dioxide is non-stereospecific since the carbon bearing the free radical loses its stereochemical configuration faster than the sulfur dioxide can add to the chain end.

$$-SO_2-\underset{\underset{CH_3}{|}}{CH}-\underset{\underset{CH_3}{|}}{CH}\cdot \xrightarrow{Fast} -SO_2-\underset{\underset{CH_3}{|}}{CH}-\overset{\cdot}{C}HCH_3 \xrightarrow[SO_2]{Slow}$$

$$-SO_2-\underset{\underset{CH_3}{|}}{CH}-CHCH_3-SO_2\cdot$$

A similar type of ideal copolymerization reaction takes place between olefins and carbon monoxide by free radical initiation to produce a polymeric ketone.[29,30]

$$CH_2{=}CH_2 + CO \xrightarrow[\substack{135° \\ 4500-14,700\ lb.}]{t\text{-Butylperoxide}} \left[CH_2-CH_2-\overset{\overset{O}{\|}}{C} \right]$$

11.2 BLOCK COPOLYMERS[31-36]

In recent years considerably more attention has been turned toward the preparation of block and graft copolymers as these tailor made polymer molecules often have quite striking properties which serve certain needs in the polymer field. Block copolymers for example, may be excellent wetting agents when the blocks are alternate hydrophilic and hydrophobic portions.

There are many techniques which may be used to prepare block co-polymers and these techniques are usually quite straightforward, utilizing chemical reactions which are well known organic and polymerization reactions. One of the major difficulties encountered in block copolymer work is the isolation of the block polymer from the homopolymers which may be present. This is necessary not only to prove the existence of the block polymer but to maintain the desirable characteristics which are inherent only in the block polymer. This often requires special fractiona-tion techniques. In the following discussion these fractionation techniques will not be mentioned. In addition, not every block polymer which has been prepared and studied will be covered, but studies which demonstrate the different methods of formation are considered.

Block polymers from living systems. One method of formation of polymer blocks involves the formation of a polymer whose growing end remains alive after all of one monomer has been consumed, and the subsequent addition of a second monomer which will then grow on the active end.

Methyl methacrylate will polymerize from the vapor under the influence of ultraviolet irradiation (Chapter 9). The poly(methyl methacrylate) which deposits on the surface of the container has active free radical ends which stay alive for a considerable length of time after all the gaseous monomer has been consumed. Subsequent addition of chloroprene to the reaction vessel results in the polymerization of chloroprene on the ends of the poly(methyl methacrylate).[34]

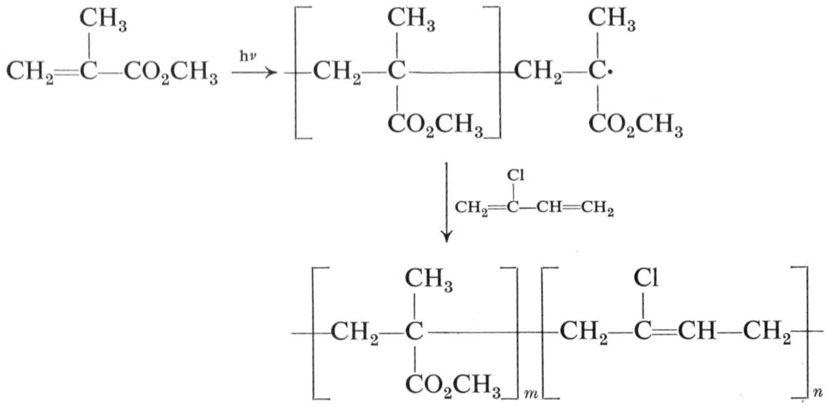

The same technique has been applied in the polymerization of styrene by sodium and naphthalene to give a living polymer system where the ends of the growing chains stay alive (Chapter 5). Addition of isoprene to this system produces a styrene-isoprene block copolymer.[38]

Polymerization by Ziegler-type catalysts also offers a method of formation of block copolymers. The first monomer which is polymerized by the conventional aluminum alkyl-titanium tetrachloride catalyst must be a polymer soluble in the reaction medium.[39] The monoölefins 1-pentene and 1-hexene or the dienes butadiene and isoprene are suitable first monomers since the polymers formed from these monomers are soluble in the reaction medium; more so than polyethylene or other poly-1-olefins. Since the metal alkyl bond remains alive, a second monomer may be introduced after the first monomer is exhausted and thus a block of the polymer formed from the second monomer is grown on the first.

With special mechanical techniques, a second monomer can be introduced even when the active radical end is comparatively short lived. By dropping a monomer such as butyl acrylate or acrylonitrile along with a photosensitizer through a capillary whose tip is illuminated with ultraviolet light, polymerization of the monomer begins to take place.[40,41] If the active polymer is passed from the capillary tip into a second monomer, such as styrene, a block of polystyrene will be formed on the poly(butyl acrylate) block or polyacrylonitrile block. By this method, a block copolymer which is a polyampholyte can be prepared from a butyl acrylate-2-vinylpyridine block copolymer by hydrolyzing the ester.[42]

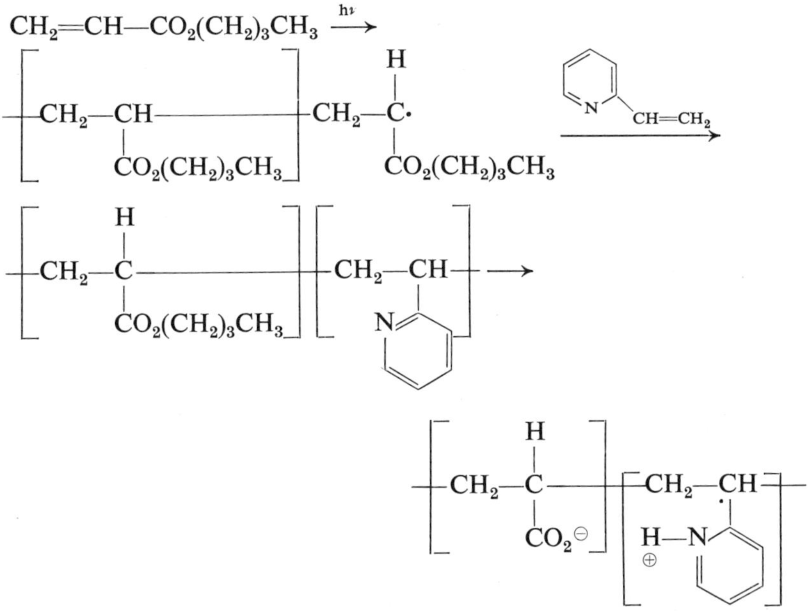

$$CH_2{=}CH{-}CO_2(CH_2)_3CH_3 \xrightarrow{h\nu}$$

Block polymers from two-phase reaction systems. The polymerization of two monomers simultaneously usually leads to a random copolymer. However, in special systems, block copolymers can be prepared by the copolymerization of two monomers one of which is soluble in the solvent engaged for the polymerization. The polymer formed in the solution from the soluble monomer migrates to the insoluble monomer phase after it has attained a certain molecular weight and the polymer then grows by addition of the insoluble monomer. Such a system is obtained by the acrylic or methacrylic acid monomers which are water soluble and styrene which is water insoluble.[43,44] With a water soluble free radical initiator, the growing polyacrylics migrate to the styrene layer and styrene blocks grow on the already formed acrylate block.

$$CH_2{=}CH{-}CO_2H \xrightarrow{S_2O_8^{-2}} \left[CH_2{-}\underset{\underset{CO_2H}{|}}{CH}\right]CH_2{-}\underset{\underset{CO_2H}{|}}{CH} \cdot \xrightarrow{C_6H_5CH{=}CH_2}$$

$$\left[CH_2{-}\underset{\underset{CO_2H}{|}}{CH}\right]\left[CH_2{-}\underset{\underset{C_6H_5}{|}}{CH}\right]$$

Block copolymers from polymeric initiators. The formation of a polymer with end groups which will decompose to generate free radical ends offers a third method of block formation. The polymerization of styrene in the presence of carbon tetrabromide gives a polystyrene with tribromomethyl end groups. When this polymer is irradiated with ultraviolet light in the presence of methyl methacrylate or methyl acrylate, the polymer acts as a free radical initiator, initiating the polymerization of the acrylate on the preformed styrene block.[43-45]

$$C_6H_5CH{=}CH_2 + CBr_4 \longrightarrow Br\left[\underset{\underset{C_6H_5}{|}}{CH}{-}CH_2\right]CBr_3 \xrightarrow{h\nu}$$

$$Br\left[\underset{\underset{C_6H_5}{|}}{CH}{-}CH_2\right]\underset{\underset{Br}{|}}{\overset{\overset{Br}{|}}{C}}\cdot \xrightarrow{\underset{}{CH_2{=}\underset{\underset{CO_2CH_3}{}}{\overset{\overset{CH_3}{|}}{C}}}} Br\left[\underset{\underset{C_6H_5}{|}}{CH}{-}CH_2\right]\underset{\underset{Br}{|}}{\overset{\overset{Br}{|}}{C}}\left[CH_2{-}\underset{\underset{CO_2CH_3}{|}}{\overset{\overset{CH_3}{|}}{C}}\right]$$

Polymeric phthaloyl peroxide initiates the polymerization of styrene or vinyl acetate to form a polymer of styrene or vinyl acetate containing polymeric phthaloyl peroxide end groups. Addition of methyl methacrylate, vinylpyrrolidone, styrene or vinyl acetate to this polymer adds a second block to the first.[46,47]

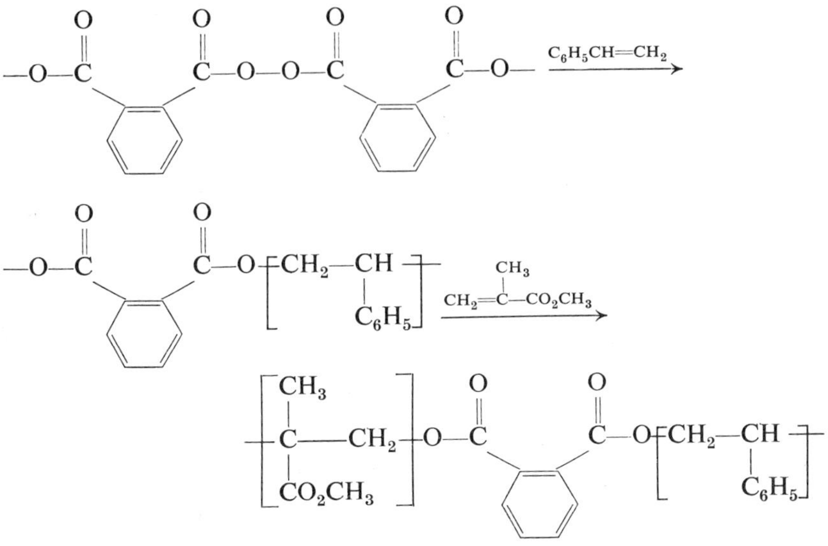

The polymerization of butadiene with a redox initiator composed of *p*-diisopropenylbenzenedihydroperoxide and ferrous ion leaves hydroperoxide end groups on the polymer.[48–50]

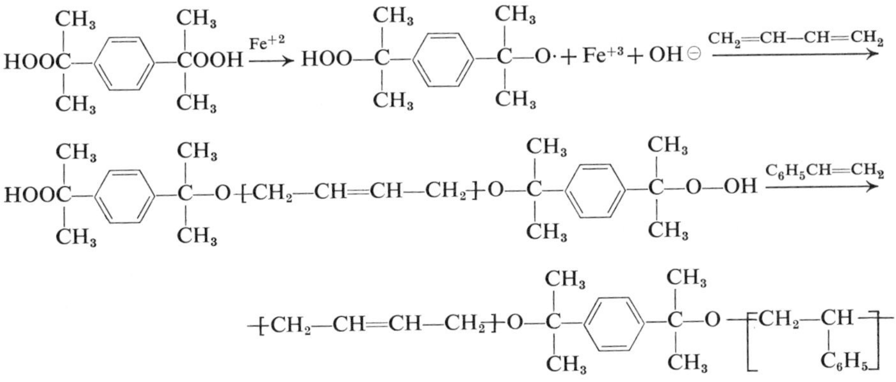

The second hydroperoxide group is not appreciably decomposed since the iron does not migrate into the polymer phase. Termination takes place mainly by coupling leaving two hydroperoxide end groups that will initiate the polymerization of styrene.

Reactive polymer end groups which decompose under the influence of ultraviolet light are obtained by the polymerization of styrene by N,N-diethylmethyldithiocarbamate.[51]

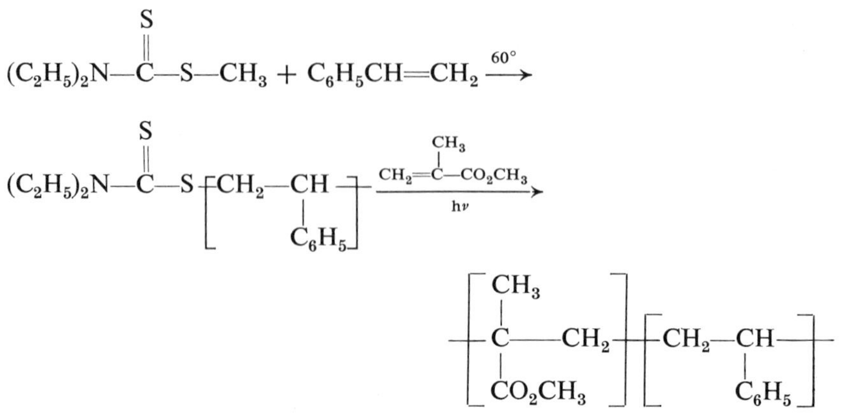

$$(C_2H_5)_2N-\overset{\overset{S}{\|}}{C}-S-CH_3 + C_6H_5CH{=}CH_2 \xrightarrow{60°}$$

$$(C_2H_5)_2N-\overset{\overset{S}{\|}}{C}-S\left[CH_2-\underset{\underset{C_6H_5}{|}}{CH}\right] \xrightarrow[h\nu]{CH_2{=}\overset{\overset{CH_3}{|}}{C}-CO_2CH_3}$$

$$\left[\overset{\overset{CH_3}{|}}{\underset{\underset{CO_2CH_3}{|}}{C}}-CH_2\right]\left[CH_2-\underset{\underset{C_6H_5}{|}}{CH}\right]$$

The polymerization of methyl methacrylate in the presence of triethylamine affords a polymer with tertiary amine end groups.[52,53] The end groups are subject to rapid chain transfer in the presence of a free radical initiator to yield free radical end groups which will initiate acrylonitrile polymerization.

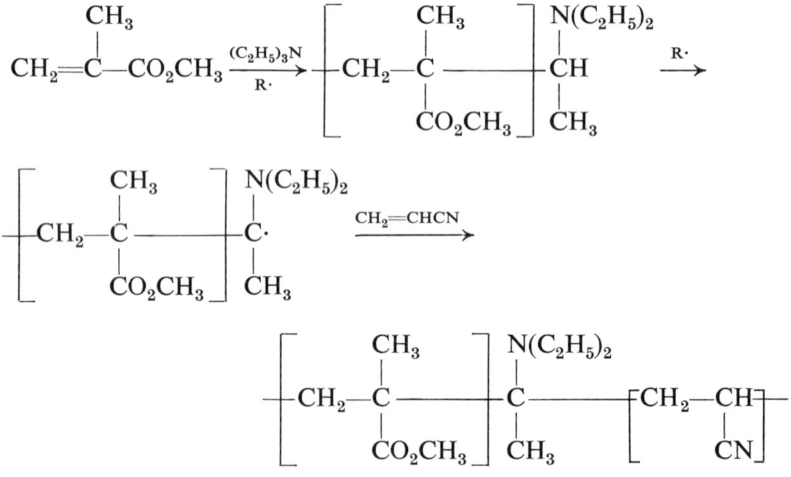

$$CH_2{=}\overset{\overset{CH_3}{|}}{C}-CO_2CH_3 \xrightarrow[R\cdot]{(C_2H_5)_3N} \left[CH_2-\overset{\overset{CH_3}{|}}{\underset{\underset{CO_2CH_3}{|}}{C}}\right]\overset{N(C_2H_5)_2}{\underset{\underset{CH_3}{|}}{CH}} \xrightarrow{R\cdot}$$

$$\left[CH_2-\overset{\overset{CH_3}{|}}{\underset{\underset{CO_2CH_3}{|}}{C}}\right]\overset{N(C_2H_5)_2}{\underset{\underset{CH_3}{|}}{C\cdot}} \xrightarrow{CH_2{=}CHCN}$$

$$\left[CH_2-\overset{\overset{CH_3}{|}}{\underset{\underset{CO_2CH_3}{|}}{C}}\right]\overset{N(C_2H_5)_2}{\underset{\underset{CH_3}{|}}{C}}\left[CH_2-\underset{\underset{CN}{|}}{CH}\right]$$

The polymeric initiators may also be obtained by forming the initiator portion on the polymer subsequent to polymer formation. The initiation of styrene by a monohydroperoxide containing a tertiary hydrogen in the molecule allows an active site in the polymer for the formation of a hydroperoxide.[54]

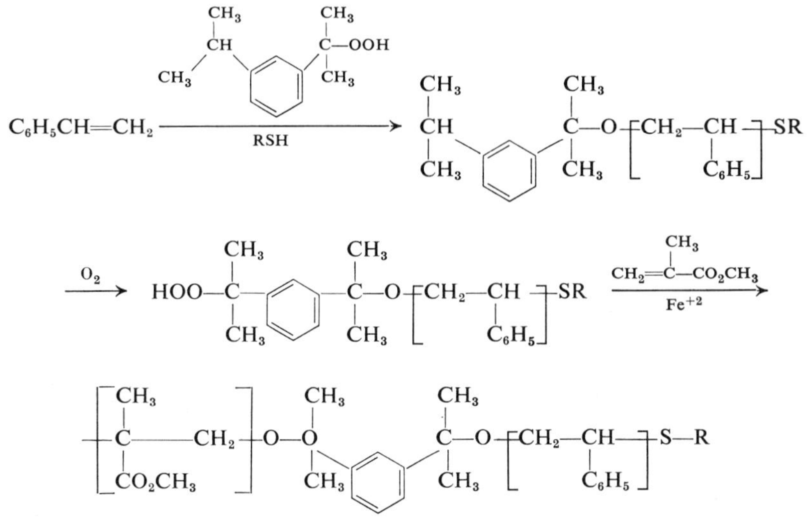

The mastication of polymers is known to form free radicals by the homolytic scission of carbon-carbon bonds. Mastication of polystyrene or poly(methyl methacrylate) which is swollen with a second monomer produces a block of the second monomer on the polystyrene or poly (methyl methacrylate) segments.[55,56]

Most of the addition polymerizations discussed have involved the formation of blocks by free radical mechanisms. Treatment of poly(ethylene oxide) with sodium forms a polymeric anionic initiator. The sodium alkoxide end serves to initiate the polymerization of acrylonitrile.[57]

$$-[O-CH_2-CH_2]-O^{\ominus}Na^{\oplus} \xrightarrow{CH_2=CHCN} -[O-CH_2-CH_2]-O-\left[CH_2-\underset{\displaystyle CN}{\underset{|}{CH}}\right]-$$

Block copolymers by condensation reactions. Polyesters with alcohol or carboxylic end groups may be joined with a diisocyanate thus forming blocks of polyester separated by diurethane or diamide single unit blocks. This type of polymer cannot be considered to be a true block polymer unless the diisocyanate joins two different polyester blocks. The vinyl polymerization of a monomer with a diazo initiator which contains carboxylic acid substituents leads to a vinyl polymer with carboxylic acid end groups.[58] Such different vinyl polymers with carboxylic end groups may be coupled with a diol by first converting the carboxyl groups to carboxylic acid chloride groups.

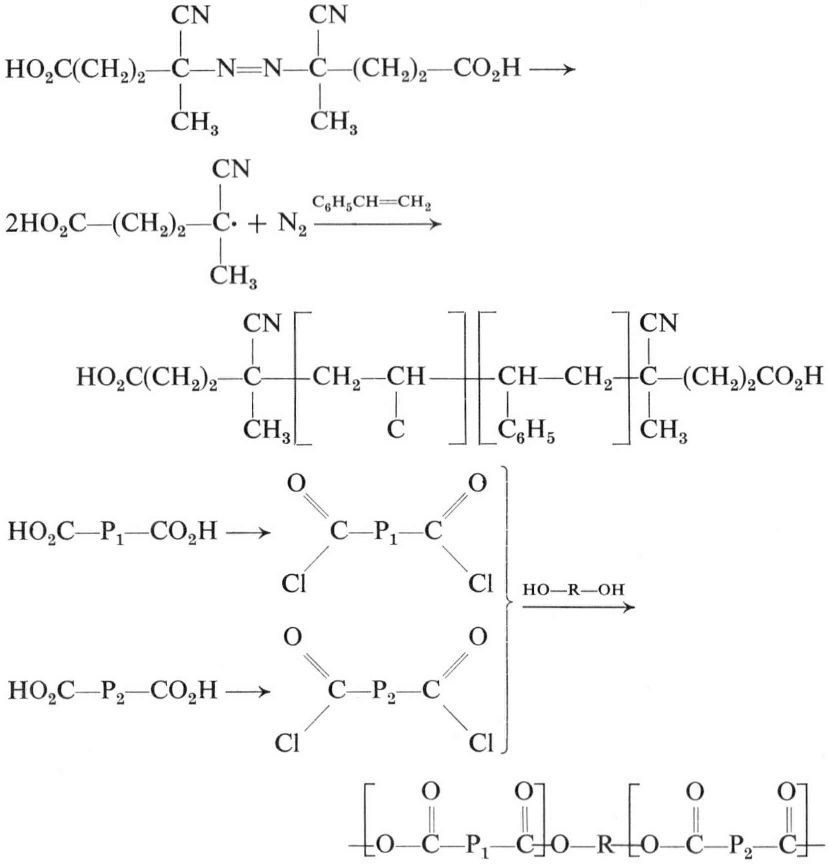

$$HO_2C(CH_2)_2-\underset{\underset{CH_3}{|}}{\overset{\overset{CN}{|}}{C}}-N{=}N-\underset{\underset{CH_3}{|}}{\overset{\overset{CN}{|}}{C}}-(CH_2)_2-CO_2H \longrightarrow$$

$$2HO_2C-(CH_2)_2-\underset{\underset{CH_3}{|}}{\overset{\overset{CN}{|}}{C}}\cdot + N_2 \xrightarrow{C_6H_5CH{=}CH_2}$$

$$HO_2C(CH_2)_2-\underset{\underset{CH_3}{|}}{\overset{\overset{CN}{|}}{C}}\left[-CH_2-\underset{\underset{C}{|}}{CH}-\right]\left[-CH-CH_2-\underset{\underset{C_6H_5}{|}}{}\right]\underset{\underset{CH_3}{|}}{\overset{\overset{CN}{|}}{C}}-(CH_2)_2CO_2H$$

$$HO_2C-P_1-CO_2H \longrightarrow \underset{Cl}{\overset{O}{C}}-P_1-\underset{Cl}{\overset{O}{C}}$$

$$HO_2C-P_2-CO_2H \longrightarrow \underset{Cl}{\overset{O}{C}}-P_2-\underset{Cl}{\overset{O}{C}}$$

$$\xrightarrow{HO-R-OH}$$

$$\left[-O-\overset{O}{\underset{}{C}}-P_1-\overset{O}{\underset{}{C}}-O-R-\right]\left[O-\overset{O}{\underset{}{C}}-P_2-\overset{O}{\underset{}{C}}-\right]$$

The condensation of poly(ethylene glycol) with dimethyl terephthalate and ethylene glycol yields block copolymers containing poly(ethylene glycol) and poly(ethylene terephthalate) blocks.[59]

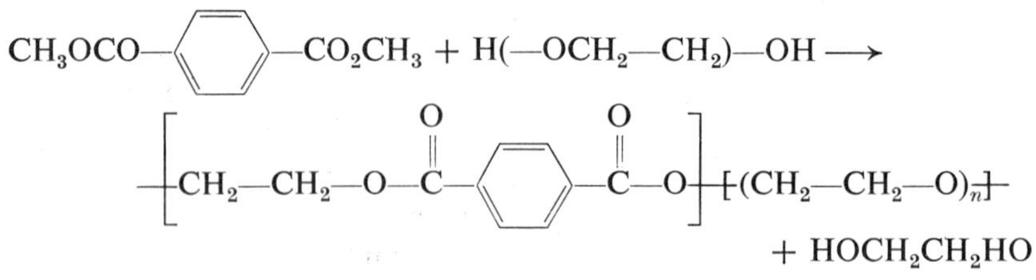

$$CH_3OCO-\langle\bigcirc\rangle-CO_2CH_3 + H(-OCH_2-CH_2)-OH \longrightarrow$$

$$\left[-CH_2-CH_2-O-\overset{O}{\underset{}{C}}-\langle\bigcirc\rangle-\overset{O}{\underset{}{C}}-O-\right]\left[-(CH_2-CH_2-O)_n-\right]$$

$$+ HOCH_2CH_2HO$$

11.3 STEREOBLOCK POLYMERS[4]

Linear polymers of 1-olefins which have block segments in the polymer chain of isotactic structure and atactic structure have been defined as stereoblock polymers. Similarly, syndiotactic-atactic segments or *d*-isotactic-*l*-isotactic segmented chains can be considered to be stereoblock polymers. These stereoblock copolymers differ from the usual block copolymers in that the former are obtained by the polymerization of a single olefin, and are also characterized by the fact that they contain ordered chain portions which are of short length compared to the total length of the polymer chain.

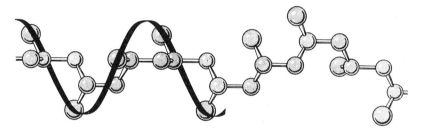

The separation of block polypropylene from the isotactic and atactic polymers requires solvent extraction with a variety of successive solvents, graded in increasing solvent power for the isotactic species.[60] In this manner, polypropylene can be fractionated into polymers with degrees of crystallinity ranging from 15 to 85% which contain the corresponding crystalline transition temperatures of 106–176°C.

The physical properties of stereoblock polymers are quite different from the properties of either completely isotactic or atactic polymers.[61,62] Elastomeric properties are observed when the isotactic portions are sufficiently long enough to form crystallites but the remaining portions are amorphous. The lattice energy of the crystallites hinders the viscous flow of the amorphous parts of the macromolecule. The polymers are characterized by an initial elastic modulus which is high, by elastic elongations of 100–200% and by a high tensile strength. The crystallites act as crosslinks in a vulcanized polymer but they can be melted and reshaped at temperatures above the crystalline melting point. This might be compared to a reversible vulcanization.

11.4 GRAFT COPOLYMERS[33–36]

The discovery that polymer molecules could grow from the backbone of a polymer molecule to produce a graft copolymer was made by Adkins and Houtz[63] when it was learned that polystyrene could increase in molecular weight in the presence of polymerizing styrene. The grafting of various polymer segments to a linear polymer chain has now become an important method in the modification or tailoring of polymer molecules.

In many cases, grafting takes place in copolymerization and homopolymerization reactions. Long chain branching in high pressure polyethylene results from a graft polymerization reaction brought about by a chain transfer reaction. In the copolymerization reaction of methyl methacrylate and styrene, methyl methacrylate grafts appear on styrene chains.

Grafting by free radical formation on a polymer chain. As indicated earlier, methyl methacrylate may be grafted to a polystyrene backbone through a chain transfer reaction occurring at the tertiary hydrogen on the polystyrene backbone:

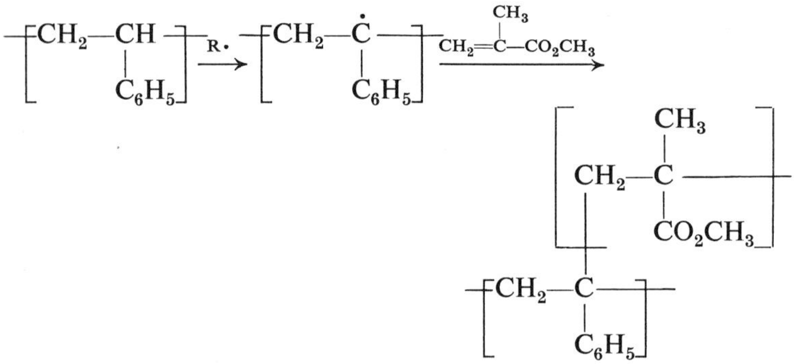

There are a variety of methods for producing a free radical on the backbone of a polymer chain. Ultraviolet and gamma irradiation have been particularly successful. Cobalt-gamma irradiation produces free radicals along the backbone of polyethylene to which monomers such as styrene may be grafted.[64–67]

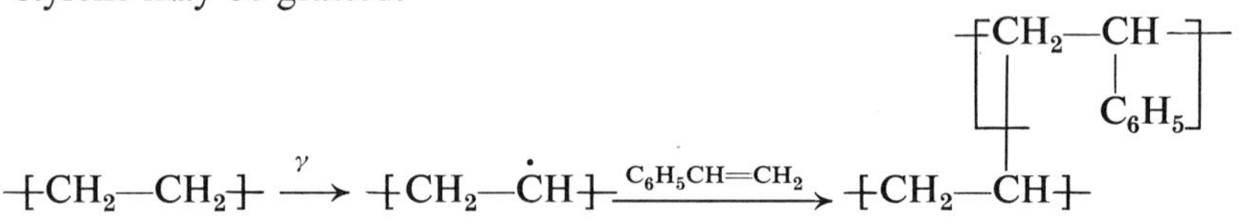

This method of grafting of polystyrene has also been quite effectively applied to Teflon.[68] The crosslinking of a rubber latex or a polyisoprene is accomplished essentially by a graft polymerization of styrene or methyl methacrylate in the presence of a strong ultraviolet source,[69] or by gamma irradiation.[70]

Grafting from a potential free radical initiator. The copolymerization of polystyrene with smaller amounts of *p*-isopropylstyrene affords a polystyrene with occasional isopropyl groups at random along the chain. Oxidation of the polymer gives a tertiary hydroperoxide at the isopropyl site which will act as a free radical initiation site in the presence of ferrous ion.[33,34] See formula on next page.

By engaging these techniques, certain grafts can be built up on polypropylene which may partially solve the dying problem associated with polypropylene fibers. Isotactic polypropylene may be treated with oxygen under pressure at 70–80°C. to introduce hydroperoxide groups at the tertiary hydrogens along the chain backbone.[71] These hydroperoxide groups, present to the extent of 0.2–0.4% peroxidic oxygen, initiate the graft polymerization of methyl methacrylate.

The polypropylene thus obtains a somewhat polar layer of poly(methyl methacrylate) 0.01–0.1 mm. thick on the surface of the polymers. Treatment of atactic polypropylene in this manner produces grafts throughout the mass of the polymer instead of only on the surface.

Treatment of poly(vinyl alcohol) with cerric ion produces free radical sites along the chain backbone to which acrylonitrile or methyl acrylate may be grafted.[72]

Copolymers of methyl acrylate and *t*-butyl peracrylate yield a polyacrylate with attached perester initiators to which polystyrene may be grafted.[73]

Grafting by condensation polymerization on a reactive polymer chain group. Groups on the backbone of a polymer chain which will enter into a

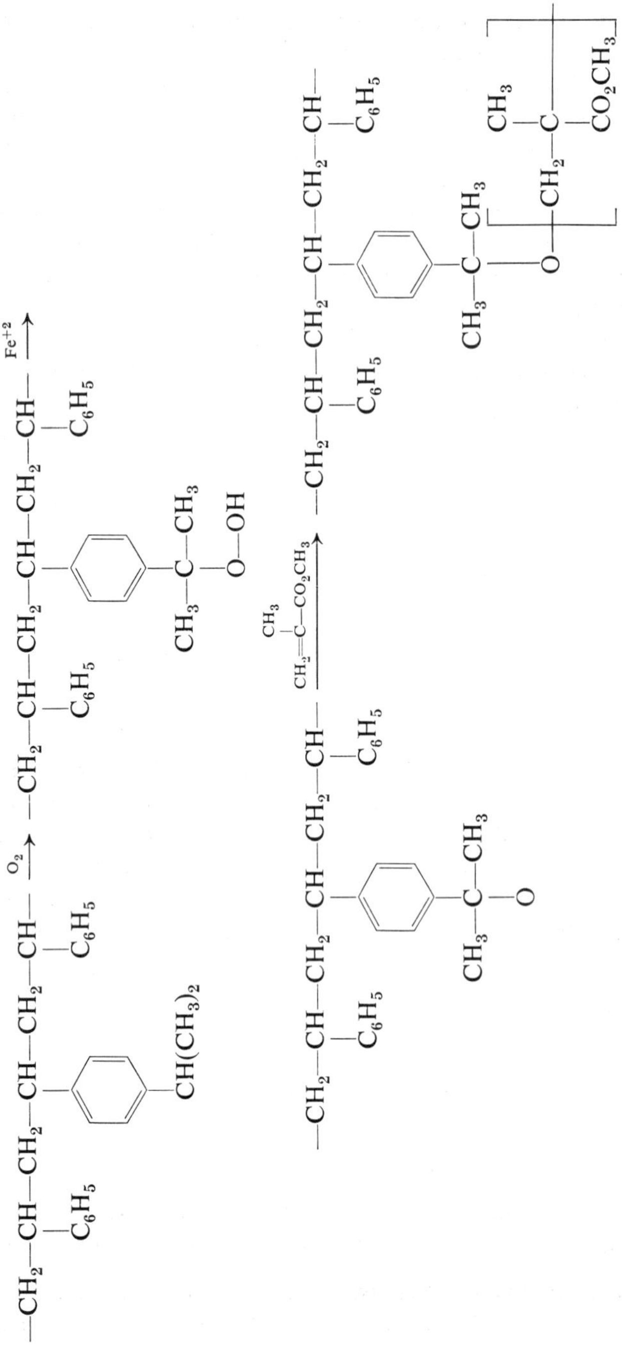

$$-CH_2-CH-CH_2-CH-CH_2-CH-\!\!\!\!\left<\!\!\!\begin{array}{c}\\ \end{array}\!\!\!\right>\!\!\!-CH(CH_3)_2 \quad \xrightarrow{O_2}$$
$$\qquad\quad\ \ C_6H_5 \qquad\quad C_6H_5$$

$$-CH_2-CH-CH_2-CH-CH_2-CH-\!\!\!\left<\!\!\!\begin{array}{c}\\ \end{array}\!\!\!\right>\!\!\!-\!\!\!\underset{CH_3}{\overset{CH_3}{C}}\!\!-O-OH \quad \xrightarrow{Fe^{+2}}$$
$$\qquad\quad\ C_6H_5 \qquad\quad C_6H_5 \qquad\qquad\qquad C_6H_5$$

$$-CH_2-CH-CH_2-CH-CH_2-CH-\!\!\!\left<\!\!\!\begin{array}{c}\\ \end{array}\!\!\!\right>\!\!\!-\!\!\!\underset{CH_3}{\overset{CH_3}{C}}\!\!-O\cdot \quad \xrightarrow[CH_2=\underset{CH_3}{C}-CO_2CH_3]{}$$
$$\qquad\quad\ C_6H_5 \qquad\quad C_6H_5 \qquad\qquad\qquad C_6H_5$$

$$-CH_2-CH-CH_2-CH-CH_2-CH-\!\!\!\left<\!\!\!\begin{array}{c}\\ \end{array}\!\!\!\right>\!\!\!-\!\!\!\underset{CH_3}{\overset{CH_3}{C}}\!\!-O-\!\!\left[CH_2-\underset{CO_2CH_3}{\overset{CH_3}{C}}\right]\!-$$
$$\qquad\quad\ C_6H_5 \qquad\quad C_6H_5 \qquad\qquad\qquad C_6H_5$$

condensation reaction with another monomer provide another method for the preparation of graft copolymers. Alcoholysis of the acetate groups on a vinyl acetate-styrene copolymer leaves such reaction sites along the backbone. To these alcoholic sites can be grafted a poly(ethylene oxide) by the addition of ethylene oxide or a polyamide graft by the addition of a carbonanhydride.

$$
\begin{array}{l}
-CH_2-CH-CH_2-CH- \\
\quad\quad\ \ | \quad\quad\quad\quad\ | \\
\quad\quad C_6H_5 \quad\quad O-C-CH_3 \\
\quad\quad\quad\quad\quad\quad\quad\quad\ \| \\
\quad\quad\quad\quad\quad\quad\quad\quad\ O
\end{array}
\longrightarrow
\begin{array}{l}
-CH_2-CH-CH- \\
\quad\quad\ \ | \quad\quad\ | \\
\quad\quad C_6H_5 \ OH
\end{array}
\xrightarrow{\ CH_2-CH_2\ O\ }
$$

$$
\begin{array}{l}
-CH_2-CH-CH_2-CH- \\
\quad\quad\ \ | \quad\quad\quad\quad\ | \\
\quad\quad C_6H_5 \quad\quad\quad\ O \\
\quad\quad\quad\quad\quad\quad\ \ | \\
\quad\quad\quad\quad\quad\ \ \{CH_2-CH_2-O\}H
\end{array}
$$

Many other polymerizable monomers such as *p*-aminostyrene may serve for the introduction of active condensation sites. Caprolactam may be grafted on the carboxyl groups of a styrene-methacrylic acid copolymer.[74] The reaction of ethanolamine with a styrene-dimethyl fumarate copolymer produces a single monomer graft containing free alcohol groups through an aminolysis reaction. Additional grafting can take place by treatment of the polymer with ethylene oxide.[75]

$$
\begin{array}{l}
-CH_2-CH-CH---CH- \\
\quad\quad\ \ | \quad\ | \quad\quad\ \ | \\
\quad\quad C_6H_5 \ CO_2CH_3 \ CO_2CH_3
\end{array}
\xrightarrow{\ H_2NCH_2CH_2OH\ }
\begin{array}{l}
-CH_2-CH-CH-CH- \\
\quad\quad\ \ | \quad\ \ | \quad\ | \\
\quad\quad C_6H_5 \ CO \quad CO \\
\quad\quad\quad\quad\ | \quad\ | \\
\quad\quad\quad\quad NH \ \ NH \\
\quad\quad\quad\quad\ | \quad\ | \\
\quad\quad\quad\ \ CH_2 \ CH_2 \\
\quad\quad\quad\quad\ | \quad\ | \\
\quad\quad\quad\ \ CH_2 \ CH_2 \\
\quad\quad\quad\quad\ | \quad\ | \\
\quad\quad\quad\ \ OH \ \ OH
\end{array}
$$

$$
\xrightarrow{\ CH_2-CH_2\ O\ }
\begin{array}{l}
-CH_2-CH-CH--------CH---- \\
\quad\quad\ \ | \quad\ \ | \quad\quad\quad\quad\quad\quad | \\
\quad\quad C_6H_5 \ CO \quad\quad\quad\quad\quad\ CO \\
\quad\quad\quad\quad\ | \quad\quad\quad\quad\quad\quad\ | \\
\quad\quad\quad\quad NH \quad\quad\quad\quad\quad\ NH \\
\quad\quad\quad\quad\ | \quad\quad\quad\quad\quad\quad\ | \\
\quad\quad\quad\ \ CH_2 \quad\quad\quad\quad\quad\ CH_2 \\
\quad\quad\quad\quad\ | \quad\quad\quad\quad\quad\quad\ | \\
\quad\quad\ \ CH_2-O(CH_2CH_2O)_xH \ CH_2-O-(CH_2CH_2O)_yH
\end{array}
$$

Methacrylylcaprolactamamide may be copolymerized with styrene. The resulting polymer with the acylcaprolactam sites is suitable for initiating the graft polymerization of caprolactam.[76]

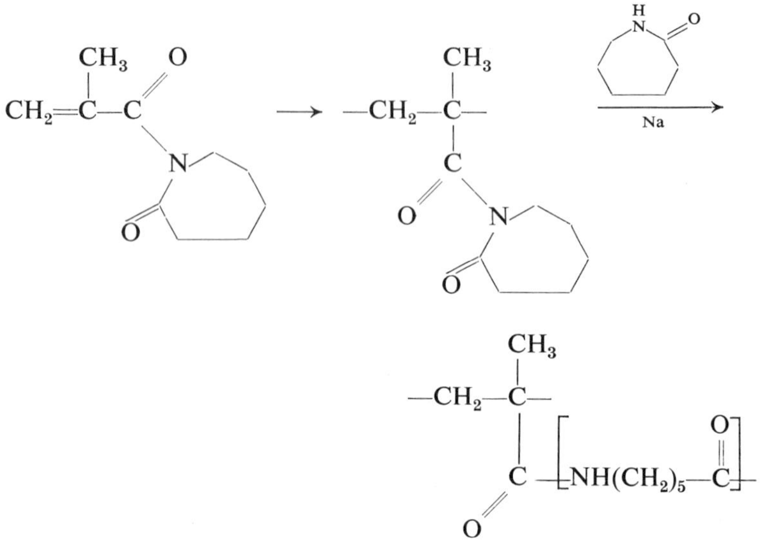

Monomer grafting prior to polymerization. Poly(ethylene oxide) with a single hydroxyl end group may be grafted to a molecule of dimethyl terephthalate by the series of reactions shown below. Copolymerization of this grafted monomer and dimethyl terephthalate with ethylene glycol provides poly(ethylene terephthalate) with a polyethylene oxide graft.

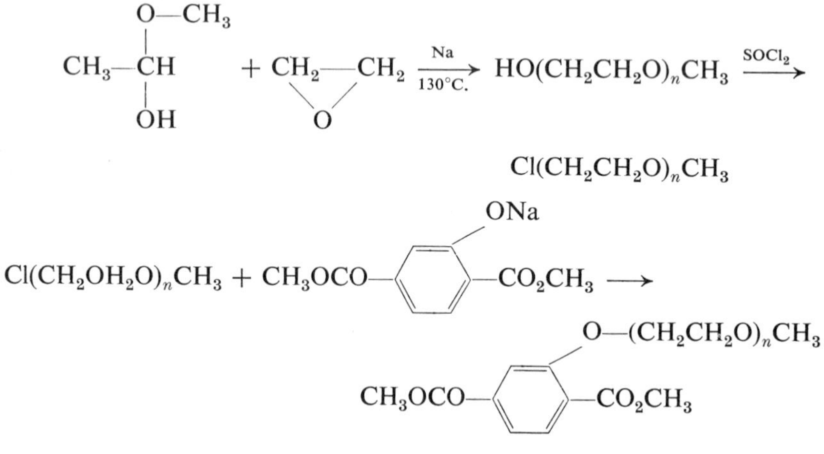

$$O\text{—}(CH_2CH_2O)_nCH_3$$

$$CH_3OCO\text{—}\langle\text{benzene}\rangle\text{—}CO_2CH_3$$

$$+$$

$$+\ HOCH_2CH_2OH \longrightarrow$$

$$CH_3OCO\text{—}\langle\text{benzene}\rangle\text{—}CO_2CH_3$$

$$O\text{—}(CH_2CH_2O)\text{—}CH_3$$

$$\begin{array}{c} O \qquad\qquad O \qquad\qquad O \qquad\qquad O \\ \parallel \qquad\qquad \parallel \qquad\qquad \parallel \qquad\qquad \parallel \end{array}$$

$$\text{—}CH_2\text{—}CH_2\text{—}O\text{—}C\text{—}\langle\text{benzene}\rangle\text{—}C\text{—}OCH_2CH_2O\text{—}C\text{—}\langle\text{benzene}\rangle\text{—}C\text{—}O\text{—}$$

REFERENCES

1. T. Alfrey, Jr., J. J. Bohrer, and H. Mark, *Copolymerization*, Interscience Publishers, New York, 1952.
2. F. R. Mayo and C. Walling, *Chem. Revs.*, **46**, 191 (1950).
3. C. E. Schildknecht, *Vinyl and Related Polymers*, John Wiley and Sons, New York, 1952.
4. N. G. Gaylord and H. F. Mark, *Linear and Stereoregular Addition Polymers*, Interscience Publishers, New York, 1959.
5. J. K. Stille, *Chem. Revs.*, **58**, 541 (1958).
6. G. Bier, *Angew. Chem.*, **73**, 186 (1961).
7. G. Natta, *Rubber and Plastics Age*, **38**, 495 (1957).
8. E. W. Rugeley, T. A. Feild, Jr., and G. H. Fremon, *Ind. Eng. Chem.*, **40**, 1724 (1948).
9. G. S. Whitby, C. C. Davis, and R. F. Dunbrook, eds., *Synthetic Rubber*, John Wiley and Sons, New York, 1954.
10. M. Morton, ed., *Introduction to Rubber Technology*, Reinhold Publishing Corp., New York, 1959.
11. H. Staudinger and B. Ritzenthaler, *Ber.*, **68**, 455 (1935).
12. M. Hunt and C. S. Marvel, *J. Am. Chem. Soc.*, **57**, 1691 (1935).
13. L. L. Ryden and C. S. Marvel, *J. Am. Chem. Soc.*, **57**, 2311 (1935).
14. F. J. Glavis, L. L. Ryden, and C. S. Marvel, *J. Am. Chem. Soc.*, **59**, 707 (1937).
15. L. L. Ryden, F. J. Glavis, and C. S. Marvel, *J. Am. Chem. Soc.*, **59**, 1014 (1937).
16. C. S. Marvel, S. J. Davis, and F. J. Glavis, *J. Am. Chem. Soc.*, **60**, 1450 (1938).
17. C. S. Marvel and W. H. Sharkey, *J. Am. Chem. Soc.*, **61**, 1603 (1939).
18. D. S. Frederick, H. D. Cogan, and C. S. Marvel, *J. Am. Chem. Soc.*, **56**, 1815 (1934).
19. C. S. Marvel and E. D. Weil, *J. Am. Chem. Soc.*, **76**, 61 (1954).
20. R. E. Cook, F. S. Dainton, and K. J. Ivin, *J. Polymer Sci.*, **29**, 549 (1958).
21. M. A. Jobard, *J. Polymer Sci.*, **29**, 275 (1958).
22. R. E. Cook, F. S. Dainton, and K. J. Ivin, *J. Polymer Sci.*, **26**, 351 (1957).
23. K. J. Ivin, *J. Polymer Sci.*, **25**, 228 (1957).
24. R. D. Snow and F. E. Frey, *Ind. Eng. Chem.*, **30**, 176 (1938).
25. F. S. Dainton and G. M. Bristow, *Nature*, **172**, 804 (1953); *Proc. Roy. Soc. (London)*, **A229**, 509, 525 (1958).
26. W. G. Barb, *Proc. Roy. Soc. (London)*, **A212,** 66 (1952).
27. F. S. Dainton and K. J. Ivin, *Proc. Roy. Soc. (London)*, **A212,** 96 (1952).

28. P. S. Skell, R. C. Woodworth, and J. H. McNamara, *J. Am. Chem. Soc.*, **79**, 1253 (1957).
29. M. M. Brubaker, D. D. Coffman, and H. H. Hoehn, *J. Am. Chem. Soc.*, **74**, 1509 (1952).
30. W. G. Barb, *J. Am. Chem. Soc.*, **75**, 224 (1953).
31. H. Mark, *Angew. Chem.*, **67**, 53 (1955).
32. H. W. Melville, *Plastics Inst. Trans.*, **23**, 146 (1955).
33. C. G. Overberger and A. Katchman, *Chem. and Eng. News*, Nov. 10 (1958) p. 80.
34. E. H. Immergut and H. Mark, *Makromol. Chem.*, **18/19**, 322 (1955).
35. W. J. Burlant and A. S. Hoffman, *Block and Graft Polymers*, Reinhold Publishing Corp., New York, 1960.
36. G. Smets and R. Hart, *Forsch. Hochpolym. Forsch.*, **2**, 173 (1960).
37. J. L. Bolland and H. W. Melville, *Proc. Rub. Tech. Conf.* (London 1939).
38. M. Szwarc, M. Levy, and B. Milkovich, *J. Am. Chem. Soc.*, **78**, 2656 (1956).
39. Goodrich-Gulf Chem. Inc., Belgium Patent 553, 720 (1956).
40. J. A. Hicks and H. W. Melville, *J. Polymer Sci.*, **12**, 461 (1954).
41. J. A. Hicks and H. W. Melville, *Proc. Roy. Soc. (London)*, **A226**, 314 (1954).
42. B. L. Funt and E. Collins, *J. Polymer Sci.*, **28**, 359 (1958).
43. A. S. Dunn and H. W. Melville, *Nature*, **169**, 699 (1952).
44. A. S. Dunn, B. D. Stead, and H. W. Melville, *Trans. Faraday Soc.*, **50**, 279 (1954).
45. J. W. Breitenback, O. F. Olaj, and A. Schindler, *Monatsh.*, **91**, 205 (1960).
46. G. Smets and A. E. Woodward, *J. Polymer Sci.*, **14**, 126 (1954).
47. A. E. Woodward and G. Smets, *J. Polymer Sci.*, **17**, 51 (1955).
48. P. E. M. Allen, J. M. Downer, G. W. Hastings, H. W. Melville, P. Molyneux, and J. R. Urwin, *Nature*, **177**, 910 (1956).
49. R. J. Orr and H. L. Williams, *J. Am. Chem. Soc.*, **79**, 3137 (1957).
50. P. Molyneux, *Makromol. Chem.*, **37**, 165 (1960).
51. T. Otsu, *J. Polymer Sci.*, **26**, 236 (1957).
52. C. H. Bamford and E. F. T. White, *Trans. Faraday Soc.*, **52**, 716 (1956); **54**, 268 (1958).
53. C. H. Bamford, A. D. Jenkins, and E. F. T. White, *J. Polymer Sci.*, **34**, 271 (1959).
54. J. R. Urwin, *J. Polymer Sci.*, **27**, 580 (1958).
55. D. J. Angier and W. F. Watson, *J. Polymer Sci.*, **18**, 129 (1955).
56. D. J. Angier, R. J. Ceresa, and W. F. Watson, *J. Polymer Sci.*, **34**, 699 (1959).
57. J. Furukawa, T. Saegusa, and N. Mise, *Makromol. Chem.*, **38**, 244 (1960).
58. C. H. Bamford and A. D. Jenkins, *Nature*, **176**, 78 (1955).
59. D. Coleman, *J. Polymer Sci.*, **14**, 15 (1954).
60. G. Natta, G. Mazzanti, G. Crespi, and G. Moraglio, *Chim. e ind. (Milan)*, **39**, 275 (1957).
61. G. Natta, *Rubber and Plastics Age*, **38**, 495 (1957).
62. G. Natta, *J. Polymer Sci.*, **34**, 531 (1959).
63. R. C. Houtz and H. Adkins, *J. Am. Chem. Soc.*, **55**, 1609 (1933).
64. D. Ballantine, A. Glines, G. Adler, and D. J. Metz, *J. Polymer Sci.*, **34**, 419 (1959).
65. A. Chapiro, *J. Polymer Sci.*, **34**, 439 (1959).
66. A. S. Hoffman, E. R. Gilliland, E. W. Merrill, and W. H. Stockmayer, *J. Polymer Sci.*, **34**, 465 (1959).
67. Y. Shinohara and K. Tomioka, *J. Polymer Sci.*, **44**, 195 (1960).
68. A. Chapiro, *J. Polymer Sci.*, **34**, 481 (1959).
69. D. T. Turner, *J. Polymer Sci.*, **35**, 17 (1959).

70. E. G. Cockbain, T. D. Pendle, and D. T. Turner, *J. Polymer Sci.*, **39,** 419 (1959).
71. G. Natta, E. Beati, and F. Severini, *J. Polymer Sci.*, **34,** 685 (1959).
72. G. Mino and S. Kaizerman, *J. Polymer Sci.*, **31,** 242 (1958).
73. G. Smets, A. Poot, M. Mullier, and J. P. Bex, *J. Polymer Sci.*, **34,** 287 (1959).
74. C. B. Chapman and L. Valentine, *J. Polymer Sci.*, **34,** 319 (1959).
75. D. Weiss, J. F. Gerecht, and I. J. Krems, *J. Polymer Sci.*, **35,** 343 (1959).
76. O. Wichterle and V. Gregor, *J. Polymer Sci.*, **34,** 309 (1959).

12

CYCLOPOLYMERIZATION[1,2]

The polymerization of diolefins such as butadiene in which the double bonds are conjugated results in a polymer that may have varying types of recurring units making up the structure of the polymer (Chapter 10). By and large these polymeric diolefins are linear and therefore are soluble in some suitable solvent. In many other cases of the polymerization of diolefins in which the double bonds are not conjugated or are separated by an insulating group, the products of polymerization are three dimensional networks, since the double bonds polymerize independently of one another. For example, p-divinyl benzene serves as a good crosslinking agent and the polymerization of biallyl by ordinary free radical initiators gives an insoluble crosslinked network.

It has been recognized, however, that nonconjugated diolefins do not always polymerize to give insoluble polymers. The monomer may be made to polymerize by using up only one of its double bonds or may undergo a polymerization reaction in which both double bonds are used up and yet no crosslinking occurs. G. B. Butler was the first to propose an intramolecular-intermolecular propagation mechanism to explain the fact that diethyldiallyl ammonium bromide could be polymerized to afford a soluble polymer which showed no residual unsaturation.[3]

Initiation:

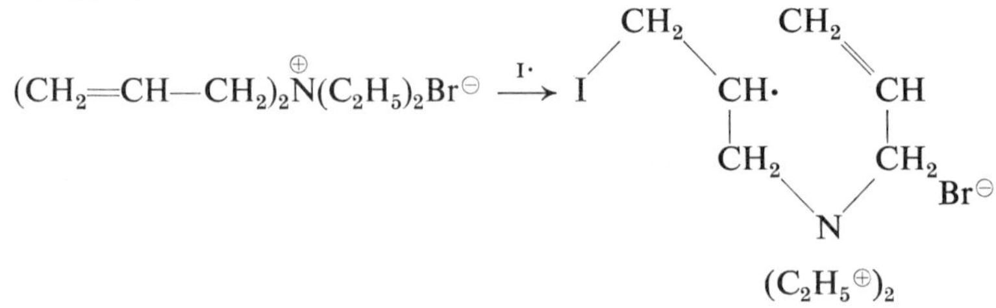

$$(CH_2\!\!=\!\!CH\!-\!CH_2)_2\overset{\oplus}{N}(C_2H_5)_2Br^{\ominus} \xrightarrow{\ I\cdot\ } $$

Intramolecular propagation:

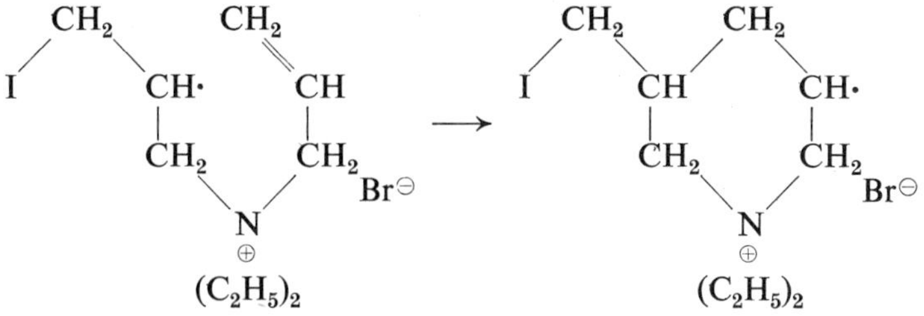

Intermolecular propagation:

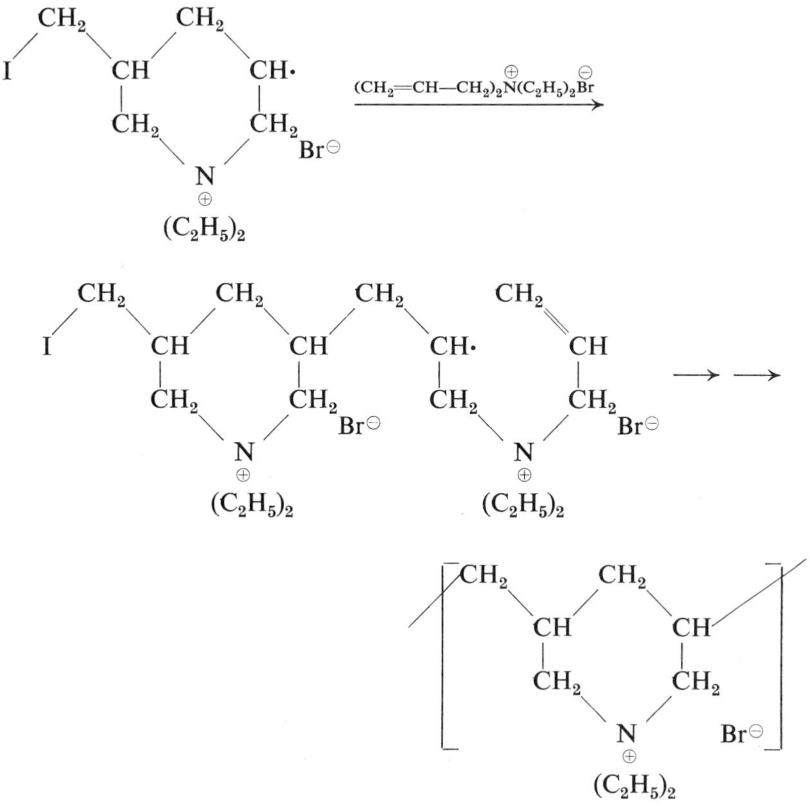

The overall result of this cyclopolymerization is that the polymer is not crosslinked and both double bonds are used up in the polymerization reaction to form cyclic recurring units along the backbone of the polymer chain. The polymerization of diallyl ammonium chloride showed similar results in a dilute solution polymerization, and the structures of these polymers were elucidated by the following reactions:[4]

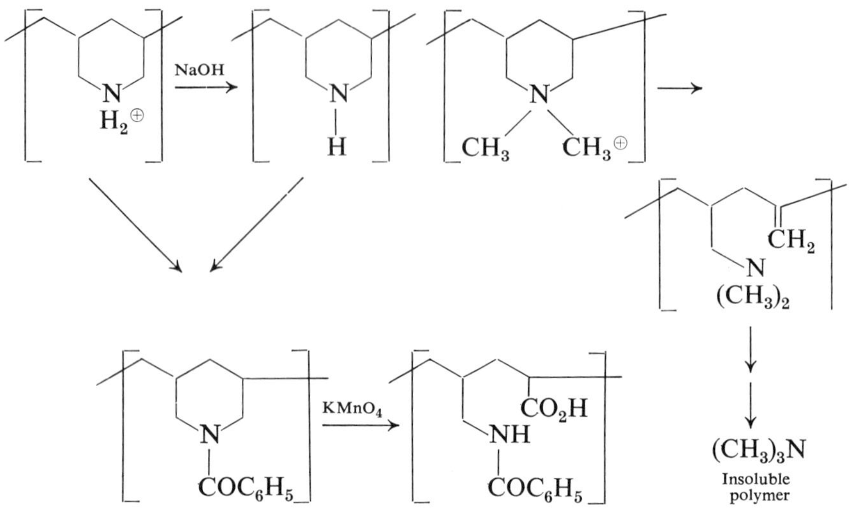

Since these initial investigations, it has been demonstrated that the cyclopolymerization is quite general for monomers of the type shown:

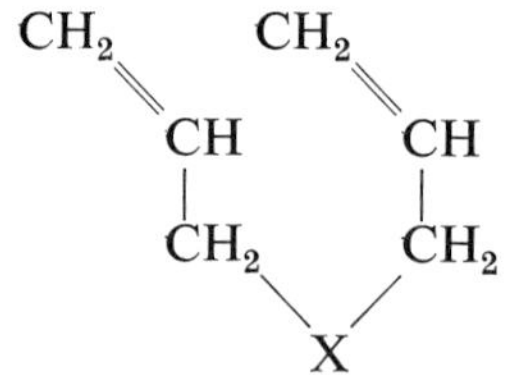

The cyclopolymerization reaction occurs most readily where five- and six-membered rings can be formed during the course of the reaction. Diallydiphenylphosphine oxide and dimethallylphenylphosphine oxide may be polymerized to low conversion by free radical initiators.[5]

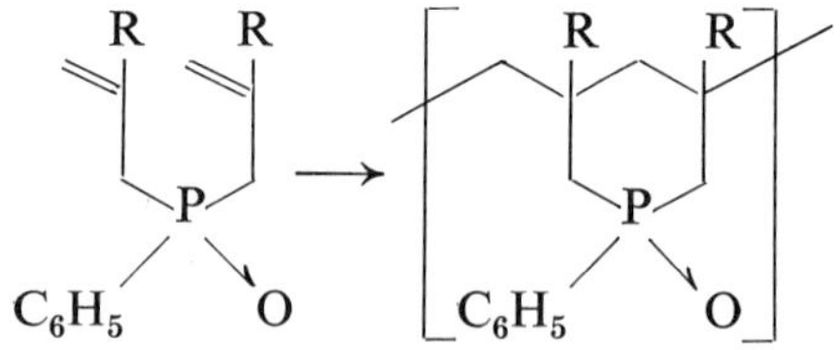

The cyclopolymerization of acrylic anhydride by peroxide initiators yields a soluble polymer for which molecular weights as high as 200,000 can be obtained.[6,7] The polymeric anhydride can be hydrolyzed to yield polyacrylic acid with a higher degree of crystallinity than polyacrylic acid obtained by the usual polymerization techniques.[6,8]

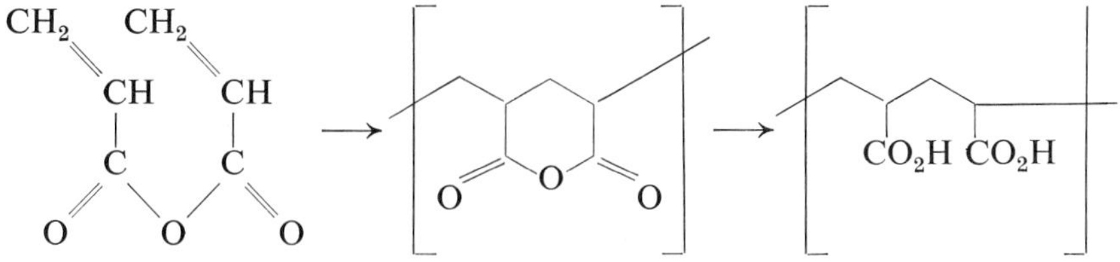

Dimethyldiallylsilane has been polymerized to give an extraordinarily heat stable polymer which contains the cyclic recurring unit.[9,10]

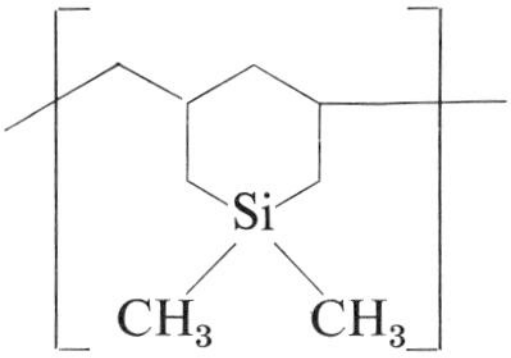

The reaction of ethylacrylate and methylvinyl ketone under the influence of strong base produces a salt of diacrylyl methane which on neutralization forms a soluble polymeric ketone, evidently from the reactive monomer diacrylylmethane.[11,12]

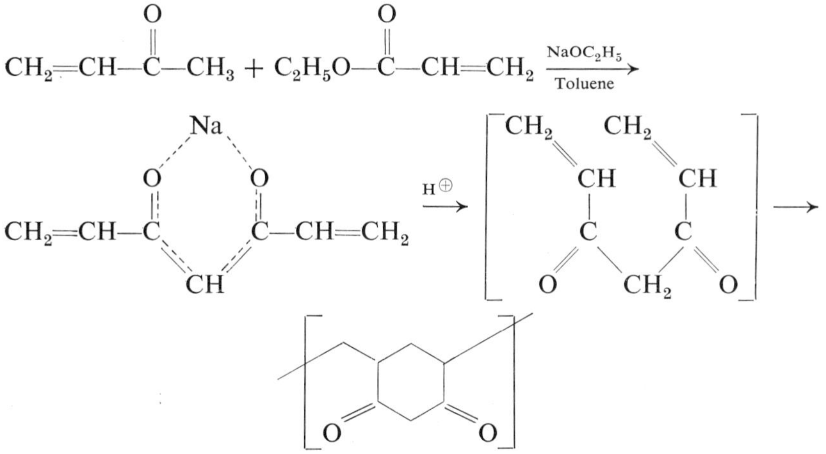

An investigation of the polymerization of the diene analogs of methacrylate monomers has shown that these reactive monomers give soluble polymers in emulsion and solution polymerization reactions, but the products polymerized in bulk tend to be mostly insoluble. Crystalline dimethyl-α-α'-dimethylene pimelate affords a polymer whose molecular weight is in the 200,000–300,000 range and forms a clear glass above its melting temperature, 300°C.[13]

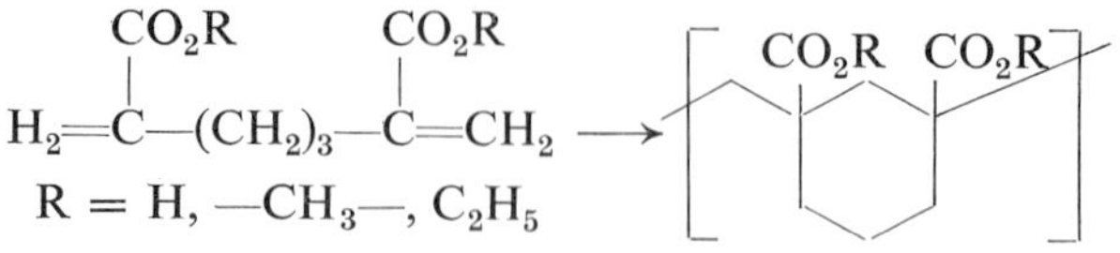

$$CH_2=C(CO_2R)-(CH_2)_3-C(CO_2R)=CH_2 \longrightarrow$$

$$R = H, -CH_3-, C_2H_5$$

High molecular weight polymers of the ethyl ester were not obtained since the liquid monomer could not be rendered entirely free from impurities. The methacrylonitrile analog, α,α'-dimethylenepimelonitrile afforded a high molecular weight polymer which did not discolor above 275°C. but turned red about 300°C. and finally black at 325°C., with a loss of 80% of its nitrogen.[14] This extraordinary stability compared to

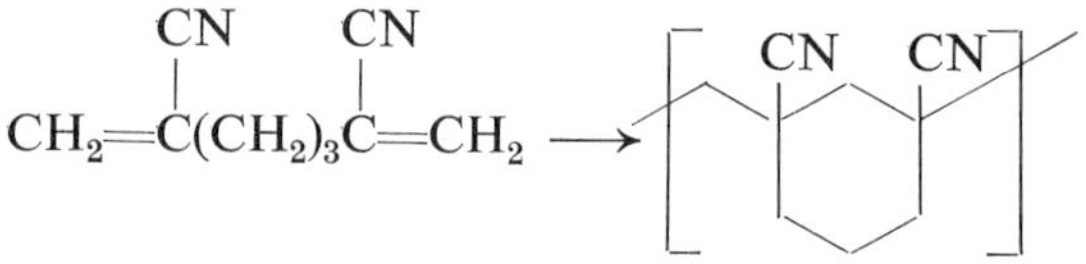

$$CH_2=C(CN)(CH_2)_3C(CN)=CH_2 \longrightarrow$$

polymethacrylonitrile (Chapter 9) may be due to either the strain which must be imposed in forming a C=N conjugated system if the polymer contains appreciable segments of an isotactic structure or to the fact that the polymer has an irregular atactic structure of the nitrile groups preventing formation of appreciably long segments of conjugated C=N links. Dimethyl-α, α'-dimethylene adipate also yields an appreciable quantity of soluble polymer for which a five-membered ring along the polymer backbone must be written.[13]

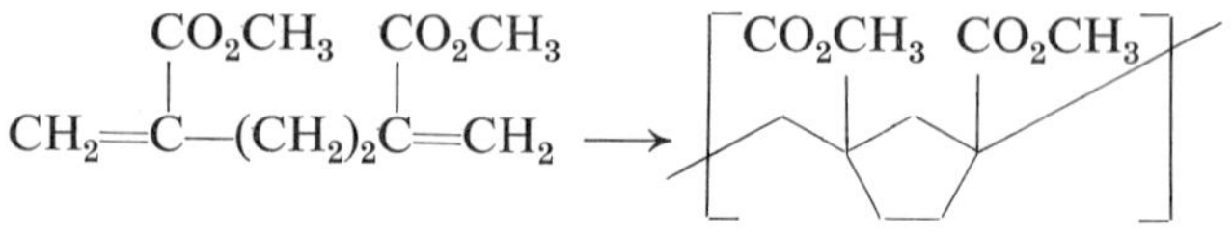

$$CH_2=C(CO_2CH_3)-(CH_2)_2C(CO_2CH_3)=CH_2 \longrightarrow$$

Nonconjugated diolefins whose double bonds are not activated by substituent groups require more vigorous conditions for the polymerization by free radical initiators. For this reason, the free radical polymerization leads to crosslinked polymers. The polymerization of these olefins by Ziegler-type catalysts, however, produces soluble polymers which contain little or no unsaturation in the resulting polymer. Biallyl, dimethallyl, and 1,6-heptadiene where the existence of five- and six-membered rings are favored in the cyclopolymerization reaction yield high molecular weight soluble polymers.[15] Poly(1,6-heptadiene) can be dehydrogenated to a polymer which contains aromatic nuclei as part of the polymer chain.

$$CH_2=CH(CH_2)_3CH=CH_2 \xrightarrow[TiCl_4]{Al(i\text{-}Bu)_3}$$ $\rightarrow$

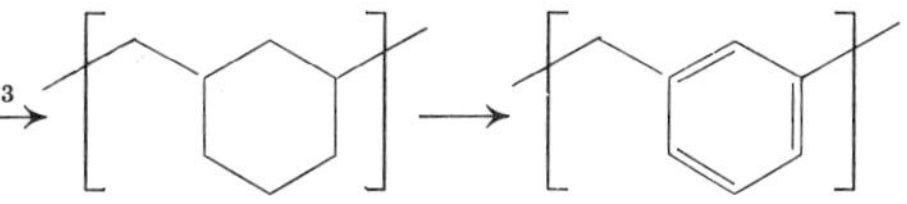

Biallyl affords a polymer only half of which is soluble, and which has appreciable residual unsaturation. That the main structural feature of this polymer is one which contains the five-membered cyclic recurring units along the backbone has been confirmed by x-ray analysis.[16]

$$CH_2=CH(CH_2)_2CH=CH_2 \longrightarrow$$

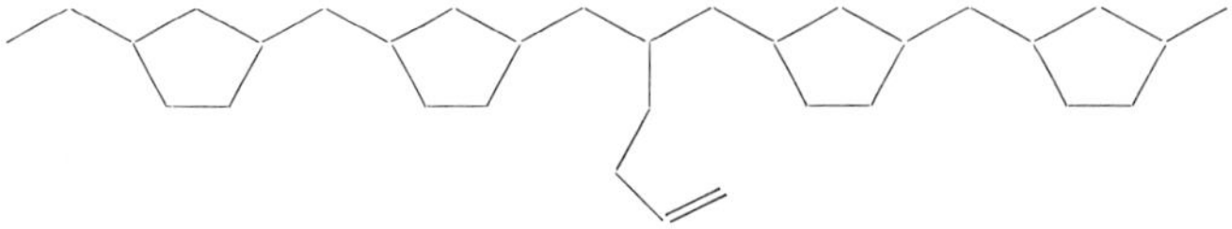

Dimethallyl forms a low molecular weight soluble polymer with an aluminum triisobutyl:titanium tetrachloride catalyst ratio of 1:1 but not with the 3:1 ratio which is effective for the 1,6-heptadiene

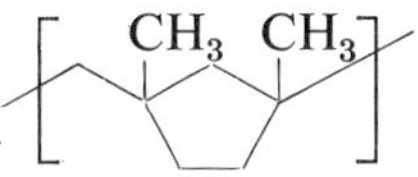

and biallyl polymerization. This polymerization may be cationic.[15] Higher nonconjugated dienes ($CH_2=CH(CH_2)_nCH=CH$ where $n =$ 4–12, 14, and 18) can be made to yield soluble polymers, but most of the polymerization takes place through only one of the double bonds.[17]

The diolefin 2,6-diphenyl-1,6-heptadiene also yields a high molecular weight heat stable polymer through polymerization by Ziegler-type catalysts.[18,19]

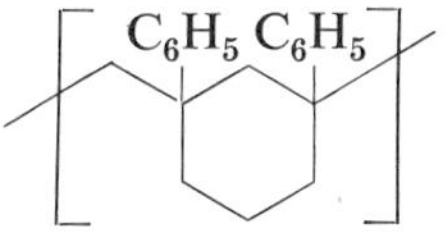

The polymerization of the diacetylene 1,6-heptadiyne with Ziegler-type catalysts gives soluble, low molecular weight (10,000–20,000), highly colored polymers.[20] These red or black polymers do not show the absorption maxima in the infrared characteristic of a monosubstituted acetylene, but instead show a highly conjugated —C≡C stretching frequency. The structure of the polymer has been proved by ozonolysis.

$$HC≡C-(CH_2)_3C≡CH \longrightarrow$$

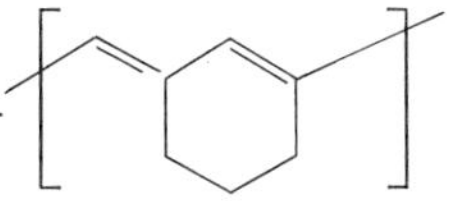

Polymerization of nonconjugated diolefins where the double bonds are not equivalent and thus the reactivity ratios of the two bonds are different will give some cyclopolymerization.[21] Most of the polymerization takes place, however, through only one (the more reactive) double bond. Investigations on such monomeric systems reveal that only 25–30% cyclic recurring units are obtained at 10% conversion. Higher conversion affords a gelled polymer.[22]

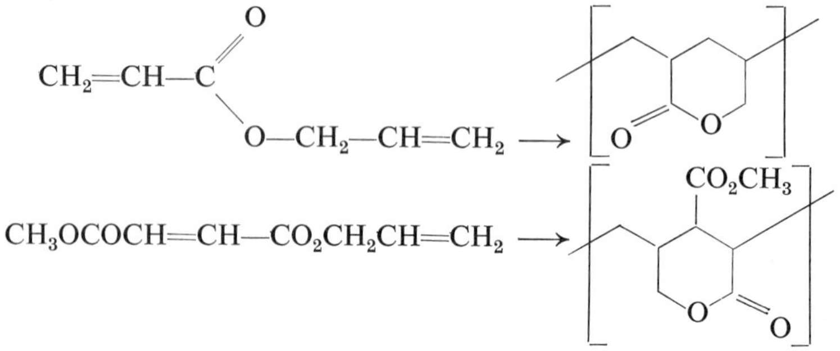

$$CH_2{=}CH{-}\overset{\displaystyle O}{C}\diagdown_{O{-}CH_2{-}CH{=}CH_2} \longrightarrow$$

$$CH_3OCOCH{=}CH{-}CO_2CH_2CH{=}CH_2 \longrightarrow$$

Copolymerization reactions between a diolefin and a monoolefin may take place to produce cyclic recurring units where rings of favorable size can be formed. The copolymerization of either maleic anhydride or nitrile with diallyl ether, diallyl sulfone or dimethyldiallylsilane gives a 2:1 copolymer.

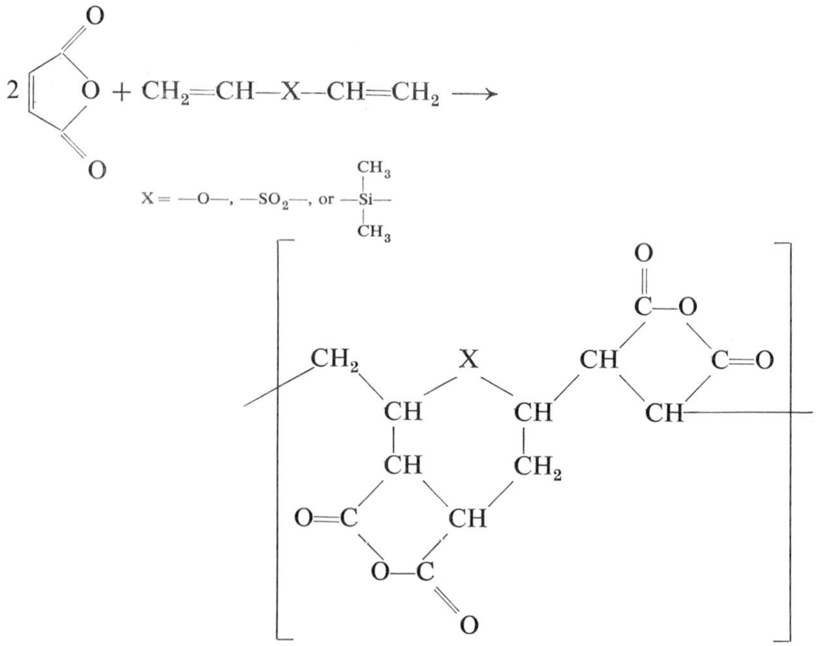

$$2 \; \underset{O}{\overset{O}{\Big\|}} O \; + \; CH_2{=}CH{-}X{-}CH{=}CH_2 \longrightarrow$$

$$X = {-}O{-}, \; {-}SO_2{-}, \; or \; {-}\underset{CH_3}{\overset{CH_3}{Si}}{-}$$

All these cyclopolymerization reactions have involved a vinyl type polymerization through carbon-carbon unsaturation. The cyclopolymerization mode has been observed, in fact, with an epoxide polymerization which favors the formation of a six-membered ring. Biallyl diepoxide will polymerize under the influence of suitable catalysts (Chapter 7) to afford a polymer with pyran recurring units.[23]

REFERENCES

1. C. S. Marvel, *J. Polymer Sci.*, **48**, 101 (1960).
2. G. B. Butler, *J. Polymer Sci.*, **48**, 279 (1960).
3. G. B. Butler and R. J. Angelo, *J. Am. Chem. Soc.*, **79**, 3128 (1957).
4. G. B. Butler, A. Crawshaw, and W. L. Miller, *J. Am. Chem. Soc.*, **80**, 3615 (1958).
5. K. D. Berlin and G. B. Butler, *J. Am. Chem. Soc.*, **82**, 2712 (1960).
6. A. Crawshaw and G. B. Butler, *J. Am. Chem. Soc.*, **80**, 5464 (1958).
7. J. F. Jones, *J. Polymer Sci.*, **33**, 15 (1958).
8. R. C. Schulz, M. Marx, and H. Hartmann, *Makromol. Chem.*, **44–46**, 281 (1961).
9. C. S. Marvel and G. Woolford, *J. Org. Chem.*, **25**, 1641 (1960).
10. G. B. Butler and R. W. Stackman, *J. Org. Chem.*, **25**, 1643 (1960).
11. J. F. Jones, *J. Polymer Sci.*, **33**, 7 (1958).
12. T. Otsu, J. E. Mulvaney, and C. S. Marvel, *J. Polymer Sci.*, **46**, 546 (1960).
13. C. S. Marvel and R. D. Vest, *J. Am. Chem. Soc.*, **79**, 5771 (1957).
14. C. S. Marvel and R. D. Vest, *J. Am. Chem. Soc.*, **81**, 984 (1959).
15. C. S. Marvel and J. K. Stille, *J. Am. Chem. Soc.*, **80**, 1740 (1958).
16. H. S. Makowski and B. K. C. Shim, Preprints of papers presented at the polymer section of the Cleveland meeting, April 1960, p. 101.
17. C. S. Marvel and W. E. Garrison, Jr., *J. Am. Chem. Soc.*, **81**, 4737 (1959).
18. N. D. Field, *J. Org. Chem.*, **25**, 1006 (1960).
19. C. S. Marvel and E. J. Gall, *J. Org. Chem.*, **25**, 1784 (1960).
20. J. K. Stille and D. A. Frey, *J. Am. Chem. Soc.*, **83**, 1697 (1961).
21. M. D. Barnett, A. Crawshaw, and G. B. Butler, *J. Am. Chem. Soc.*, **81**, 5946 (1959).
22. M. D. Barnett and G. B. Butler, *J. Org. Chem.*, **25**, 309 (1960).
23. J. K. Stille, Preprints of papers presented at the Petroleum Section of the St. Louis Meeting, A. C. S., March 1961.

13

NATURALLY
OCCURRING
POLYMERS

Of the many naturally occurring polymers, two industrially important classes as determined from production and sales are cellulose and keratin. (Natural rubber has been considered along with the conjugated diene polymers in Chapter 9). Cellulose may be obtained from various parts of plants but most of the cellulose and derived cellulose products are obtained from cotton or wood pulp. Keratin is a protein found mainly in animal hair and silk. Cellulose and modified or derived cellulosic products are still the most important fibers while wool stands second. Perhaps the most important naturally occurring polymers are the nucleic acids. These polyesters are apparently the key to life in that they manufacture proteins and play a leading role in cell reproduction and heredity.

13.1 CELLULOSE[1-4]

Structure and properties. Cellulose is a linear polysaccharide made up of glucose recurring units joined by a 1,4-β-glucosidic union.

The hydroxyl groups, hydroxymethyl groups and 1,4-ether linkages are all in equatorial positions. The relatively small portions of amorphous regions in native cellulose are only slightly less ordered than the crystalline regions. The monoclinic unit cell has a diagonal screw axis parallel to the fiber axis so that adjacent polymer chains lie along the fiber axis (Fig.

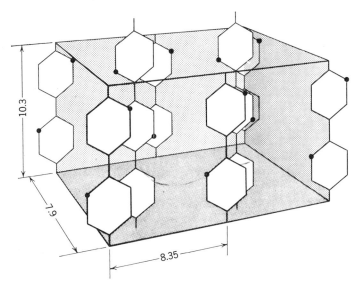

Fig. 13.1. Crystalline cellulose.[5]

13.1). The polymer chains are held together by hydrogen bonds from the hydroxyl groups which accounts for its high degree of crystallinity, high melting point and low solubility, even in hydrogen bonding solvents. The amorphous regions will swell, however, in water.

It must be understood that naturally occurring cellulosic material is not pure β-1,4-polyanhydroglucose. Cotton is about 95% cellulose and contains various other related materials such as lignin, xylans, and other polysaccharides. Physical removal of these substances affords a cellulose which may contain small portions of carboxyl groups and chemically bound hemicelluloses, xylan, or lignin.

Since cellulose is insoluble, molecular weight measurements must either be made on a soluble derivative of cellulose or a complexing solution such as a cuprammonium solution. Treatment of cellulose with some reagent which will form a derivative of cellulose results in some degradation of the polymer such that the molecular weight values are lower than the native cellulose. Molecular weights as high as 20 million have been reported for cotton cellulose but there is a broad molecular weight distribution in naturally occurring cellulose and the molecular weight varies with the source. Cellulose derivatives have molecular weights between 5000 and 500,000.

Reactions of cellulose and cellulose derivatives. The reaction of cellulose with sodium hydroxide produces an alkali cellulose in which a sodium alcoholate is formed. At weak alkali concentrations, the reaction occurs only at the surface of the crystallites and in the amorphous portions. The alcoholate ions are formed on about half of the recurring units. At higher alkali concentrations (above 13%) the alkali penetrates into the crystal lattice and a 1:1 compound is formed. The reaction probably takes place at the hydroxymethyl group.

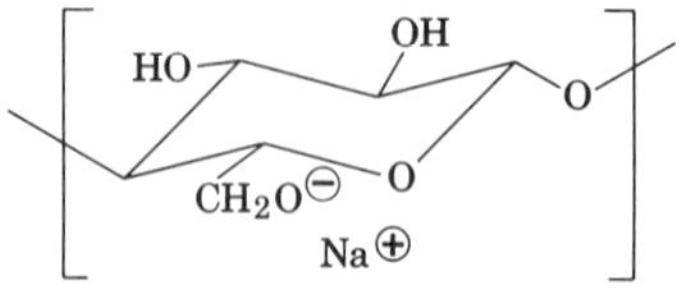

This reaction is of great commercial importance in the mercerization of cotton. The result of the reaction of stretched cellulose fibers with dilute alkali at the amorphous regions is a waving, an increased luster a better dyeability, lower tensile strength and increased water absorption. The luster is brought about by a smoothing of the surface and amorphous regions.

The production of viscose alkali cellulose is the first step in the manufacture of viscose rayon. The alkali cellulose which has been prepared with 18% sodium hydroxide and a wood pulp cellulose is pressed and brought into contact with air. This air ripening process serves to oxidatively break down the cellulose chains so that the subsequent viscose solution will have a viscosity suitable for spinning and handling.

The alkali cellulose pulp is treated either with carbon disulfide vapor or the pulp is dissolved in a dilute sodium hydroxide solution to form a sludge which is treated with liquid carbon disulfide in an emulsion. The pulp which is vapor treated becomes soluble in water and the end result of both methods is an orange solution containing about 6% alkali and 10% xanthate. These reactions have not been completely elucidated. There is on the average about one xanthate group for every two glucose recurring units.

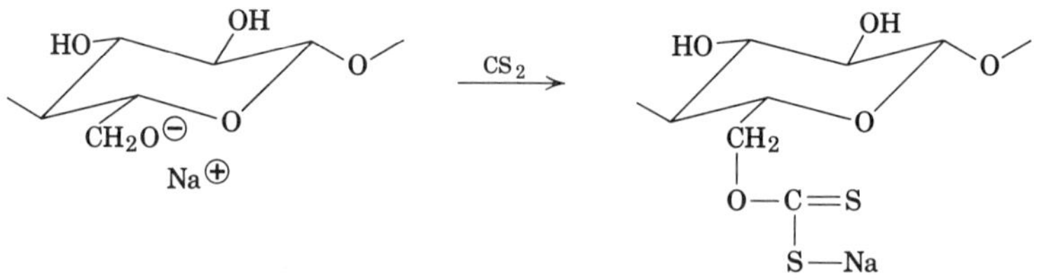

The viscose solution is ripened during which time xanthate groups decompose and bring the viscose to a gell point which will insure coagulation during spinning. The viscose solution is forced through spinnerettes into a sulfuric acid-salt bath to produce the fiber.

Products from this rayon fiber include a variety of fabrics and tire cord. An improvement on the process provides a more uniform viscose which has a more even xanthate distribution and chain length. This affords a stronger rayon which is used for the tire cord Tyrex.

In the acetylation of cellulose, the cotton or wood pulp is dried to a low moisture content in order to reduce the water content in the reaction mixture, but not low enough to yield a product resistant to swelling. The acetylation is carried out in an acetic acid-acetic anhydride-sulfuric acid mixture below 50°C. Under these conditions, the cellulose dissolves completely and the triacetate is formed. The solution is aged to produce some chain degradation.

The triacetate may be spun into fibers but its low solubility in solvents makes this operation difficult. The acylation is usually reversed by the addition of acetic acid and water so that the final water content of the mixture is 5–10%. The resulting diacetate rayon is precipitated by the addition of acetic acid and is spun from an acetone solution by flashing off the acetone solvent. Acetate films are cast from a benzene-alcohol solution with added plasticizer.

13.2   KERATIN[2]

A large group of naturally occurring high polymers is the proteins. These polyamides composed of α-amino acid segments are found in plants and animals and have a variety of compositions and structures. Proteins may occur as the insoluble proteins fibroin, collagen, keratin, and elastin or as the soluble globular proteins. Only keratin, a fibrous protein will be considered here as an example of a naturally occurring polyamide.

Structure. The keratins of wool and hair are insoluble in all solvents but will swell to a certain extent. Of the amino acids in wool which comprise the polyamide chain, leucine, cystine, glutamic acid, and arginine account for about half the amino acid content of the fiber. Alanine, valine, tyrosine, aspartic acid, and proline account for another fourth of the weight and smaller amounts of glycine, serine, lanthionin, oxyglutamic acid, histidine, and tryptophane are also present.

The polyamide chains in wool and hair are crosslinked by the disulfide links from cystine which account for the insolubility of these fibers. Wool and hair fibers are not homogeneous but are comprised of different cellular layers which have different amino acid contents.

Keratin may exist in two crystalline modifications. In the unstretched state, the polyamide chains are folded into an α-helical configuration (Fig. 13.2). When keratin is stretched the polyamide chains arrange themselves into the extended sheet structure, β-keratin (Fig. 13.3).

Properties and reactions. Wool and hair absorb large amounts of water and can be stretched up to 100% of their original length after softening with alkali or hot water. When tension is released, it returns to almost its original length. This stretching involves a transformation into the β-keratin structure.

The machine waving in hair involves a rupture of the disulfide crosslinks by steam into sulfhydryl and sulfenic acid groups. The sulfenic acid group decomposes into an aldehyde which reacts with amino groups present on an adjacent chain to recrosslink the hair. Thus, if the hair is wound into a new configuration, old crosslinks are broken and new ones are formed which relieve the strain and hold the chains in new positions relative to one another.

A cold wave process accomplishes the same realignment by a two-step

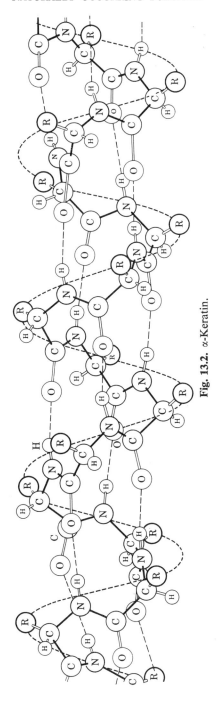

Fig. 13.2. α-Keratin.

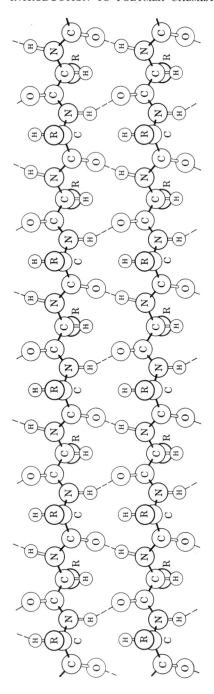

Fig. 13.3. β-Keratin.

operation. Reduction of the disulfide links with thioglycolic acid uncrosslinks the hair through the formation of sulfhydryl groups. After the hair is set, the chains may be recrosslinked by a variety of reagents, including alkyldibromides.

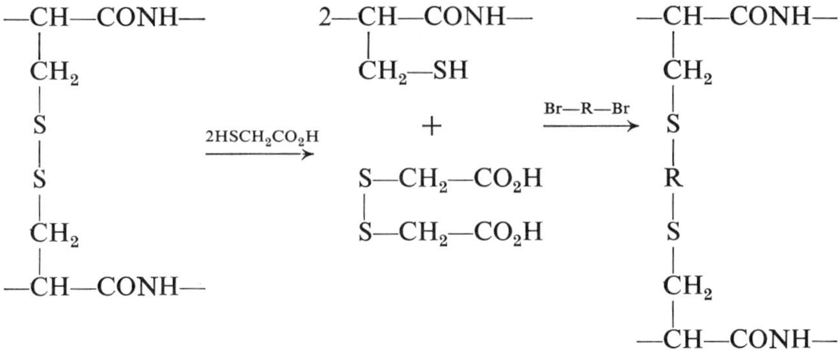

13.3 NUCLEIC ACIDS[7,8]

Nucleic acids were discovered in 1869 but it was not until 1944 that most of the substances or building blocks of the nucleic acids were known. Much of our knowledge of the polynucleotides, particularly the gross structure and an understanding of the biochemical significance, had been advanced however since 1944.

There are two types of nucleic acids, deoxyribonucleic acid (DNA) and ribonucleic acid (RNA). DNA is found in plant and animal cell nuclei while RNA occurs both in cell nuclei and in the cytoplasm. In order to fully understand the structure of the nucleic acids, the component parts of the polymer molecules are discussed first and finally built into the complete molecule.

The two major purine bases present in *both* DNA and RNA are adenine and guanine.

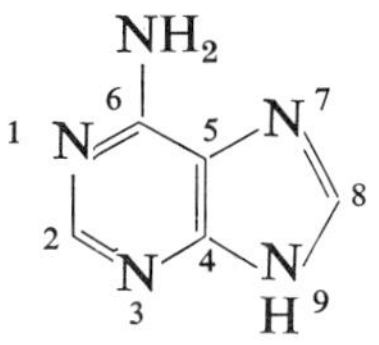

Adenine 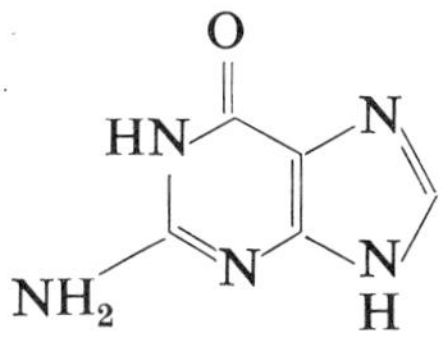   Guanine

Other trace purines have been found, but these are all methyl derivatives (usually N-methyl) of adenine or guanine. The other bases present are the pyrimidines. Cytosine is common to both DNA and RNA while thymine is found only in DNA and uracil only in RNA.

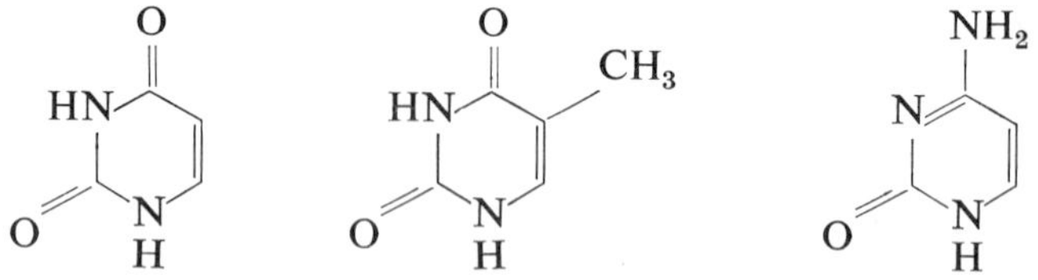

Uracil   Thymine   Cytosine

The base 5-methyl cytosine may be found in DNA and RNA in varying amounts, and is present in addition to the other two pyrimidine bases in either DNA or RNA. The 5-methyl cytosine may replace cytosine one for one and to the extent of 25 %.

Thus the nucleic acids contain four different bases, two purines and two pyrimidines, three of which are common to DNA and RNA and the fourth different. In a wide variety of DNA preparations which are mixtures of individual DNA molecules, an important observation has been made: The ratio of adenine to thymine and the ratio of guanine to cytosine is very close to one.

Nucleosides are pentose derivatives of the purines or pyrimidines. D-ribose is the sugar from RNA and D-2-deoxyribose is the sugar from DNA which make up the nucleoside. In both the ribose and deoxyribose nucleosides, the linkages occur from the 1-position on the β-D-furanoside to the 9-position on the purines and the 1-position on the pyrimidines. Two examples of nucleosides are shown.

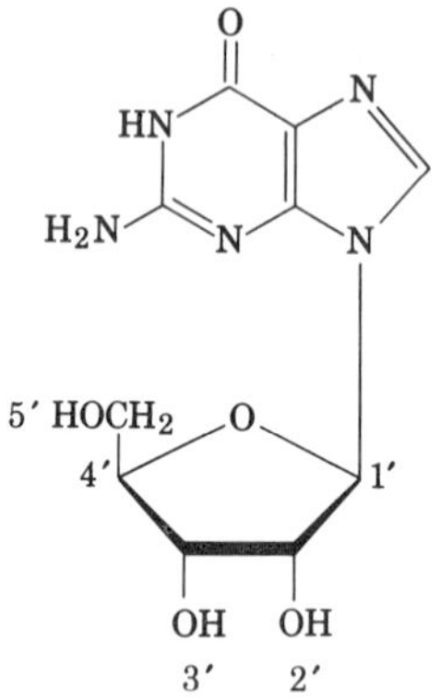

Guanosine 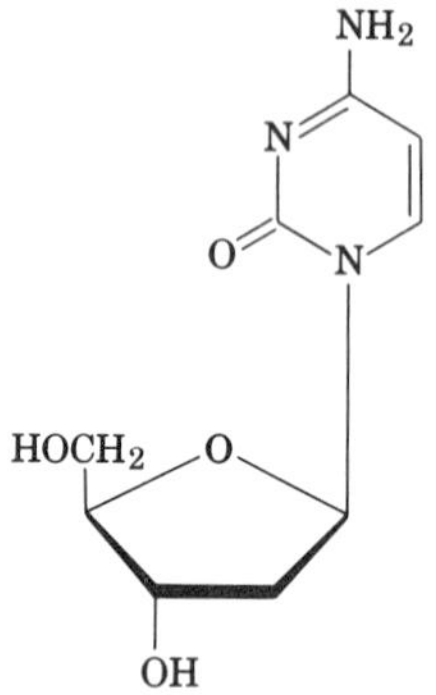   Deoxycytidine

A nucleotide is a phosphate ester of a nucleoside. The phosphate moiety may occur on any of the hydroxyl positions or may be a cyclic

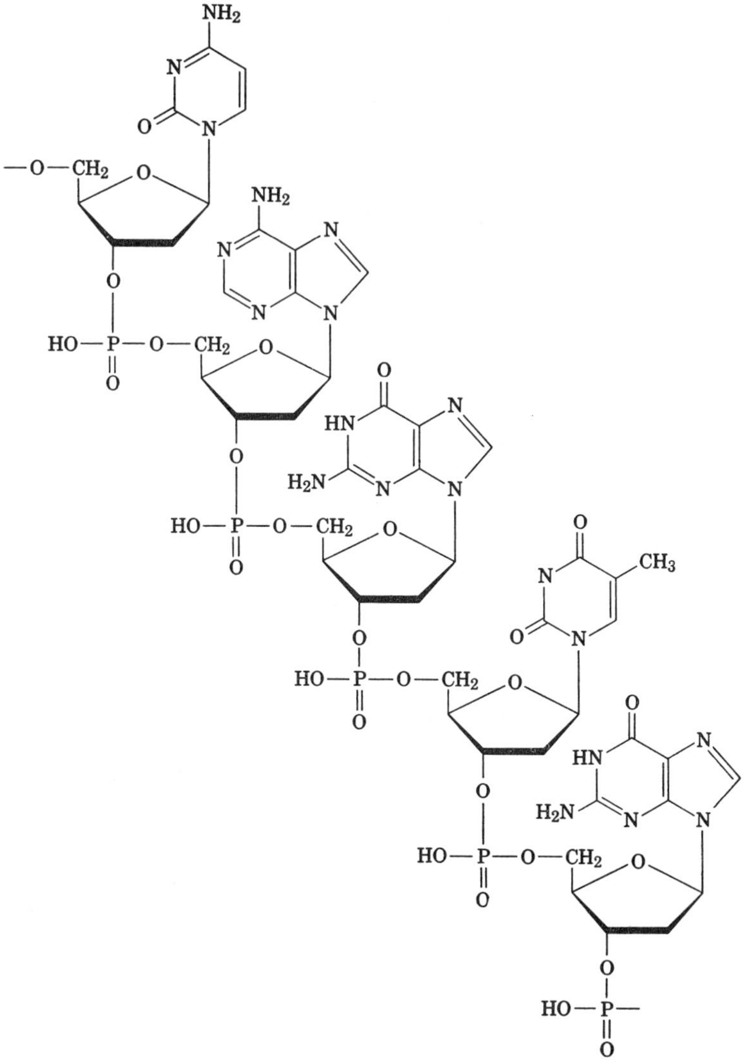

Fig. 13.4. A portion of a DNA molecule.

phosphate in the case of a RNA nucleotide. Hydrolytic or enzymatic cleavage of a nucleic acid may result in a 3′ or 5′ phosphate or both depending on the enzyme or method of hydrolysis, and a mass of evidence has been provided for the linkage of the nucleosides at the 3′ or 5′ positions to form the nucleic acid polyesters (polynucleotide).

The same type of structure can be drawn for RNA. The different nucleotide units do not follow a definite sequence in different nucleic acids,

Fig. 13.5. The DNA double helix. (By permission from Van R. Potter, DNA Model Kit. Burgess Publishing Co., Minneapolis, Minn., 1959.)

but nucleic acids apparently are different in the sequence which is peculiar to the individual molecule. The fact that in DNA molecules the ratios of adenine to thymine and guanine to thymine is nearly 1:1 lead to the proposed three dimensional structure of DNA. The DNA molecule is a double helix, consisting of two chains, side by side and twisted together (Fig. 13.5). The purine or pyrimidine moieties are arranged, however, such that there are suitable geometric requirements for hydrogen bonding through the core of the double helix. There are only two purine to pyrimidine pairs, adenine-thymine on one hand and guanine-cytosine on the other which may be properly hydrogen bonded in the helix. Each of these four bases can occur in either chain and must be paired from the opposite direction in the corresponding chains. This gives rise to four possible pairings: cytosine-guanine, guanine-cytosine, thymine-adenine, and adenine-thymine. RNA apparently does not have the distinctive base pairing peculiar to DNA. One interesting fact is that RNA contains a ratio of total adenine and cytosine to total guanine and uracil of nearly one.

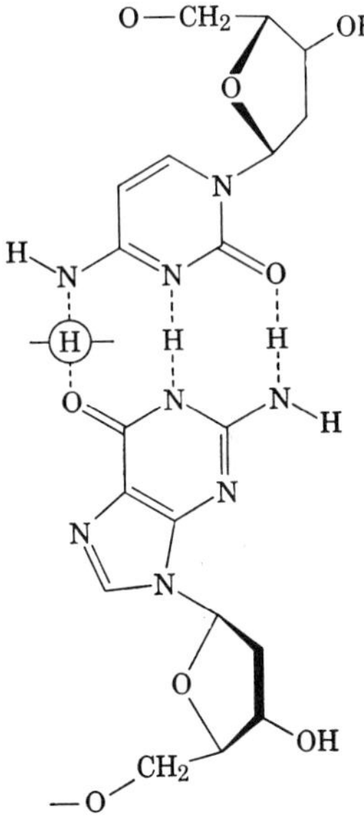

Fig. 13.6. Looking down the core of the helix at a guanine-cytosine pair.

What is the purpose or role of DNA or RNA in the cell? The answer is only a series of educated guesses. DNA probably has two important functions: to reproduce itself in cell division through RNA and to produce RNA which synthesize protein. DNA may act as a mold in which RNA may be constructed. (Note the helical space in the DNA double helix). The RNA thus formed may serve as a pattern for the synthesis of a duplicate DNA. The RNA may also carry out the synthesis of the proteins that make up the enzymes and cell structure according to the instructions (pattern) obtained from DNA. This is obviously a much oversimplified picture, but is a working hypothesis which may provide more questions and answers.

REFERENCES

1. E. Ott, H. M. Spurlin, and M. N. Grafflin, eds., *Cellulose and Cellulose Derivatives*, 2nd ed., Interscience Publishers, New York and London. Parts I and II, (1954). Part III (1955).
2. K. H. Meyer, *Natural and Synthetic High Polymers*, Interscience Publishers, New York and London, 1950.

3. J. Grant, *Cellulose Pulp and Allied Products*, Interscience Publishers, New York, 1959.
4. W. D. Paist, *Cellulosics*, Reinhold Publishing Corp., New York, 1958.
5. R. D. Preston, *Scientific American*, **197**, No. 3, 157 (1957).
6. P. Doty, *Scientific American*, **197**, No. 3, 173 (1957).
7. E. Chargaff and J. N. Davidson, *The Nucleic Acids*, Academic Press, New York and London, I (1955), II (1955), III (1960).
8. Van R. Potter, *Nucleic Acid Outlines I*, Burgess Publishing Company, Minneapolis, Minnesota, 1960.

INDEX

243